ENGINEERING FORMULAS

Kurt Gieck

Fifth Edition

McGraw-Hill Book Company

New York St. Louis San Francisco Montreal Toronto

Library of Congress Cataloging-in-Publication Data

Gieck, Kurt.
Engineering formulas.

Translation of: Technische Formelsammlung.
Includes index.
1. Engineering – Tables. I. Title.
TA151.G4713 1986   620'.00212   85-23153
ISBN 0-07-023231-8

ISBN 0-07-023231-8

First published in the English Language under the title
A COLLECTION OF TECHNICAL FORMULAE

Fifth American edition
published by McGraw-Hill, Inc. in 1986
English translation by J. Walters

Printed in West Germany

Preface

The purpose of this collection of technical formulae is to provide a brief, clear and handy guide to the more important technical and mathematical formulae.

Since the book has been printed on one side of the page only, the facing pages are available for additional notes.

Each separate subject has been associated with a capital letter. The various formulae have been grouped under corresponding small letters and numbered serially. This method enables the formulae used in any particular calculation to be indicated.

Preface
to the enlarged and revised 6th edition

A new section on STATISTICS has been included because of its growing importance in connection with probability distribution, quality control and reliability.

Fourier and Laplace transformations have been added to the section called ARITHMETIC together with a section on partial fractions.

K. Gieck

Reference to BS, DIN and VDE

BS · British Standards Institution
(Address: 2 Park St, LONDON W 1 A 2 BS)

DIN · Deutsches Institut für Normung
(Address: D-1000 BERLIN 30, Postfach 1107)

VDI · Verein Deutscher Ingenieure
(Address: D-4000 DUESSELDORF 1, Postfach 1139).

Method of Presentation and Use of Units

Most of the equations clearly reveal the physical relationships which they describe and are valid regardless of the system of units employed, provided that they are consistent.

Some of the equations are empirical in origin and the units quoted must be used in the formula to obtain the correct result, these are mainly to be found in sections Q and R.

It is intended that the Stroud notation is used when evaluating the formulae i.e. both the quantity and the unit is substituted for a given symbol and the subsequent calculation involves manipulation of numbers and units together.

For example, taking equation I 23: $t = \dfrac{s}{v}$

$$\begin{aligned} \text{if } s \text{ (distance)} &= 2\cdot 8 \text{ metres} \\ v \text{ (speed)} &= 8 \text{ metres/second} \end{aligned}$$

then $\qquad t = \dfrac{2\cdot 8 \text{ metres} \times \text{second}}{8 \text{ metres}}$

hence $\qquad t = 0\cdot 35$ seconds (time)
cancelling the unit 'metres'

It is clear that t should have the units of time; if it does not, then it is obvious that an error has been made and the working should be checked. As a help, in many cases, the anticipated units are quoted using the abbreviation "EU", Example-Unit.

When the numerical values and the units are included in the calculations, their equivalents or definitions are best written so that they are dimensionless and have the value of 1·0. In this form they are sometimes called "Unity Brackets" and their use can be illustrated in three ways:

with consistent units,

equation a 6

$$1 \text{ km} = 10^3 \text{ m} \qquad \text{becomes} \quad 1 = \left[\frac{1 \text{ km}}{10^3 \text{ m}} \right]$$

equation a 62

$$12 \text{ in} = 1 \text{ ft} \qquad \text{becomes} \quad 1 = \left[\frac{1 \text{ ft}}{12 \text{ in}} \right]$$

equation a 90

$$778 \cdot 6 \text{ ft lbf} = 1 \text{ Btu} \qquad \text{becomes} \quad 1 = \left[\frac{778 \cdot 6 \text{ ft lbf}}{1 \text{ Btu}} \right]$$

for example, to convert $14 \cdot 7$ lbf/in^2 to lbf/ft^2

$$14 \cdot 7 \frac{\text{lbf}}{\text{in}^2} = 14 \cdot 7 \frac{\text{lbf}}{\text{in}^2} \left[\frac{12 \text{ in}}{1 \text{ ft}} \right]^2 = 14 \cdot 7 \times 144 \frac{\text{lbf}}{\text{ft}^2} = 2117 \frac{\text{lbf}}{\text{ft}^2}$$

in the conversion between different systems of units,

equation a 36

$$1 \text{ N} = 0 \cdot 102 \text{ kgf} \qquad \text{becomes} \quad 1 = \left[\frac{0 \cdot 102 \text{ kgf}}{1 \text{ N}} \right]$$

equation a 65

$$1 \text{ m} = 3 \cdot 281 \text{ ft} \qquad \text{becomes} \quad 1 = \left[\frac{1 \text{ m}}{3 \cdot 281 \text{ ft}} \right]$$

equation a 110

$$1 \text{ Btu/lb} = 0 \cdot 556 \text{ kcal/kg becomes} \quad 1 = \left[\frac{0 \cdot 556 \text{ kcal lb}}{1 \text{ kg Btu}} \right]$$

For example, to convert 1000 kgf/cm^2 to S.I. units,

$$1000 \frac{\text{kgf}}{\text{cm}^2} = 1000 \frac{\text{kgf}}{\text{cm}^2} \left[\frac{9 \cdot 81 \text{ N}}{1 \text{ kgf}} \right] \left[\frac{10^4 \text{ cm}^2}{1 \text{ m}^2} \right] \left[\frac{1 \text{ MN}}{10^6 \text{ N}} \right]$$

$$= 98 \cdot 1 \frac{\text{MN}}{\text{m}^2}$$

in the use of definitions:

1 lbf is the force required to accelerate a mass of 1 lb at the rate of 32·174 ft/s².

$$1 \text{ lbf} = 1 \text{ lb} \times 32 \cdot 174 \, \frac{ft}{s^2} \qquad \text{becomes} \quad 1 = \left[\frac{32 \cdot 174 \text{ lb ft}}{1 \text{ s}^2 \text{ lbf}} \right]$$

Similarly, the Newton is defined by the equation

$$1 \text{ N} = 1 \text{ kg} \times \frac{1 \text{ m}}{s^2} \qquad \text{which becomes} \quad 1 = \left[\frac{1 \text{ N s}^2}{1 \text{ kg m}} \right]$$

and

$$1 \text{ kgf} = 1 \text{ kg} \times 9 \cdot 81 \, \frac{m}{s^2} \qquad \text{becomes} \quad 1 = \left[\frac{9 \cdot 81 \text{ kg m}}{1 \text{ kgf s}^2} \right]$$

For example, to find the force in S.I. units required to accelerate a mass of 3 lb at the rate of 2·5 ft/s², proceed as follows:

$$F = m \, a, \text{ equation m 1.}$$
$$F = 3 \text{ lb} \times 2 \cdot 5 \, \frac{ft}{s^2} \left[\frac{0 \cdot 4536 \text{ kg}}{1 \text{ lb}} \right] \left[\frac{1 \text{ m}}{3 \cdot 281 \text{ ft}} \right] \left[\frac{1 \text{ N s}^2}{1 \text{ kg m}} \right]$$
$$= \frac{3 \times 2 \cdot 5 \times 0 \cdot 4536}{3 \cdot 281} \text{ N} = 1 \cdot 036 \text{ N}$$

which is a unit of force.

Base Quantities and Base Units
of the International System of Measurement

base quantity		base unit	
name	symbol (*italic letters*)	name	symbol (vertical letters)
length	l	metre	m
mass	m	kilogram	kg
time	t	second	s
electric current			
absolute temperature	I	ampere	A
amount of substance	T	kelvin	K
light intensity	n	mole	mol
	I_v	candela	cd

(Old units are put in [ ] brackets)

List of symbols

Space and time

α,	β, γ	angles
Ω		solid angle
b,	B	breadth
d,	D	diameter (diagonal)
h,	H	height
l,	L	length
p		pitch
r,	R	radius
s		distance covered, perimeter
t		thickness
u,	U	circumference
A		area, cross section
A_m		generated surface
A_o		surface area
V		volume
t		time
v		velocity, linear
ω		velocity, angular
a		acceleration, linear
α		acceleration, angular
g		acceleration, gravitational

Periodical and related phenomens

T	period
f	frequency
n	rotational speed
ω	angular frequency
λ	wavelength
c	velocity of light

Mechanics

m	mass
ϱ	density
F	force, direct force

f, σ	direct stress
q, τ	shear stress
p	normal pressure
ε	extension, strain
E	modulus of elasticity (Young's modulus)
G	modulus of rigidity (shear modulus)
M	bending moment
T	torsional moment, torque
Z	modulus of section
Q	shear force, shear load
V	vertical reaction
W	weight or load, work
w	uniformly distributed load
I	moment of inertia, second moment of area
I_p	polar moment of inertia
J	torsion constant
Z	modulus of section
μ	coefficient of sliding friction
μ_o	coefficient of static friction
μ_q	coefficient of friction of a radial bearing
μ_l	coefficient of friction of a longitudinal bearing
f	coefficient of rolling friction
η	dynamic viscosity
ν	kinematic viscosity
P	power
η	efficiency

Heat

T	absolute temperature
t	temperature
α	linear coefficient of expansion
γ	cubic coefficient of expansion
Φ	heat current or flow
φ	density of heat flow
q	quantity of heat per unit mass
Q	quantity of heat
c_p	specific heat at constant pressure
c_v	specific heat at constant volume
γ	ratio of c_p to c_v
R	gas constant
λ	thermal conductivity
α	heat transfer coefficient
k	coefficient of heat transmission
C	radiation constant
v	specific volume

Electricity and magnetism

I	current
J	current density
V, U	voltage
U_q	source voltage
R	resistance
G	conductance
Q	quantity of electricity (charge)
C	capacitance
D	dielectric displacement
E	electric field strength
Φ	magnetic flux
B	magnetic induction
L	inductance
H	magn. field strength
Θ	circulation (magnetic potential)

V	magnetic voltage
R_m	magnetic resistance
Λ	magnetic conductance
δ	length of air gap
α	temperature coefficient of resistance
γ	conductivity
ϱ	resistivity
ε	permittivity, dielectric constant
ε_0	absolute permittivity
ε_r	relative permittivity
N	number of turns
μ	permeability
μ_0	absolute permeability
μ_r	relative permeability
p	number of pairs of poles
z	number of conductors
Q	quality, figure of merit
δ	loss angle
Z	impedance
X	reactance
P_s	apparent power
P_q	reactive power
C_M	moment constant

Light and related electromagnetic radiations

I_e	radiant intensity
I_v	luminous intensity
Φ_e	radiant power, radiant flux
Φ_v	luminous flux
Q_e	radiant energy
Q_v	quantity of light
E_e	irradiance
E_v	illuminance
H_e	radiant exposure
H_v	light exposure
L_e	radiance
L_v	luminance
c	velocity of light
n	refractive index
f	focal length
D	refractive power

Decimal multiples and fractions of units

da	=	deca	=	10^1	d	=	deci	=	10^{-1}
h	=	hecto	=	10^2	c	=	centi	=	10^{-2}
k	=	kilo	=	10^3	m	=	milli	=	10^{-3}
M	=	mega	=	10^6	μ	=	micro	=	10^{-6}
G	=	giga	=	10^9	n	=	nano	=	10^{-9}
T	=	tera	=	10^{12}	p	=	pico	=	10^{-12}
P	=	peta	=	10^{15}	f	=	femto	=	10^{-15}
E	=	exa	=	10^{18}	a	=	atto	=	10^{-18}

Units of length

			m	μm	mm	cm	dm	km
a 1	1 m	=	1	10^6	10^3	10^2	10	10^{-3}
a 2	1 μm	=	10^{-6}	1	10^{-3}	10^{-4}	10^{-5}	10^{-9}
a 3	1 mm	=	10^{-3}	10^3	1	10^{-1}	10^{-2}	10^{-6}
a 4	1 cm	=	10^{-2}	10^4	10	1	10^{-1}	10^{-5}
a 5	1 dm	=	10^{-1}	10^5	10^2	10	1	10^{-4}
a 6	1 km	=	10^3	10^9	10^6	10^5	10^4	1

Units of length (continued)

			mm	μm	nm	[Å] [1]	pm	[m Å] [2]
a 7	1 mm	=	1	10^3	10^6	10^7	10^9	10^{10}
a 8	1 μm	=	10^{-3}	1	10^3	10^4	10^6	10^7
a 9	1 nm	=	10^{-6}	10^{-3}	1	10	10^3	10^4
a 10	[1 Å]	=	10^{-7}	10^{-4}	10^{-1}	1	10^2	10^3
a 11	1 pm	=	10^{-9}	10^{-6}	10^{-3}	10^{-2}	1	10
a 12	[1 mÅ]	=	10^{-10}	10^{-7}	10^{-4}	10^{-3}	10^{-1}	1

Units of area

			m^2	μm^2	mm^2	cm^2	dm^2	km^2
a 13	1 m^2	=	1	10^{12}	10^6	10^4	10^2	10^{-6}
a 14	1 μm^2	=	10^{-12}	1	10^{-6}	10^{-8}	10^{-10}	10^{-18}
a 15	1 mm^2	=	10^{-6}	10^6	1	10^{-2}	10^{-4}	10^{-12}
a 16	1 cm^2	=	10^{-4}	10^8	10^2	1	10^{-2}	10^{-10}
a 17	1 dm^2	=	10^{-2}	10^{10}	10^4	10^2	1	10^{-8}
a 18	1 km^2	=	10^6	10^{18}	10^{12}	10^{10}	10^8	1

[1] Å = Ångström   [2] 1 mÅ = 1 XE = 1 X-unit

A₂ UNITS

Units of volume

	m^3	mm^3	cm^3	dm^3 [1]	km^3	
1 m^3 =	1	10^9	10^6	10^3	10^{-9}	a 19
1 mm^3 =	10^{-9}	1	10^{-3}	10^{-6}	10^{-18}	a 20
1 cm^3 =	10^{-6}	10^3	1	10^{-3}	10^{-15}	a 21
1 dm^3 =	10^{-3}	10^6	10^3	1	10^{-12}	a 22
1 km^3 =	10^9	10^{18}	10^{15}	10^{12}	1	a 23

Units of mass

	kg	mg	g	dt	t = Mg	
1 kg =	1	10^6	10^3	10^{-2}	10^{-3}	a 24
1 mg =	10^{-6}	1	10^{-3}	10^{-8}	10^{-9}	a 25
1 g =	10^{-3}	10^3	1	10^{-5}	10^{-6}	a 26
1 dt =	10^2	10^8	10^5	1	10^{-1}	a 27
1 t = 1 Mg =	10^3	10^9	10^6	10	1	a 28

Units of time

	s	ns	μs	ms	min	
1 s =	1	10^9	10^6	10^3	16.66×10^{-3}	a 29
1 ns =	10^{-9}	1	10^{-3}	10^{-6}	16.66×10^{-12}	a 30
1 μs =	10^{-6}	10^3	1	10^{-3}	16.66×10^{-9}	a 31
1 ms =	10^{-3}	10^6	10^3	1	16.66×10^{-6}	a 32
1 min =	60	60×10^3	60×10^6	60×10^3	1	a 33
1 h =	3600	3.6×10^{12}	3.6×10^9	3.6×10^6	60	a 34
1 d =	86.4×10^3	86.4×10^{12}	86.4×10^9	86.4×10^6	1440	a 35

Units of force (gravitational force also)

	N [2]	kN	MN	[kgf]	[dyn]	
1 N =	1	10^{-3}	10^{-6}	0.102	10	a 36
1 kN =	10^3	1	10^{-3}	0.102×10^3	10^8	a 37
1 MN =	10^6	10^3	1	0.102×10^6	10^{11}	a 38

[1] 1 dm^3 = 1 l = 1 liter   [2] 1 N = 1 kg m/s² = 1 Newton

UNITS

Units of pressure

		Pa	N/mm²	bar	[kgf/cm²]	[torr]
a 39	1 Pa = 1 N/m² =	1	10^{-6}	10^{-5}	1.02×10^{-5}	0.0075
a 40	1 N/mm² =	10^{6}	1	10	10.2	7.5×10^{3}
a 41	1 bar =	10^{5}	0.1	1	1.02	750
a 42	[1 kgf/cm² = 1 at] =	98 100	9.81×10^{-2}	0.981	1	736
a 43	[1 torr]¹⁾ =	133	0.133×10^{-3}	1.33×10^{-3}	1.36×10^{-3}	1

Units of work

		J	kW h	[kgf m]	[kcal]	[hp h]
a 44	1 J ²⁾ =	1	0.278×10^{-6}	0.102	0.239×10^{-3}	0.378×10^{-6}
a 45	1 kW h =	3.60×10^{6}	1	367×10^{3}	860	1.36
a 46	[1 kgf m] =	9.81	2.72×10^{-6}	1	2.345×10^{-3}	3.70×10^{-6}
a 47	[1 kcal] =	4186.8	1.16×10^{-3}	426.9	1	1.58×10^{-3}
a 48	[1 hp h] =	2.65×10^{6}	0.736	0.27×10^{6}	632	1

Units of power

		W	kW	[kgf m/s]	[kcal/h]	[hp]
a 49	1 W ³⁾ =	1	10^{-3}	0.102	0.860	1.36×10^{-3}
a 50	1 kW =	1000	1	102	860	1.36
a 51	[1 kgf m/s] =	9.81	9.81×10^{-3}	1	8.43	13.3×10^{-3}
a 52	[1 kcal/h] =	1.16	1.16×10^{-3}	0.119	1	1.58×10^{-3}
a 53	[1 hp] =	736	0.736	75	632	1

Unit of mass for jewels

a 54   1 carat = 200 mg = 0.2×10^{-3} kg = 1/5000 kg

Unit of fineness for precious metals

a 55	24 carat ≙ 1000.00 ‰	18 carat ≙ 750.00 ‰
a 56	14 carat ≙ 583.33 ‰	8 carat ≙ 333.33 ‰

Units of temperature

a 57 $T = \left(\dfrac{t}{°C} + 273.15\right) K = \dfrac{5}{9}\cdot\dfrac{T_R}{Rank}\ K$

a 58 $T_R = \left(\dfrac{t_F}{°F} + 459.67\right) Rank = \dfrac{9}{5}\cdot\dfrac{T}{K}\ Rank$

a 59 $t = \dfrac{5}{9}\left(\dfrac{t_F}{°F} - 32\right)°C = \left(\dfrac{T}{K} - 273.15\right)°C$

a 60 $t_F = \left(\dfrac{9}{5}\cdot\dfrac{t}{°C} + 32\right)°F = \left(\dfrac{T_R}{Rank} - 459.67\right)°F$

	K	°C	°F	Rank
boiling point of water at 760 torr	373.15	100	212	671.67
	273.15	0 -----	32	491.67
absol. zero	0	-273.15	-459.67	0

T, T_R, t and t_F are the temperatures in the scales for Kelvin, Rankine, Celsius, Fahrenheit.

¹⁾ 1 torr = 1/760 atm = 1.33322 mbar = 1 mm Hg at $t = 0\ °C$
²⁾ 1 J = N m = 1 W s   ³⁾ 1 W = 1 J/s = 1 N m/s

UNITS

Conversion, Anglo-American to metric units

Units of length

		in	ft	yd	mm	m	km	
1 in	=	1	0·08333	0·02778	25·4	0·0254	−	a 61
1 ft	=	12	1	0·3333	304·8	0·3048	−	a 62
1 yd	=	36	3	1	914·4	0·9144	−	a 63
1 mm	=	0·03937	3281×10⁻⁶	1094×10⁻⁶	1	0·001	10⁻⁶	a 64
1 m	=	39·37	3·281	1·094	1000	1	0·001	a 65
1 km	=	39370	3281	1094	10⁶	1000	1	a 66

Units of area

		sq in	sq ft	sq yd	cm²	dm²	m²	
1 sq in	=	1	6·944×10⁻³	0·772×10⁻³	6·452	0·06452	64·5×10⁻⁵	a 67
1 sq ft	=	144	1	0·1111	929	9·29	0·0929	a 68
1 sq yd	=	1296	9	1	8361	83·61	0·8361	a 69
1 cm²	=	0·155	1·076×10⁻³	1·197×10⁻⁴	1	0·01	0·0001	a 70
1 dm²	=	15·5	0·1076	0·01196	100	1	0·001	a 71
1 m²	=	1550	10·76	1·196	10000	100	1	a 72

Units of volume

		cu in	cu ft	cu yd	cm³	dm³	m³	
1 cu in	=	1	5·786×10⁻⁴	2·144×10⁻⁵	16·39	0·01639	1·64×10⁻⁵	a 73
1 cu ft	=	1728	1	0·037	28316	28·32	0·0283	a 74
1 cu yd	=	46656	27	1	764555	764·55	0·7646	a 75
1 cm³	=	0·06102	3532×10⁻⁸	1·31×10⁻⁶	1	0·001	10⁻⁶	a 76
1 dm³	=	61·02	0·03532	0·00131	1000	1	0·001	a 77
1 m³	=	61023	35·32	1·307	10⁶	1000	1	a 78

Units of mass

		dram	oz	lb	g	kg	Mg	
1 dram	=	1	0·0625	0·003906	1·772	0·00177	1·77×10⁻⁶	a 79
1 oz	=	16	1	0·0625	28·35	0·02832	28·3×10⁻⁶	a 80
1 lb	=	256	16	1	453·6	0·4531	4·53×10⁻⁴	a 81
1 g	=	0·5643	0·03527	0·002205	1	0·001	10⁻⁶	a 82
1 kg	=	564·3	35·27	2·205	1000	1	0·001	a 83
1 Mg	=	564·4×10³	35270	2205	10⁶	1000	1	a 84

continued A 5

continued from A 4

Units of work

		ft lb	kgf m	J = W s	kW h	kcal	Btu
a 85	1 ft lb =	1	0·1383	1·356	$376·8×10^{-9}$	$324×10^{-6}$	$1·286×10^{-3}$
a 86	1 kgf m =	7·233	1	9·807	$2·725×10^{-6}$	$2·344×10^{-3}$	$9·301×10^{-3}$
a 87	1 J = 1 W s =	0·7376	0·102	1	$277·8×10^{-9}$	$239×10^{-6}$	$948·4×10^{-6}$
a 88	1 kW h =	$2·655×10^{6}$	$367·1×10^{3}$	$3·6×10^{6}$	1	860	3413
a 89	1 kcal =	$3·087×10^{3}$	426·9	4187	$1·163×10^{-3}$	1	3·968
a 90	1 Btu =	778·6	107·6	1055	$293×10^{-6}$	0·252	1

Units of power

		hp	kgf m/s	J/s = W	kW	kcal/s	Btu/s
a 91	1 hp =	1	76·04	745·7	0·7457	0·1782	0·7073
a 92	1 kgf m/s=	$13·1×10^{-3}$	1	9·807	$9·807×10^{-3}$	$2·344×10^{-3}$	$9·296×10^{-3}$
a 93	1 J/s = 1 W=	$1·341×10^{-3}$	0·102	1	10^{-3}	$239×10^{-6}$	$948·4×10^{-6}$
a 94	1 kW =	1·341	102	1000	1	0·239	0·9484
a 95	1 kcal/s =	5·614	426·9	4187	4·187	1	3·968
a 96	1 Btu/s =	1·415	107·6	1055	1·055	0·252	1

Other units

a 97	1 mil = 10^{-3} in	=	0·0254 mm
a 98	1 sq mil = 10^{-6} sq in	=	645·2 μm^2
a 99	1 yard = 3 ft	=	0·914 m
a100	1 English mile = 1760 yds	=	1609 m
a101	1 Nautical mile	=	1852 m
a102	1 Geographical mile	=	7420 m
a103	1 long ton = 2240 lb	=	1·016 Mg
a104	1 short ton (US) = 2000 lb	=	0·9072 Mg
a105	1 long ton = 2240 lbf	=	9·96 MN
a106	1 short ton (US) = 2000 lbf	=	9·00 MN
a107	1 Imp. gallon (Imperial gallon)	=	4·546 dm^3
a108	1 US gallon	=	3·785 dm^3
a109	1 BTU/ft^3 = 9·547 kcal/m^3	=	39·964 kJ/m^3
a110	1 BTU/lb = 0·556 kcal/kg	=	2·327 kJ/kg
a111	1 lbf/ft^2 = 4·882 kgf/m^2	=	47·892 N/m^2
a112	1 lbf/in^2 (p.s.i.) = 0·0703 kgf/cm^2	=	0·6896 N/cm^2
a113	1 chain = 22 yds	=	20·11 m
a114	1 Hundredweight (GB) (cwt) = 112 lbf	=	498 kN
a115	1 Quarter (GB) = 28 lbf	=	124·5 kN
a116	1 Stone (GB) = 14 lbf	=	62·3 kN

AREAS

1

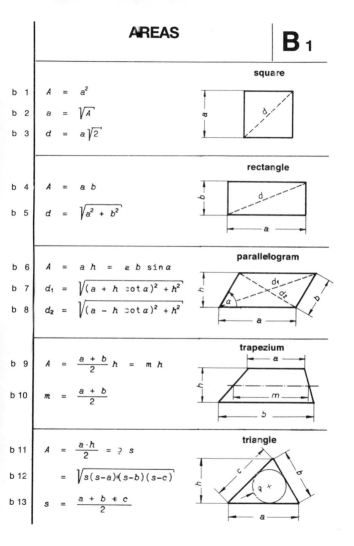

square

b 1 $\quad A = a^2$

b 2 $\quad a = \sqrt{A}$

b 3 $\quad d = a\sqrt{2}$

rectangle

b 4 $\quad A = a\,b$

b 5 $\quad d = \sqrt{a^2 + b^2}$

parallelogram

b 6 $\quad A = a\,h = a\,b\,\sin\alpha$

b 7 $\quad d_1 = \sqrt{(a + h\cot\alpha)^2 + h^2}$

b 8 $\quad d_2 = \sqrt{(a - h\cot\alpha)^2 + h^2}$

trapezium

b 9 $\quad A = \dfrac{a + b}{2}\,h = m\,h$

b 10 $\quad m = \dfrac{a + b}{2}$

triangle

b 11 $\quad A = \dfrac{a\cdot h}{2} = \varrho\,s$

b 12 $\quad\quad = \sqrt{s(s-a)(s-b)(s-c)}$

b 13 $\quad s = \dfrac{a + b + c}{2}$

B₂ | **AREAS**

equilateral triangle

$$A = \frac{a^2}{4}\sqrt{3}$$ b 14

$$h = \frac{a}{2}\sqrt{3}$$ b 15

pentagon

$$A = \frac{5}{8}\,r^2\sqrt{10 + 2\sqrt{5}}$$ b 16

$$a = \frac{1}{2}\,r\sqrt{10 - 2\sqrt{5}}$$ b 17

$$\varrho = \frac{1}{4}\,r\sqrt{6 + 2\sqrt{5}}$$ b 18

construction :
$\overline{AB} = 0.5\,r, \;\; \overline{BC} = \overline{BD}, \;\; \overline{CD} = \overline{CE}$

hexagon

$$A = \frac{3}{2}\,a^2\sqrt{3}$$ b 19

$$d = 2\,a$$ b 20

$$= \frac{2}{\sqrt{3}}\,s \;\approx\; 1 \cdot 155\,s$$ b 21

$$s = \frac{\sqrt{3}}{2}\,d \;\approx\; 0 \cdot 866\,d$$ b 22

octagon

$$A = 2\,a\,s \;\approx\; 0 \cdot 83\,s^2$$ b 23

$$= 2\,s\sqrt{d^2 - s^2}$$ b 24

$$a = s\,\tan 22 \cdot 5^0 \approx 0 \cdot 415\,s$$ b 25

$$s = d\,\cos 22 \cdot 5^0 \approx 0 \cdot 924\,d$$ b 26

$$d = \frac{s}{\cos 22 \cdot 5^0} \;\approx\; 1 \cdot 083\,s$$ b 27

polygon

$$A = A_1 + A_2 + A_3$$ b 28

$$= \frac{a\,h_1 + b\,h_2 + b\,h_3}{2}$$ b 29

		circle
b 30	$A = \dfrac{\pi}{4} d^2 = \pi r^2$	
b 31	$\approx 0.785 \, d^2$	
b 32	$U = 2\pi r = \pi d$	

		annulus
b 33	$A = \dfrac{\pi}{4} (D^2 - d^2)$	
b 34	$= \pi (d + b) b$	
b 35	$b = \dfrac{D - d}{2}$	

		sector of a circle
b 36	$A = \dfrac{\pi}{360^0} r^2 \alpha = \dfrac{\hat{a}}{2} r^2$	
b 37	$= \dfrac{b r}{2}$	
b 38	$b = \dfrac{\pi}{180^0} r \alpha$	
b 39	$\hat{a} = \dfrac{\pi}{180^0} \alpha \quad (\hat{a} = \alpha \text{ in circular measure})$	

		segment of a circle
b 40	$s = 2 r \sin\dfrac{\alpha}{2}$	
b 41	$A = \dfrac{h}{6 s} (3 h^2 + 4 s^2) = \dfrac{r^2}{2} (\hat{a} - \sin \alpha)$	
b 42	$r = \dfrac{h}{2} + \dfrac{s^2}{8 h}$	
b 43	$h = r(1 - \cos\dfrac{\alpha}{2}) = \dfrac{s}{2} \tan\dfrac{\alpha}{4}$	
b 44	$\hat{a}$ see formula b 39	

		ellipse
b 45	$A = \dfrac{\pi}{4} D d = \pi a b$	
b 46	$U \approx \pi \dfrac{D + d}{2}$	
b 47	$= \pi(a+b)\left[1 + \dfrac{1}{4}\lambda^2 + \dfrac{1}{64}\lambda^4 + \dfrac{1}{256}\lambda^6 + \dfrac{25}{16384}\lambda^8 + \ldots\right], \text{ where } \lambda = \dfrac{a - b}{a + b}$	

SOLID BODIES

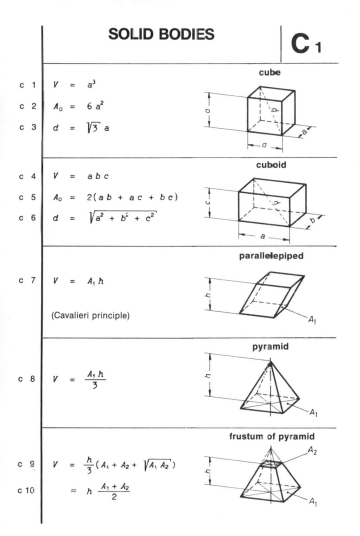

cube

c 1 $V = a^3$

c 2 $A_0 = 6\,a^2$

c 3 $d = \sqrt{3}\,a$

cuboid

c 4 $V = a\,b\,c$

c 5 $A_0 = 2(a\,b + a\,c + b\,c)$

c 6 $d = \sqrt{a^2 + b^2 + c^2}$

parallelepiped

c 7 $V = A_1\,h$

(Cavalieri principle)

pyramid

c 8 $V = \dfrac{A_1\,h}{3}$

frustum of pyramid

c 9 $V = \dfrac{h}{3}(A_1 + A_2 + \sqrt{A_1\,A_2})$

c 10 $\approx h\,\dfrac{A_1 + A_2}{2}$

cylinder	$V = \dfrac{\pi}{4} d^2 h$ c 11
	$A_m = 2\pi r h$ c 12
	$A_o = 2\pi r (r + h)$ c 13

hollow cylinder	$V = \dfrac{\pi}{4} h (D^2 - d^2)$ c 14

cone	$V = \dfrac{\pi}{3} r^2 h$ c 15
	$A_m = \pi r m$ c 16
	$A_o = \pi r (r + m)$ c 17
	$m = \sqrt{h^2 + r^2}$ c 18
	$A_2 : A_1 = x^2 : h^2$ c 19

frustum of cone	$V = \dfrac{\pi}{12} h (D^2 + Dd + d^2)$ c 20
	$A_m = \dfrac{\pi}{2} m (D + d) = 2\pi p m$ c 21
	$m = \sqrt{\left(\dfrac{D - d}{2}\right)^2 + h^2}$ c 22

sphere	$V = \dfrac{4}{3} \pi r^3 = \dfrac{1}{6} \pi d^3$ c 23
	$\approx 4 \cdot 189 \, r^3$ c 24
	$A_o = 4\pi r^2 = \pi d^2$ c 25

zone of a sphere

c 26 $V = \frac{\pi}{6} h (3 a^2 + 3 b^2 + h^2)$

c 27 $A_m = 2 \pi r h$

c 28 $A_0 = \pi(2 r h - a^2 + b^2)$

segment of a sphere

c 29 $V = \frac{\pi}{6} h (\frac{3}{4} s^2 + h^2)$

        $= \pi h^2 (r - \frac{h}{3})$

c 30 $A_m = 2 \pi r h$

c 31 $= \frac{\pi}{4} (s^2 + 4 h^2)$

sector of a sphere

c 32 $V = \frac{2}{3} \pi r^2 h$

c 33 $A_0 = \frac{\pi}{2} r (4 h + s)$

sphere with cylindrical boring

c 34 $V = \frac{\pi}{6} h^3$

c 35 $A_0 = 2 \pi h (R + r)$

sphere with conical boring

c 36 $V = \frac{2}{3} \pi r^2 h$

c 37 $A_0 = 2 \pi r \left(h + \sqrt{r^2 - \frac{h^2}{4}} \right)$

torus

$$V = \frac{\pi^2}{4} D d^2 \qquad \text{c 38}$$

$$A_o = \pi^2 D d \qquad \text{c 39}$$

sliced cylinder

$$V = \frac{\pi}{4} d^2 h \qquad \text{c 40}$$

ungula

$$V = \frac{2}{3} r^2 h \qquad \text{c 41}$$

$$A_m = 2 r h \qquad \text{c 42}$$

$$A_o = A_m + \frac{\pi}{2} r^2 + \frac{\pi}{2} r \sqrt{r^2 + h^2} \qquad \text{c 43}$$

barrel

$$V \approx \frac{\pi}{12} h (2 D^2 + d^2) \qquad \text{c 44}$$

prismoid

$$V = \frac{h}{6} (A_1 + A_2 + 4 A) \qquad \text{c 45}$$

This formula may be used for calculations involving solids shown in fig. C1...C3 and thus spheres and parts of spheres.

Rules for powers and roots

	general	numerical examples
d 1	$p\,a^n \pm q\,a^n = (p \pm q)a^n$	$3a^4 + 4a^4 = 7a^4$
d 2	$a^m\,a^n = a^{m+n}$	$a^8 \times a^4 = a^{12}$
d 3	$a^m/a^n = a^{m-n}$	$a^8/a^2 = a^{8-2} = a^6$
d 4	$(a^m)^n = (a^n)^m = a^{mn}$	$(a^3)^2 = (a^2)^3 = a^{2\times 3} = a^6$
d 5	$a^{-n} = 1/a^n$	$a^{-4} = 1/a^4$
d 6	$\dfrac{a^n}{b^n} = \left(\dfrac{a}{b}\right)^n$	$\dfrac{a^3}{b^3} = \left(\dfrac{a}{b}\right)^3$
d 7	$p\sqrt[n]{a} \pm q\sqrt[n]{a} = (p \pm q)\sqrt[n]{a}$	$4\sqrt[3]{x} + 7\sqrt[3]{x} = 11\sqrt[3]{x}$
d 8	$\sqrt[n]{a\,b} = \sqrt[n]{a} \times \sqrt[n]{b}$	$\sqrt[4]{16 \times 81} = \sqrt[4]{16} \times \sqrt[4]{81}$
d 9	$\dfrac{\sqrt[n]{a}}{\sqrt[n]{b}} = \sqrt[n]{\dfrac{a}{b}} = \left(\dfrac{a}{b}\right)^{\frac{1}{n}}$	$\dfrac{\sqrt{8}}{\sqrt{2}} = \sqrt{4} = 2$
d10	$\sqrt[nx]{a^{mx}} = \sqrt[n]{a^m}$	$\sqrt[6]{a^8} = \sqrt[3]{a^4}$
d11	$\sqrt[n]{a^m} = \left(\sqrt[n]{a}\right)^m = a^{\frac{m}{n}}$ +)	$\sqrt[4]{a^3} = \left(\sqrt[4]{a}\right)^3 = a^{\frac{3}{4}}$
d12	$\sqrt{-a} = i\sqrt{a}$	$\sqrt{-9} = i\sqrt{9} = i\,3$

+) Not applicable to special calculations } e.g. $\sqrt{(-2)^2} = \pm 2$; or $(\sqrt{-2})^2 = -2$.

Exponents of powers and roots have to be non-dimensional quantities!

Quadratic equation (equation of the second degree)

d13	Normal form	$x^2 + px + q = 0$
d14	Solutions	$x_1\,;\quad x_2 = -\dfrac{p}{2} \pm \sqrt{\dfrac{p^2}{4} - q}$
d15	Vieta's rule	$p = -(x_1 + x_2);\quad q = x_1 \cdot x_2$

Iterative calculation of an n-th root

d16 When $x = \sqrt[n]{A}$, then $x = \dfrac{1}{n}\left[(n-1)x_0 + \dfrac{A}{x_0^{\,n-1}}\right]$,

where x_0 is the initially estimated value of x. Repeatedly inserting the obtained x as a new value of x_0 gradually increases the accuracy of x.

Expansion of general algebraic expressions

d 17 $\quad (a \pm b)^2 = a^2 \pm 2ab + b^2$

d 18 $\quad (a \pm b)^3 = a^3 \pm 3a^2 b + 3ab^2 \pm b^3$

d 19 $\quad (a + b)^n = a^n + \dfrac{n}{1} a^{n-1} b + \dfrac{n(n-1)}{1 \cdot 2} a^{n-2} b^2 +$
$$+ \dfrac{n(n-1)(n-2)}{1 \times 2 \times 3} a^{n-3} b^3 + \ldots b^n$$

d 20 $\quad (a + b + c)^2 = a^2 + 2ab + 2ac + b^2 + 2bc + c^2$

d 21 $\quad (a - b + c)^2 = a^2 - 2ab + 2ac + b^2 - 2bc + c^2$

d 22 $\quad a^2 - b^2 = (a + b)(a - b)$

d 23 $\quad a^3 + b^3 = (a + b)(a^2 - ab + b^2)$

d 24 $\quad a^3 - b^3 = (a - b)(a^2 + ab + b^2)$

d 25 $\quad a^n - b^n = (a - b)(a^{n-1} + a^{n-2} b + a^{n-3} b^2 + \ldots$
$$\ldots + ab^{n-2} + b^{n-1})$$

Binomial theorem

d 26 $\quad (a + b)^n = \dbinom{n}{0} a^n + \dbinom{n}{1} a^{n-1} b + \dbinom{n}{2} a^{n-2} b^2 + \dbinom{n}{3} a^{n-3} b^3 + \ldots$ *)

d 27 $\quad \dbinom{n}{k} = \dfrac{n(n-1)(n-2) \ldots (n-k+1)}{1 \times 2 \times 3 \ldots k}$ *)

*) n must be a whole number

d 28 $\quad (a + b)^4 = 1a^4 + \dfrac{4}{1} a^{4-1} b + \dfrac{4 \times 3}{1 \times 2} a^{4-2} b^2 + \dfrac{4 \times 3 \times 2}{1 \times 2 \times 3} a^{4-3} b^3 + b^4$

$\qquad\qquad\quad = a^4 + 4a^3 b + 6a^2 b^2 + 4 a \times b^3 + b^4$

Diagrammatic solution

d 29 **Coefficient – Pascal triangle**

$(a + b)^0$ $\qquad\qquad\qquad\qquad\qquad\qquad 1$

$(a + b)^1$ $\qquad\qquad\qquad\qquad\qquad 1 \quad 1$

$(a + b)^2$ $\qquad\qquad\qquad\qquad 1 \quad 2 \quad 1$

$(a + b)^3$ $\qquad\qquad\qquad 1 \quad 3 \quad 3 \quad 1$

$(a + b)^4$ $\qquad\qquad 1 \quad 4 \quad \boxed{6 \quad 4} \quad 1$

$(a + b)^5$ $\qquad\quad 1 \quad \boxed{5 \quad 10} \quad 10 \quad 5 \quad 1$

$(a + b)^6$ $\quad 1 \quad 6 \quad 15 \quad 20 \quad 15 \quad 6 \quad 1$

Continue with each line starting and finishing with 1. The second and penultimate numbers should be the exponents, the others the sum of those to the right and left immediately above them.

d 30 **Exponents:** The sum of the exponents a and b in each separate term is equal to the binomial exponent n. As the power of a decreases the power of b increases.

d 31 **Signs:** $(a + b)$ is always positive
$\qquad\quad (a - b)$ is initially positive and changes from term to term.

d 32 **Examples:**

$\quad (a + b)^5 = a^5 + 5a^4 b + 10a^3 b^2 + 10a^2 b^3 + 5ab^4 + b^5$

$\quad (a - b)^5 = +a^5 - 5a^4 b + 10a^3 b^2 - 10a^2 b^3 + 5ab^4 - b^5$

Proper fraction rational function

$$y(x) = \frac{P(x)}{Q(x)} = \frac{a_0 + a_1 x + a_2 x^2 + \ldots + a_m x^m}{b_0 + b_1 x + b_2 x^2 + \ldots + b_n x^n} \qquad n > m$$

n and m whole numbers

Coefficients a_v, b_μ can be real or complex. If n_i are the zeros of the denominator $Q(x)$ the factorized form from $y(x)$ is:

d 33
$$y(x) = \frac{P(x)}{Q(x)} = \frac{P(x)}{\alpha(x-n_1)^{k_1} \cdot (x-n_2)^{k_2} \ldots (x-n_q)^{k_q}}$$

where real or complex zeros of $Q(x)$ can occur $k_1, k_2 \ldots k_q$ times; α is a constant factor.

Partial fraction expansion

For easy manipulation of $y(x)$, e.g. for integration, the expansion $y(x)$ into partial fractions is often appropriate

d 34
$$y(x) = \frac{P(x)}{Q(x)} = \frac{A_{11}}{x-n_1} + \frac{A_{12}}{(x-n_1)^2} + \ldots + \frac{A_{1k1}}{(x-n_1)^{k_1}} +$$
$$+ \frac{A_{21}}{x-n_2} + \frac{A_{22}}{(x-n_2)^2} + \ldots + \frac{A_{2k2}}{(x-n_2)^{k_2}} + \ldots +$$
$$+ \frac{A_{q1}}{x-n_q} + \frac{A_{q2}}{(x-n_q)^2} + \ldots + \frac{A_{qkq}}{(x-n_q)^{kc}}$$

Complex zeros occur in pairs (conjugate complex numbers) when $Q(x)$ has real coefficients. For expansion these pairs are combined to real partial fractions. If in d 33 the zeros $n_2 = \bar{n}_1$ (n_2 is conjugate complex to n_1) and if due to the pairwise occurrence $k_1 = k_2 = k$, the partial fractions of d 34 with the constants $A_{11} \ldots A_{2k2}$ can be combined to the following partial fractions:

d 35
$$\frac{B_{11} x + C_{11}}{x^2 + ax + b} + \frac{B_{12} x + C_{12}}{(x^2 + ax + b)^2} + \ldots + \frac{B_{1k} x + C_{1k}}{(x^2 + ax + b)^k}$$

To obtain the constants A_{11} to A_{qkq} resp. B_{11}, C_{11} to B_{1k}, C_{1k} coefficients of equal power in x at the left side of the equation are compared with those at the right side after having converted to the common denominator $Q(x)$.

Example:
$$y(x) = \frac{2x-1}{(x+1-2i)(x+1+2i)(x+1)^2} = \frac{2x-1}{Q(x)} = \frac{B_{11}x + C_{11}}{x^2+2x+5} + \frac{A_{q1}}{x+1} + \frac{A_{q2}}{(x+1)^2}$$

$$\frac{2x-1}{Q(x)} = \frac{B_{11}x(x+1)^2 + C_{11}(x+1)^2 + A_{q1}(x+1)(x^2+2x+5) + A_{q2}(x^2+2x+5)}{Q(x)}$$

$$2x-1 = (A_{q1} + B_{11})x^3 + (3A_{q1} + A_{q2} + 2B_{11} + C_{11})x^2 +$$
$$+ (7A_{q1} + 2A_{q2} + B_{11} + 2C_{11})x + 5A_{q1} + 5A_{q2} + C_1$$

Comparison of coefficients between left and right side:

$B_{11} = -1/2$; $C_{11} = 1/4$; $A_{q1} = 1/2$; $A_{q2} = -3/4$.

If there are single zeros n_i, the constants $A_{11}, A_{21} \ldots A_{q1}$ of equation d 34 can be obtained by:

d 36
$$A_{11} = P(n_1)/Q'(n_1); \quad A_{21} = P(n_2)/Q'(n_2); \ldots A_q = P(n_q)/Q'(n_q)$$

General

	system	log to the base of	terminology
d 37	$\log_a$	a	log to base a
d 38	$\log_{10} = \log$	10	common log
d 39	$\log_e = \ln$	e	natural log
d 40	$\log_2 = \text{ld}$	2	log to base 2

The symbols in $\log_a x = b$ are called: a base
     x antilogarithm
     b logarithm (log)

Rules for logarithmic calculations

d 41	$\log_a (x\,y) = \log_a x + \log_a y$
d 42	$\log_a \dfrac{x}{y} = \log_a x - \log_a y$
d 43	$\log_a x^n = n \times \log_a x$
d 44	$\log_a \sqrt[n]{x} = \dfrac{1}{n} \log_a x$

Exponential equation

d 45	$a^x = b = e^{x \ln a}$
d 46	hence $\quad x = \dfrac{\log b}{\log a} \quad \bigg| \quad a = \sqrt[x]{b}$

Conversion of logarithms

d 47	$\log x =$	$\log e \times \ln x$	$= 0{\cdot}434294 \times \ln x$
d 48	$\ln x =$	$\dfrac{\log x}{\log e}$	$= 2{\cdot}302585 \times \log x$
d 49	$\text{ld}\, x =$	$1{\cdot}442695 \times \ln x$	$= 3{\cdot}321923 \times \log x$

Base of the natural logs $e = 2{\cdot}71828183\ldots$

Key to common logarithm of a number

d 50	$\log 0{\cdot}01$	$= -2.$	or	$8.\ \ldots-10$
d 51	$\log 0{\cdot}1$	$= -1.$	or	$9.\ \ldots-10$
d 52	$\log 1$	$= 0.$		
d 53	$\log 10$	$= 1.$		
d 54	$\log 100$	$= 2.$		
		etc.		

Note: The antilogarithm always has to be a non-dimensional quantity.

Permutations

An ordered selection or arrangement of r out of n things is called a "permutation" of the n things taken r at a time. The number of these permutations is denoted by:

d 55

$$P_r^n = n(n-1)(n-2)\ldots(n-r+1), \qquad n \geq r$$

If $r = n$, this becomes

$$P_n^n = P_n = n(n-1)(n-2)\ldots 1 = n! \quad *)$$

Example: The $n = 3$ things a, b, c can be permutated with each other (i.e. 3 at a time) in the following 6 ways:

$$\begin{array}{ccc} abc & bac & cab \\ acb & bca & cba. \end{array} \qquad \text{Here } r = n = 3.$$

d 56

$$P_3 = 3! = 1 \times 2 \times 3 = 6.$$

Special case: The number of permutations of n things taken all together incorporating n_1 of one sort, n_2 of another sort and n_r of a rth sort is:

d 57

$$P_{n,r} = \frac{n!}{n_1! \times n_2! \times \ldots n_r!}$$

Example: The $n = 3$ things a, a, b can be permutated the following 3 ways:

$$aab \quad aba \quad baa. \qquad \text{Here } n = 3, n_1 = 2, n_2 = 1.$$

$$P_{3,2} = \frac{3!}{2! \times 1!} = \frac{1 \times 2 \times 3}{1 \times 2 \times 1} = 3.$$

Combinations

A selection of r out n things without regard to order is called "combination" of n things taken r at a time. The number of these combinations is denoted by

d 58

$$C_r^n = \frac{n!}{r!(n-r)!} = \binom{n}{r} \quad **)$$

Example: The $n = 3$ things a, b, c taken together give only the one combination abc. Here $n = 3$, $r = 3$.

Hence

$$C_3^3 = \binom{3}{3} = \frac{3 \times 2 \times 1}{1 \times 2 \times 3} = 1.$$

The table on page D 6 compares combinations and permutations (with and without the things repeating).

---

*) $n!$ is pronounced „n factorial"
**) Symbol usual for binomial coefficient (see d 27)

Combinations and Permutations
(Explanations see D 5)

	d 59	d 60	d 61	d 62
	Number of permutations **with** repeating taking into account the positions of things	Number of permutations **without** repeating taking into account the positions of things	Number of combinations **with** repeating regardless of the positions of things	Number of combinations **without** repeating regardless of the positions of things
Formula	$wP_r^n = n^r$	$P_r^n = \dfrac{n!}{(n-r)!} = \left(\dbinom{n}{r}\right) r!$ *) $= n(n-1)\cdots(n-r+1)$	$wC_r^n = \dbinom{n+r-1}{r}$ *) $= \dfrac{n(n+1)\cdots(n+r-1)}{r!}$	$C_r^n = \dfrac{n!}{r!(n-r)!} = \left(\dbinom{n}{r}\right)$ *) $= \dfrac{n(n-1)\cdots(n-r+1)}{r!}$
Explanation of symbols	*P:* Number of possible permutations		*C:* Number of possible combinations *n:* Number of things given *r:* Number of things selected from *n* given things	
Examples — Given	*r* = 2 things selected from the 3 given things			*n* = 3 things *a, b, c*
Possibilities	aa ab ac ba bb bc ca cb cc	· ab ac ba · bc ca cb ·	aa ab ac · bb bc · · cc	· ab ac · · bc · · ·
Calculation of the number of possibilities	$wP_2^3 = 3^2$ $= 9$	$P_2^3 = \left(\dbinom{3}{2}\right) 2!$ $= \dfrac{3!}{(3-2)!} = \dfrac{3!}{1!}$ $= \dfrac{1\times2\times3}{1} = 6$	$wC_2^3 = \left(\dbinom{3+2-1}{2}\right)$ $= \left(\dbinom{4}{2}\right)$ $= \dfrac{4\times3}{1\times2} = 6$	$C_2^3 = \dfrac{3!}{2!(3-2)!}$ $= \left(\dbinom{3}{2}\right)$ $= \dfrac{3\times2}{1\times2} = 3$
Note	*ab* and *ba* for example are different permutations		*ab* and *ba* for example are the same combination	

*) calculation according to d 27

w : with repeating

Second order determinants

d 63

$$a_{11}\,x + a_{12}\,y = r_1$$
$$a_{21}\,x + a_{22}\,y = r_2$$

$$D = \begin{vmatrix} a_{11} & a_{12} \\ a_{21} & a_{22} \end{vmatrix} = a_{11}\,a_{22} - a_{21}\,a_{12}$$

insert r column in place of

| column x | column y |

d 64

$$D_1 = \begin{vmatrix} r_1 & a_{12} \\ r_2 & a_{22} \end{vmatrix} = \begin{matrix} r_1\,a_{22} \\ -r_2\,a_{12} \end{matrix}$$

$$D_2 = \begin{vmatrix} a_{11} & r_1 \\ a_{21} & r_2 \end{vmatrix} = \begin{matrix} r_2\,a_{11} \\ -r_1\,a_{21} \end{matrix}$$

$$x = \frac{D_1}{D}$$

$$y = \frac{D_2}{D}$$

Third order determinants (Sarrus rule)

d 65

$$a_{11}\,x + a_{12}\,y + a_{13}\,z = r_1$$
$$a_{21}\,x + a_{22}\,y + a_{23}\,z = r_2$$
$$a_{31}\,x + a_{32}\,y + a_{33}\,z = r_3$$

d 66

$$D = \begin{vmatrix} a_{11} & a_{12} & a_{13} \\ a_{21} & a_{22} & a_{23} \\ a_{31} & a_{32} & a_{33} \end{vmatrix} \begin{matrix} a_{11} & a_{12} \\ a_{21} & a_{22} \\ a_{31} & a_{32} \end{matrix} = \begin{matrix} a_{11}\,a_{22}\,a_{33} + a_{12}\,a_{23}\,a_{31} \\ +a_{13}\,a_{21}\,a_{32} - a_{13}\,a_{22}\,a_{31} \\ -a_{11}\,a_{23}\,a_{32} - a_{12}\,a_{21}\,a_{33} \end{matrix}$$

insert r column for x column:

d 67

$$D_1 = \begin{vmatrix} r_1 & a_{12} & a_{13} \\ r_2 & a_{22} & a_{23} \\ r_3 & a_{32} & a_{33} \end{vmatrix} \begin{matrix} r_1 & a_{12} \\ r_2 & a_{22} \\ r_3 & a_{32} \end{matrix} = \begin{matrix} r_1\,a_{22}\,a_{33} + a_{12}\,a_{23}\,r_3 \\ +a_{13}\,r_2\,a_{32} - a_{13}\,a_{22}\,r_3 \\ -r_1\,a_{23}\,a_{32} - a_{12}\,r_2\,a_{33} \end{matrix}$$

determine D_2 and D_3 similarly by replacing the y- and z-column by the r-column:

d 68

$$x = \frac{D_1}{D} \qquad y = \frac{D_2}{D} \qquad z = \frac{D_3}{D}$$

continued on D 8

Determinants of more than the 2nd order:

(The Sarrus Rule, see D 7, may be used for determinants of higher order than the 3rd).

By adding or subtracting suitable multiples of two rows or columns, endeavour to obtain zero values. Expand the determinant starting from the row or column containing most zeros. Alternate the signs of terms, starting with a_{11} as +.

Example:

d 69

$$
\begin{vmatrix}
c_{11}^{+} & a_{12}^{-} & a_{13}^{+} & 0^{-} \\
c_{21} & a_{22} & a_{23} & a_{24}^{+} \\
c_{31} & a_{32} & a_{33} & a_{34}^{-} \\
c_{41} & a_{42} & a_{43} & 0^{+}
\end{vmatrix}
$$

Expand on 4th column:

d 70

$$
a_{24}\begin{vmatrix} a_{11}^{+} & a_{12}^{-} & a_{13}^{+} \\ a_{31} & a_{32} & a_{33} \\ a_{41} & a_{42} & a_{43} \end{vmatrix} \quad -a_{34}\begin{vmatrix} a_{11}^{+} & a_{12}^{-} & a_{13}^{+} \\ a_{21} & a_{22} & a_{23} \\ a_{41} & a_{42} & a_{43} \end{vmatrix}
$$

Further expand as

d 71

$$
D = a_{24}\left(a_{11}\begin{vmatrix} a_{32} & a_{33} \\ a_{42} & a_{43} \end{vmatrix} -a_{12}\begin{vmatrix} a_{31} & a_{33} \\ a_{41} & a_{43} \end{vmatrix} +a_{13}\begin{vmatrix} a_{31} & a_{32} \\ a_{41} & a_{42} \end{vmatrix} \right) -a_{34}(\ldots)
$$

To form the determinants $D_1, D_2, \ldots$ (see D 7) substitute the r column for the first, second, ... column of D, and evaluate in the same way as for D.

For determinant of the nth order, find $u_{1 \ldots n}$ from the formulae:

d 72

$$
u_1 = \frac{D_1}{D} , \quad u_2 = \frac{D_2}{D} , \quad \ldots u_n = \frac{D_n}{D}
$$

Note: For determinants of the nth order continue until determinants of the 3rd order have been obtained.

Arithmetic series

The sequence 1, 4, 7, 10 etc. is called an arithmetic series. (The difference between two consecutive terms is constant).

Formulae:

d 73
$$a_n = a_1 + (n - 1)d$$

d 74
$$s_n = \frac{n}{2}(a_1 + a_n) = a_1 n + \frac{n(n-1)d}{2}$$

Arithmetic mean:

Each term of an arithmetic series is the arithmetic mean a_m of its adjacent terms a_{m-1} and a_{m+1}.

Thus, the mth term is

d 75
$$a_m = \frac{a_{m-1} + a_{m+1}}{2} \qquad \text{for} \quad 1 < m < n$$

(e.g. in the above series) $\qquad a_3 = \dfrac{4 + 10}{2} = 7$)

Geometric series

The sequence 1, 2 4, 8 etc is called a geometric series. (The quotient of two consecutive terms is constant).

Formulae:

d 76
$$a_n = a_1 \, q^{n-1}$$

d 77
$$s_n = a_1 \frac{q^n - 1}{q - 1} = \frac{q \times a_n - a_1}{q - 1}$$

Geometric mean:

Each term of a geometric series is the geometric mean a_m of its adjacent terms a_{m-1} and a_{m+1}.

Thus, the mth term is

d 78
$$a_m = \sqrt{a_{m-1} \; a_{m+1}} \qquad \text{for} \quad 1 < m < n$$

(e.g. in the above series) $\qquad a_3 = \sqrt{2 \times 8} = 4$)

For infinite geometric series $(n \to \infty; \; |q| < 1)$ the following statements apply

d 79
$$a_n = \lim_{n \to \infty} a_n = 0 \; ; \qquad s_n = \lim_{n \to \infty} s_n = a_1 \frac{1}{1 - q}$$

a_1 : initial term	n : number of terms
a_n : final term	s_n : sum to n terms
d : difference between two consecutive terms	q : quotient of two consecutive terms

Binominal series

d 80
$$f(x) = (1 \pm x)^{\alpha} = 1 \pm \binom{a}{1}x + \binom{a}{2}x^2 \pm \binom{a}{3}x^3 + \ldots$$

a may be either positive or negative, a whole number or a fraction.

Expansion of the binomia coefficient:

$$\binom{a}{n} = \frac{a(a-1)(a-2)(a-3)\ldots(a-n+1)}{1 \times 2 \times 3 \ldots \times n}$$

Examples:
	for

d 81
$$\frac{1}{1 \pm x} = (1 \pm x)^{-1} = 1 \mp x + x^2 \mp x^3 + \ldots \quad |x| < 1$$

d 82
$$\sqrt{1 \pm x} = (1 \pm x)^{\frac{1}{2}} = 1 \pm \frac{1}{2}x - \frac{1}{8}x^2 \pm \frac{1}{16}x^3 - \ldots \quad |x| < 1$$

d 83
$$\frac{1}{\sqrt{1 \pm x}} = (1 \pm x)^{-\frac{1}{2}} = 1 \mp \frac{1}{2}x + \frac{3}{8}x^2 \mp \frac{5}{16}x^3 + \ldots \quad |x| < 1$$

Taylor series

d 84
$$f(x) = f(a) + \frac{f'(a)}{1!}(x-a) + \frac{f''(a)}{2!}(x-a)^2 + \ldots$$

putting $a = 0$ gives the MacLaurin series:

d 85
$$f(x) = f(0) + \frac{f'(0)}{1!}x + \frac{f''(0)}{2!}x^2 + \ldots$$

Examples:
	for

d 86
$$e^x = 1 + \frac{x}{1!} + \frac{x^2}{2!} + \frac{x^3}{3!} + \ldots \quad \text{all } x$$

d 87
$$a^x = 1 + \frac{x \ln a}{1!} + \frac{(x \ln a)^2}{2!} + \frac{(x \ln a)^3}{3!} + \ldots \quad \text{all } x$$

d 88
$$\ln x = 2\left[\frac{x-1}{x+1} + \frac{1}{3}\left(\frac{x-1}{x+1}\right)^3 + \frac{1}{5}\left(\frac{x-1}{x+1}\right)^5 + \ldots\right] \quad x > 0$$

d 89
$$\ln(1+x) = x - \frac{x^2}{2} + \frac{x^3}{3} - \frac{x^4}{4} + \frac{x^5}{5} - \ldots \quad \begin{array}{l} -1 < x \\ x \leq +1 \end{array}$$

d 90
$$\ln 2 = 1 - \frac{1}{2} + \frac{1}{3} - \frac{1}{4} + \frac{1}{5} - \ldots$$

continued on D 11

Taylor series
(continued)

	Examples	for
d 91	$\sin x = x - \dfrac{x^3}{3!} + \dfrac{x^5}{5!} - \dfrac{x^7}{7!} + \ldots$	all x
d 92	$\cos x = 1 - \dfrac{x^2}{2!} + \dfrac{x^4}{4!} - \dfrac{x^6}{6!} + \ldots$	all x
d 93	$\tan x = x + \dfrac{1}{3} x^3 + \dfrac{2}{15} x^5 + \dfrac{17}{315} x^7 + \ldots$	$|x| < \dfrac{\pi}{2}$
d 94	$\cot x = \dfrac{1}{x} - \dfrac{1}{3} x - \dfrac{1}{45} x^3 - \dfrac{2}{945} x^5 - \ldots$	$0 < |x|$ $|x| < \pi$
d 95	$\arcsin x = x + \dfrac{1}{2} \dfrac{x^3}{3} + \dfrac{1 \times 3}{2 \times 4} \dfrac{x^5}{5} + \dfrac{1 \times 3 \times 5}{2 \times 4 \times 6} \dfrac{x^7}{7} + \ldots$	$|x| \leqq 1$
d 96	$\arccos x = \dfrac{\pi}{2} - \arcsin x$	$|x| \leqq 1$
d 97	$\arctan x = x - \dfrac{x^3}{3} + \dfrac{x^5}{5} - \dfrac{x^7}{7} + \dfrac{z^9}{9} - \quad \ldots$	$|x| \leqq 1$
d 98	$\text{arccot } x = \dfrac{\pi}{2} - \arctan x$	$|x| \leqq 1$
d 99	$\sinh x = x + \dfrac{x^3}{3!} + \dfrac{x^5}{5!} + \dfrac{x^7}{7!} + \dfrac{x^9}{9!} + \ldots$	all x
d100	$\cosh x = 1 + \dfrac{x^2}{2!} + \dfrac{x^4}{4!} + \dfrac{x^6}{6!} + \dfrac{x^8}{8!} + \ldots$	all x
d101	$\tanh x = x - \dfrac{1}{3} x^3 + \dfrac{2}{15} x^5 - \dfrac{17}{315} x^7 + \ldots$	$|x| < \dfrac{\pi}{2}$
d102	$\coth x = \dfrac{1}{x} + \dfrac{1}{3} x - \dfrac{1}{45} x^3 + \dfrac{2}{945} x^5 - \ldots$	$0 < |x|$ $|x| < \pi$
d103	$\text{arsinh } x = x - \dfrac{1}{2} \dfrac{x^3}{3} + \dfrac{1 \times 3}{2 \times 4} \dfrac{x^5}{5} - \dfrac{1 \times 3 \times 5}{2 \times 4 \times 6} \dfrac{x^7}{7} + \ldots$	$|x| < 1$
d104	$\text{arcosh } x = \ln 2x - \dfrac{1}{2} \dfrac{1}{2x^2} - \dfrac{1 \times 3}{2 \times 4} \dfrac{1}{4x^4} - \dfrac{1 \times 3 \times 5}{2 \times 4 \times 6} \dfrac{1}{6x^6} + \ldots$	$|x| > 1$
d105	$\text{artanh } x = x + \dfrac{x^3}{3} + \dfrac{x^5}{5} + \dfrac{x^7}{7} + \dfrac{x^9}{9} + \ldots$	$|x| < 1$
d106	$\text{arcoth } x = \dfrac{1}{x} + \dfrac{1}{3x^3} + \dfrac{1}{5x^5} + \dfrac{1}{7x^7} + \quad \ldots$	$|x| > 1$

Fourier series

General: Each periodic function $f(x)$, which can be subdivided into a finite number of continuous intervals within its period $-\pi \leq x \leq \pi$, may be expanded in this interval into convergent series of the following form ($x = \omega t$):

d107
$$f(x) = \frac{a_0}{2} + \sum_{n=1}^{\infty} \left[a_n \cos(nx) + b_n \sin(nx) \right]$$

The various coefficients can be calculated by:

d108
$$a_k = \frac{1}{\pi} \int_{-\pi}^{\pi} f(x) \cos(kx)\,dx \qquad b_k = \frac{1}{\pi} \int_{-\pi}^{\pi} f(x) \sin(kx)\,dx$$

with the index $k = 0, 1, 2 \ldots$ $2, \ldots$

Simplified calculation of coefficient for symmetr. waveforms:

Even function: $f(x) = f(-x)$

d109
$$a_k = \frac{2}{\pi} \int_{0}^{\pi} f(x) \cos(kx)\,dx$$

with the index $k = 0, 1, 2 \ldots$

d110 $b_k = 0$

Odd function: $f(x) = -f(-x)$

d111 $a_k = 0$

d112
$$b_k = \frac{2}{\pi} \int_{0}^{\pi} f(x) \sin(kx)\,dx$$

with the index $k = 0, 1, 2, \ldots$

Even-harmonic functions	Odd-harmonic functions
d113 $f(x) = f(-x)$ and	$f(x) = -f(x)$ and
d114 $f(\frac{\pi}{2} + x) = -f(\frac{\pi}{2} - x)$ give:	$f(\frac{\pi}{2} + x) = -f(\frac{\pi}{2} - x)$ give:
d115 $a_k = \frac{4}{\pi} \int_{0}^{\pi/2} f(x) \cos(kx)\,dx$	$b_k = \frac{4}{\pi} \int_{0}^{\pi/2} f(x) \sin(kx)\,dx$
for $k = 1, 3, 5, \ldots$	for $k = 1, 3, 5, \ldots$
d116 $a_k = 0$ for $k = 0, 2, 4, \ldots$	$c_k = 0$ for $k = 0, 1, 2, \ldots$
d117 $b_k = 0$ for $k = 1, 2, 3, \ldots$	$b_k = 0$ for $k = 2, 4, 6, \ldots$

Table of Fourier expansions

d118	$y = a$	for	$0 < x < \pi$
d119	$y = -a$	for	$\pi < x < 2\pi$

d120
$$y = \frac{4a}{\pi}\left[\sin x + \frac{\sin (3x)}{3} + \frac{\sin (5x)}{5} + \dots\right]$$

d121	$y = a$	for	$a < x < \pi-a$
d122	$y = -a$	for	$\pi+a < x < 2\pi-a$

d123
$$y = \frac{4a}{\pi}\left[\cos a \sin x + \frac{1}{3}\cos (3a) \sin (3x) + \frac{1}{5}\cos (5a) \sin (5x) + \dots\right]$$

d124	$y = a$	for	$a < x < 2\pi-a$
d125	$y = f(2\pi + x)$		

d126
$$y = \frac{2a}{\pi}\left[\frac{\pi-a}{2} - \frac{\sin(\pi-a)}{1}\cos x + \frac{\sin 2(\pi-a)}{2}\cos (2x) - \frac{\sin 3(\pi-a)}{3}\cos (3x) + \dots\right]$$

d127	$y = ax/b$	for	$0 \leqq x \leqq b$
d128	$y = a$	for	$b \leqq x \leqq \pi-b$
d129	$y = a(\pi - x)/b$	for	$\pi-b \leqq x \leqq \pi$

d130
$$y = \frac{4}{\pi}\frac{a}{b}\left[\frac{1}{1^2}\sin b \sin x + \frac{1}{3^2}\sin (3b) \sin (3x) + \frac{1}{5^2}\sin (5b) \sin (5x) + \dots\right]$$

d131	$y = \dfrac{ax}{2\pi}$	for	$0 < x < 2\pi$
d132	$y = f(2\pi + x)$		

d133
$$y = \frac{a}{2} - \frac{a}{\pi}\left[\frac{\sin x}{1} + \frac{\sin (2x)}{2} + \frac{\sin (3x)}{3} + \dots\right]$$

continued on D 14

Continuation of D 13

d134	$y = 2ax/\pi$	for $0 \leqq x \leqq \pi/2$
d135	$y = 2a(\pi-x)/\pi$	for $\pi/2 \leqq x \leqq \pi$
d136	$y = -f(\pi + x)$	

d137
$$y = \frac{8}{\pi^2}a\left[\sin x - \frac{\sin(3x)}{3^2} + \frac{\sin(5x)}{5^2} - \dots\right]$$

d138	$y = ax/\pi$	for $0 \leqq x \leqq \pi$
d139	$y = a(2\pi-x)/\pi$	for $\pi \leqq x \leqq 2\pi$
d140	$y = f(2\pi+x)$	

d141
$$y = \frac{a}{2} - \frac{4a}{\pi^2}\left[\frac{\cos x}{1^2} + \frac{\cos(3x)}{3^2} + \frac{\cos(5x)}{5^2} + \dots\right]$$

d142	$y = a\sin x$	for $0 \leqq x \leqq \pi$
d143	$y = -a\sin x$	for $\pi \leqq x \leqq 2\pi$
d144	$y = f(\pi + x)$	

d145
$$y = \frac{2a}{\pi} - \frac{4a}{\pi}\left[\frac{\cos(2x)}{1\times3} + \frac{\cos(4x)}{3\times5} + \frac{\cos(6x)}{5\times7} + \dots\right]$$

d146	$y = 0$	for $0 \leqq x \leqq \pi/2$
d147	$y = a\sin\left(x-\frac{\pi}{2}\right)$	for $\frac{\pi}{2} \leqq x \leqq \frac{3\pi}{2}$
d148	$y = f(2\pi + x)$	

d149
$$y = \frac{2a}{\pi}\left[\frac{1}{2} - \frac{\pi}{4}\cos x + \frac{\cos(2x)}{2^2-1} - \frac{\cos(4x)}{4^2-1} + \frac{\cos(6x)}{6^2-1} - \dots\right]$$

| d150 | $y = x^2$ | for $-\pi \leqq x \leqq \pi$ |
| d151 | $y = f(-x) = f(2\pi + x)$ | |

d152
$$y = \frac{\pi^2}{3} - 4\left[\frac{\cos x}{1^2} - \frac{\cos(2x)}{2^2} + \frac{\cos(3x)}{3^2} - \dots\right]$$

| d153 | $y = ax/\pi$ | for $0 \leqq x \leqq \pi$ |
| d154 | $y = f(2\pi + x)$ | |

d155
$$y = \frac{a}{4} - \frac{2a}{\pi^2}\left[\frac{\cos x}{1^2} + \frac{\cos(3x)}{3^2} + \frac{\cos(5x)}{5^2} + \dots\right]$$
$$+ \frac{a}{\pi}\left[\frac{\sin x}{1} - \frac{\sin(2x)}{2} + \frac{\sin(3x)}{3} - \dots\right]$$

General

The Fourier-Transformation $F\{s(t)\}$ based on the Fourier integral converts the time function $s(t)$ in a continuous spectrum (spectral density) $S(\omega)$ in a way that frequency ω corresponds to the spectral density. $s(t)$ must have the following characteristics:

a) be piecewise smooth in a defined number of finite intervals

d 156
b) have defined values at the jumps $s(t+0)$ and $s(t-0)$, so that the value is equal to the average

d 157
$$s(t) = 1.2\ [s(t-0) + s(t+0)]$$

d 158
c) $\int\limits_{-\infty}^{+\infty} |s(t)|\ dt$ must be absolutely convergent.

The inverse Fourier transformation $F^{-1}\{S(\omega)\}$ gives the time function $s(t)$.

Definitions

d 159
$$F\{s(t)\} = S(\omega) = \int\limits_{-\infty}^{+\infty} s(t)\ e^{-i\omega t}\ dt; \qquad\qquad i = \sqrt{-1}$$

d 160
$$F^{-1}\{S(\omega)\} = s(t) = \frac{1}{2\pi}\int\limits_{-\infty}^{+\infty} S(\omega)\ e^{i\omega t}\ d\omega; \qquad\qquad i = \sqrt{-1}$$

d 161
Spectral energy
$$\int\limits_{-\infty}^{+\infty} |s(t)|^2\ dt = \frac{1}{2\pi}\int\limits_{-\infty}^{+\infty} |S(\omega)|^2\ d\omega$$

Calculation rules

d 162
Time translation
$$F\{s(t-\tau)\} = S(\omega)\ e^{-i\omega\tau}; \quad i = \sqrt{-1}$$

d 163
Convolution
$$s_1(t) * s_2(t) = \int\limits_{-\infty}^{+\infty} s_1(\tau)\ s_2(t-\tau)\ d\tau$$

d 164
$$= \int\limits_{-\infty}^{+\infty} s_2(\tau)\ s_1(t-\tau)\ d\tau$$

d 165
$$F\{s_1(t) * s_2(t)\} = S_1(\omega)\ S_2(\omega)$$

d 166
$$F\{s(t)\} = S(\omega)$$

d 167
$$F\{s(at)\} = \frac{1}{|a|} S(\frac{\omega}{a}) \qquad a \text{ real} > 0$$

d 168
$$F\{s_1(t) + s_2(t)\} = S_1(\omega) + S_2(\omega)$$

continued on D 16

continued from D 15

Using equation d 159 calculated spectral densities are given for some important time functions. Correspondence between time function and spectral density:

d 169
$$s(t) = \frac{1}{2\pi} \int_{-\infty}^{\infty} S(\omega)\, e^{i\omega t}\, d\omega \; ; \qquad S(\omega) = \int_{-\infty}^{\infty} s(t)\, e^{-i\omega t}\, dt$$

	Time function $s(t)$	Spectral density $S(\omega)$
d 170	Rectangle function $A\,R_T(t)$	$2\,A\,T\,\sin(\omega T)/(\omega T)$
d 171 d 172	Dirac-Pulse $A\,\delta(t)$	$S(\omega) = A$ (spectral density is constant over ω)
d 173 d 174	Rectangle funct. with change of polarity $A\,R_{T/2}(t-T/2)- A\,R_{T/2}(t+T/2)$	$S(\omega) = -j\,2\,A\,T\,\dfrac{\sin^2\dfrac{\omega T}{2}}{\dfrac{\omega T}{2}}$
d 175		$S(\omega) = 4AT\,\cos(2\omega T)\dfrac{\sin(\omega T)}{\omega T}$
76/177	$s(t)=\dfrac{A}{\pi}\,\omega_o\dfrac{\sin(\omega_o t)}{\omega_o t}$ with $\omega_o=\dfrac{2\pi}{T}$	$S(\omega) = A\,R_{\omega_o}(\omega)$ $\begin{pmatrix}\text{Rectangle}\\\text{function}\end{pmatrix}$

continued on D 17

continued from D 16

Time function $s(t)$	Spectral density $S(\omega)$

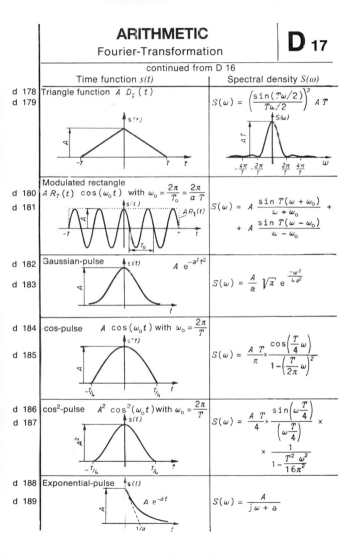

d 178
d 179 · Triangle function $A\, D_T(t)$

$$S(\omega) = \left(\frac{\sin(T\omega/2)}{T\omega/2}\right)^2 A\,T$$

d 180 Modulated rectangle
d 181 · $A\,R_T(t)\,\cos(\omega_0 t)$ with $\omega_0 = \frac{2\pi}{T_0} = \frac{2\pi}{\alpha\,T}$

$$S(\omega) = A\,\frac{\sin T(\omega + \omega_0)}{\omega + \omega_0} + A\,\frac{\sin T(\omega - \omega_0)}{\omega - \omega_0}$$

d 182 Gaussian-pulse $\quad A\,e^{-a^2 t^2}$
d 183

$$S(\omega) = \frac{A}{a}\,\sqrt{\pi}\; e^{\frac{-\omega^2}{4\,a^2}}$$

d 184 · cos-pulse $\quad A\,\cos(\omega_0 t)$ with $\omega_0 = \frac{2\pi}{T}$
d 185

$$S(\omega) = \frac{A\,T}{\pi} \times \frac{\cos\left(\frac{T}{4}\omega\right)}{1 - \left(\frac{T}{2\pi}\omega\right)^2}$$

d 186 $\cos^2$-pulse $\quad A^2\,\cos^2(\omega_0 t)$ with $\omega_0 = \frac{2\pi}{T}$
d 187

$$S(\omega) = \frac{A\,T}{4} \times \frac{\sin\left(\omega\frac{T}{4}\right)}{\left(\omega\frac{T}{4}\right)} \times \frac{1}{1 - \frac{T^2\,\omega^2}{16\pi^2}}$$

d 188 Exponential-pulse
d 189 $\quad A\,e^{-at}$

$$S(\omega) = \frac{A}{j\,\omega + a}$$

General: The Laplace-Transformation $L\{f(t)\}$ based on the Integral-function

d 190
$$F(p) = \int_0^\infty f(t)\, e^{-pt}\, dt$$

converts the time function $f(t)$, which has to be zero for $t < 0$ and which must be given completely for $t \geq 0$, into a picture function. The part e^{-pt} in d 190 is used as an attention factor

d 191
to get convergency of the integral for as many time functions as possible; here is $p = \sigma + i\omega$ with $\sigma \geq 0$ a complex operation variable. In this picture-domain differential equations can be solved and unique, non periodical processes (e.g. oscillating) can be handled; the desired time behaviour is reached finally by inverse transformation in the t-domain (see D 20).

Definitions

192/193
$$L\{f(t)\} = F(p) = \int_0^\infty f(t)\ e^{-pt}dt \quad \Bigg| \quad L^{-1}\{F(p)\} = f(t) = \frac{1}{2\pi i}\int_{\sigma_0-i\infty}^{\sigma_0+i\infty} F(p)\ e^{pt}\, dp$$

abbreviated description:

$$f(t)\ \circ\!\!-\!\!-\!\!-\!\!\bullet\ F(p)$$

abbreviatec description:

$$F(p)\ \bullet\!\!-\!\!-\!\!-\!\!\circ\ f(t)$$

Calculation rules (operation rules)

d 194	Linearity	$L\{f_1(t) + f_2(t)\} = F_1(p) + F_2(p)$
d 195		$L\{c\ f_1(t)\} = c\ F_1(p)$
d 196	Translation	$L\{f(t-a)\} = e^{-ap}\ F(p)$
d 197	Convolution	$f_1(t) * f_2(t) = \int_0^t f_1(t-\tau)\ f_2(\tau)\ d\tau$
d 198		$= \int_0^t f_1(\tau)\ f_2(t-\tau)\ d\tau$
d 199		$f_1(t) * f_2(t)\ \circ\!\!-\!\!-\!\!\bullet\ F_1(p)\ F_2(p)$
d 200	Variable transform.	$L\left\{\dfrac{1}{a}\ f\left(\dfrac{t}{a}\right)\right\} = F(a\,p)$
d 201	Differen-tiation	$L\{f'(t)\} = p\ F(p) - f(0^+)$
d 202		$L\{f''(t)\} = p^2 F(p) - p\ f(0^+) - f'(0^+)$
d 203		$L\{f^n(t)\} = p^n\ F(p) - \sum_{k=0}^{n-1} f^{(k)}(0^+)p^{n-k-1}$
d 204	Integration	$L\left\{\int_0^t f(t)\ dt\right\} = \dfrac{1}{p}\ F(p)$

Application of the _L_-Transformation to differential equations

Scheme

d 205

d 206

Difficulty of the solution of the differential equations is transferred to the inverse transformation. This can be simplified by expansion from $Y(p)$ into partial fractions (see D 3) or into such partial functions, for which in D 20 conversions are given back in the time domain.

d 207

Example: $2y' + y = f(t)$; $f(t)$ is startfunction
$y(0^+) = 2 \triangleq$ start condition

with $\left| \begin{array}{l} \text{d 201} \\ \text{d 205} \end{array} \right\}$ $2p\,Y(p) - 2y(0^+) + Y(p) = F(p)$

$\left| \text{d 206} \right.$ $y(t) \circ\!\!-\!\!\bullet Y(p) = \dfrac{F(p) + 2y(0^+)}{1 + 2p} = \dfrac{1/p + 2y(0^+)}{1 + 2p}$

According to $f(t) \circ\!\!-\!\!\bullet F(p)$ there are different solutions for $y(t)$. [Here $f(t)$ is assumed to be a step function. In this case referring to d 213 $F(p) = 1/p$.]

Application $\left.\right\}$ of D 3 $Y(p) = \dfrac{1}{p(1+2p)} + \dfrac{2y(0^+)}{1+2p} = \dfrac{1}{p} - \dfrac{2}{1+2p} + \dfrac{2y(0^+)}{1+2p}$

after D 20 $y(t) = 1 - 2\frac{1}{2}e^{-t/2} + 2 \times 2\frac{1}{2}e^{-t/2} = 1 - e^{-t/2}$

Application of the convolution rule to the _L_-Transformation on linear networks

The originate function $f_1(t)$ is changed to a response $y(t)$ after having passed a network. The network is defined by its transfer function $F_2(p)$. $F_2(p)$ has the inverse transformate $f_2(t)$.

d 208

d 209

$y(t) = f_1(t) * f_2(t) \circ\!\!-\!\!\bullet Y(p) = F_1(p) \times F_2(p)$

For a given network the response $y(t)$ depends on $f_1(t)$. $y(t)$ can be found by d 205. After having found $Y(p)$ calculation is continued on line d 206. Complete inverse transformation to the t-domain is possible when $F_2(p)$ is given as proper fraction rational function in p and when _L_-Transformate $F(p)$ is given in D 20.

Table of correlation

d 210
$$F(p) = \int_0^\infty f(t)\, e^{-pt}\, dt; \qquad f(t) = \frac{1}{2\pi i}\int_{G_0-i\infty}^{G_0+i\infty} F(p)\, e^{pt}\, dp$$

with $p = i\omega = i\,2\pi f$; $\quad i = \sqrt{-1}$

	p-domain Laplace transf. $F(p)$	t-domain original-function $f(t)$	p-domain Laplace transf. $F(p)$	t-domain original function $f(t)$
d 211 d 212	1	$\delta(t) \triangleq$ Dirac	$\dfrac{p^2}{(p^2+k^2)^2}$	$\dfrac{1}{2k}\sin(kt) +$
d 213 d 214	$1/p$	1 for $t>0$ 0 for $t<0$ │Step-function		$+\dfrac{t}{2}\cos(kt)$
d 215 d 216	$1/p^2$	t	$\dfrac{p^3}{(p^2+k^2)^2}$	$\cos(kt) -$ $-\dfrac{k}{2}t\sin(kt)$
d 217 d 218	$1/p^n$	$\dfrac{t^{n-1}}{(n-1)!}$	$\dfrac{1}{(p-a)(p-b)}$	for $b \neq a$:
d 219 d 220	$1/(p-a)$	$\exp(at)$		$\dfrac{e^{bt}-e^{at}}{b-a}$
d 221 d 222	$1/(p-a)^2$	$t\exp(at)$	$\dfrac{1}{(p+a)^2+k^2}$	$\dfrac{1}{k}e^{-at}\sin(kt)$
d 223 d 224	$\dfrac{a}{p(p-a)}$	$\exp(at)-1$	$\dfrac{1}{\sqrt{p}}$	$\dfrac{1}{\sqrt{\pi\,t}}$
d 225 d 226	$\dfrac{1}{1+Tp}$	$\dfrac{1}{T}\exp(-t/T)$	$\dfrac{1}{p\sqrt{p}}$	$2\sqrt{\dfrac{t}{\pi}}$
d 227 d 228	$\dfrac{a}{p^2-a^2}$	$\sinh(at)$	$\sqrt{p}$	$-1/(2\sqrt{\pi}\,t^{3/2})$
d 229 d 230	$\dfrac{p}{p^2-a^2}$	$\cosh(at)$	$p\sqrt{p}$	$3/(4\sqrt{\pi}\,t^{5/2})$
			$\ln\dfrac{p+b}{p+a}$	$\dfrac{1}{t}\left(e^{-at}-e^{-bt}\right)$
d 231 d 232	$\dfrac{k}{p^2+k^2}$	$\sin(kt)$	$\arctan(a/p)$	$1/t\,\sin(at)$
d 233 d 234	$\dfrac{p}{p^2+k^2}$	$\cos(kt)$	for $a>0$: $e^{-a\sqrt{p}}$	$\dfrac{a}{2t\sqrt{\pi t}}\,e^{\frac{-a^2}{4t}}$
d 235 d 236	$\dfrac{1}{(p^2+k^2)^2}$	$\dfrac{1}{2k^3}\sin(kt) -$ $-\dfrac{1}{2k^2}t\cos(kt)$	for $a \geq 0$: $\dfrac{1}{p}e^{-a\sqrt{p}}$	$\operatorname{erfc}\dfrac{a}{2\sqrt{t}}$
237/238	$\dfrac{p}{(p^2+k^2)^2}$	$\dfrac{1}{2k}\sin(kt)$	$\dfrac{1}{\sqrt{p^2+k^2}}$	$J_0(kt)$ { Bessel function

Complex numbers

General

$$z = r\,e^{\widehat{\varphi}} = a + ib$$

a = real part of z
b = imaginary part of z
r = absolute value of z
   = or modulus of z
φ = argument of z
a and b are real

	$i = \sqrt{-1}$		
d 239	$i^1 = +1$	$i^{-1} = -i$
d 240	$i^2 = -1$	$i^{-2} = -1$
d 241	$i^3 = -i$	$i^{-3} = +i$
d 242	$i^4 = +1$	$i^{-4} = +1$
d 243	$i^5 = +1$	$i^{-5} = -i$

etc.

Note: In electrical engineering the letter j is used for i to avoid confusion.

In the Cartesian coordinate system:

d 245
$$z = a + ib$$

d 246
$$z_1 + z_2 = (a_1 + a_2) + i(b_1 + b_2)$$

d 247
$$z_1 - z_2 = (a_1 - a_2) + i(b_1 - b_2)$$

d 248
$$z_1 \times z_2 = (a_1 a_2 - b_1 b_2) + i(a_1 b_2 + a_2 b_1)$$

d 249
$$\frac{z_1}{z_2} = \frac{a_1 a_2 + b_1 b_2}{a_2^2 + b_2^2} + i\frac{-a_1 b_2 + a_2 b_1}{a_2^2 + b_2^2}$$

d 250
$$a^2 + b^2 = (a + ib)(a - ib)$$

d 251
$$\sqrt{a \pm ib} = \sqrt{\frac{a + \sqrt{a^2 + b^2}}{2}} \pm i\sqrt{\frac{-a + \sqrt{a^2 + b^2}}{2}}$$

Where $a_1 = a_2$ and $b_1 = b_2$, then $z_1 = z_2$

continued on D 22

Complex numbers
(continued)

In the polar coordinate system:

d 252 $$z = r(\cos\varphi + i \sin\varphi) = a + ib$$

d 253 $$r = +\sqrt{a^2 + b^2}$$

d 254 $$\varphi = \arctan\frac{b}{a}$$

d 255 $$\sin\varphi = \frac{b}{r} \quad \Big| \quad \cos\varphi = \frac{a}{r} \quad \Big| \quad \tan\varphi = \frac{b}{a}$$

d 256 $$z_1 \times z_2 = r_1 \times r_2\left[\cos(\varphi_1 + \varphi_2) + i \sin(\varphi_1 + \varphi_2)\right]$$

d 257 $$\frac{z_1}{z_2} = \frac{r_1}{r_2}\left[\cos(\varphi_1 - \varphi_2) + i \sin(\varphi_1 - \varphi_2)\right] \quad (z_2 \neq 0)$$

d 258 $$z^n = r^n\left[\cos(n\varphi) + i \sin(n\varphi)\right] \quad (n > 0 \text{ integral})$$

d 259 $$\sqrt[n]{z} = \left|\sqrt[n]{r}\right|\left(\cos\frac{\varphi + 2\pi k}{n} + i \sin\frac{\varphi + 2\pi k}{n}\right)$$

d 260 $$\sqrt[n]{1} = \cos\frac{2\pi k}{n} + i \sin\frac{2\pi k}{n} \quad (n\text{th roots of unity})$$

In formula d 259 and d 260 $\quad k = 0, 1, 2, \ldots, n-1$

d 261 $$e^{i\widehat{\varphi}} = \cos\varphi + i \sin\varphi$$

d 262 $$e^{-i\widehat{\varphi}} = \cos\varphi - i \sin\varphi = \frac{1}{\cos\varphi + i \sin\varphi}$$

d 263 $$\left|e^{-i\widehat{\varphi}}\right| = \sqrt{\cos^2\varphi + \sin^2\varphi} = 1$$

d 264 $$\cos\varphi = \frac{e^{i\widehat{\varphi}} + e^{-i\widehat{\varphi}}}{2} \qquad \sin\varphi = \frac{e^{i\widehat{\varphi}} - e^{-i\widehat{\varphi}}}{2i}$$

d 265 $$\ln z = \ln r + i(\widehat{\varphi} + 2\pi k) \quad (k = 0, \pm1, \pm2, \ldots)$$

Where $r_1 = r_2$ and $\varphi_1 = \varphi_2 + 2\pi k$, then $z_1 = z_2$

Note: φ should be measured along the arc,
k is any arbitrary whole number

Compound interest calculation

d 266
$$k_n = k_0 \, q^n$$

d 267
$$n = \frac{\log \dfrac{k_n}{k_0}}{\log q}$$

$$q = \sqrt[n]{\frac{k_n}{k_0}}$$

Annuity interest calculation

d 268
$$k_n = k_c \, q^r - r \, q \, \frac{q^n - 1}{q - 1}$$

d 269
$$r = \frac{(k_0 \, q^n - k_n)(q - 1)}{(q^n - 1) q}$$

d 270
$$n = \frac{\log \dfrac{r \, q - k_n(q - 1)}{r \, q - k_0(q - 1)}}{\log q}$$

Where $k_n = 0$, we get the 'redemption formulae"

Deposit calculation
(savings bank formula)

d 271
$$k_n = k_0 \, q^n + r \, q \, \frac{q^n - 1}{q - 1}$$

d 272
$$r = \frac{(k_n - k_0 \, q^n)(q - 1)}{(q^n - 1) q}$$

d 273
$$n = \frac{\log \dfrac{k_n(q - 1) + r \, q}{k_0(q - 1) + r \, q}}{\log q}$$

Letters

k_0 : initial capital
k_n : capital after n years
r : annual pensions (withdrawals)

n : number of years
q : $1 + p$
p : rate of interest (e.g. 0·06 at 6%)

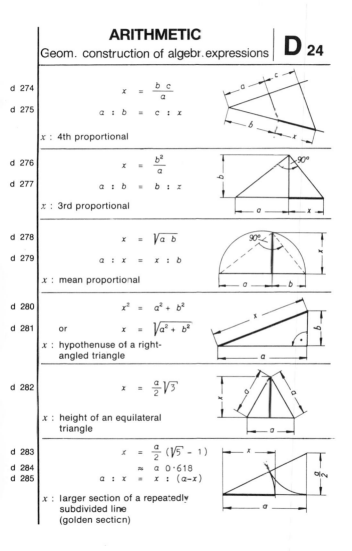

d 274

d 275

$$x = \frac{b\,c}{a}$$

$$a : b = c : x$$

x : 4th proportional

d 276

d 277

$$x = \frac{b^2}{a}$$

$$a : b = b : x$$

x : 3rd proportional

d 278

d 279

$$x = \sqrt{a\,b}$$

$$a : x = x : b$$

x : mean proportional

d 280

d 281

$$x^2 = a^2 + b^2$$

$$\text{or} \qquad x = \sqrt{a^2 + b^2}$$

x : hypothenuse of a right-angled triangle

d 282

$$x = \frac{a}{2}\sqrt{3}$$

x : height of an equilateral triangle

d 283

d 284

d 285

$$x = \frac{a}{2}(\sqrt{5} - 1)$$

$$\approx a\ 0 \cdot 618$$

$$a : x = x : (a-x)$$

x : larger section of a repeatedly subdivided line (golden section)

Circular and angular measure of a plane angle

Circular measure

Circular measure is the ratio of the distance d measured along the arc to the radius r.

It is given the unit "radian" which has no dimensions.

e 1
$$\alpha = \frac{d}{r} \quad \text{(rad)}$$

Unit: rad

Angular measure

Angular measure is obtained by dividing the angle subtended at the centre of a circle into 360 equal divisions known as "degrees".

Unit: °

e 2
e 3
A degree is divided into 60 minutes (unit: '),
a minute is divided into 60 seconds (unit: ").

Relation between circular and angular measure

By considering a circle, it may be seen that

e 4
$$360° = 2\pi \text{ radians}$$

e 5
$$\text{or} \quad 1 \text{ rad} = 57 \cdot 2958°$$

e 6

degrees	0°	30°	45°	60°	75°	90°	180°	270°	360°
radians	0	$\frac{\pi}{6}$	$\frac{\pi}{4}$	$\frac{\pi}{3}$	$\frac{5}{12}\pi$	$\frac{\pi}{2}$	π	$\frac{3}{2}\pi$	2π
	0	0·52	0·79	1·05	1·31	1·57	3·14	4·71	6·28

FUNCTIONS OF A CIRCLE

General terms

E 2

Right angled triangle

e 7 $\quad \sin \alpha = \dfrac{\text{opposite}}{\text{hypotenuse}} = \dfrac{a}{c}$

e 8 $\quad \cos \alpha = \dfrac{\text{adjacent}}{\text{hypotenuse}} = \dfrac{b}{c}$

e 9 $\quad \tan \alpha = \dfrac{\text{opposite}}{\text{adjacent}} = \dfrac{a}{b} \qquad \cot \alpha = \dfrac{\text{adjacent}}{\text{opposite}} = \dfrac{b}{a}$

Functions of the more important angles

e 10

angle α	0°	30°	45°	60°	75°	90°	180°	270°	360°
$\sin \alpha$	0	0,500	0,707	0,366	0,966	1	0	−1	0
$\cos \alpha$	1	0,866	0,707	0,500	0,259	0	−1	0	1
$\tan \alpha$	0	0,577	1,000	1.732	3,732	∞	0	∞	0
$\cot \alpha$	∞	1,732	1,000	0 577	0,268	0	∞	0	∞

Relations between sine and cosine functions

Basic equations

e 13 $\quad$ Sine function $\qquad y = A \sin (k \alpha - \varphi)$

e 14 $\quad$ Cosine function $\qquad y = A \cos (k \alpha - \varphi)$

——— sine curve
—·— sine curve $\qquad$ with an
— — — cosine curve $\qquad$ amplitude of
$\qquad$ or sine curve with a phase shift of

$A = 1$	and $k = 1$
$A = 1 \cdot 5$	and $k = 2$
$A = 1$	and $k = 1$
$\varphi = -\dfrac{\pi}{2}$	

FUNCTIONS OF A CIRCLE
Quadrants

E 3

e 15	$\sin(90° - \alpha)$	$=$	$+\cos\alpha$		$\sin(90° + \alpha)$	$=$	$+\cos\alpha$
e 16	$\cos($ " $)$	$=$	$+\sin\alpha$		$\cos($ " $)$	$=$	$-\sin\alpha$
e 17	$\tan($ " $)$	$=$	$+\cot\alpha$		$\tan($ " $)$	$=$	$-\cot\alpha$
e 18	$\cot($ " $)$	$=$	$+\tan\alpha$		$\cot($ " $)$	$=$	$-\tan\alpha$
e 19	$\sin(180° - \alpha)$	$=$	$+\sin\alpha$		$\sin(180° + \alpha)$	$=$	$-\sin\alpha$
e 20	$\cos($ " $)$	$=$	$-\cos\alpha$		$\cos($ " $)$	$=$	$-\cos\alpha$
e 21	$\tan($ " $)$	$=$	$-\tan\alpha$		$\tan($ " $)$	$=$	$+\tan\alpha$
e 22	$\cot($ " $)$	$=$	$-\cot\alpha$		$\cot($ " $)$	$=$	$+\cot\alpha$
e 23	$\sin(270° - \alpha)$	$=$	$-\cos\alpha$		$\sin(270° + \alpha)$	$=$	$-\cos\alpha$
e 24	$\cos($ " $)$	$=$	$-\sin\alpha$		$\cos($ " $)$	$=$	$+\sin\alpha$
e 25	$\tan($ " $)$	$=$	$+\cot\alpha$		$\tan($ " $)$	$=$	$-\cot\alpha$
e 26	$\cot($ " $)$	$=$	$+\tan\alpha$		$\cot($ " $)$	$=$	$-\tan\alpha$
e 27	$\sin(360° - \alpha)$	$=$	$-\sin\alpha$		$\sin(360° + \alpha)$	$=$	$+\sin\alpha$
e 28	$\cos($ " $)$	$=$	$+\cos\alpha$		$\cos($ " $)$	$=$	$+\cos\alpha$
e 29	$\tan($ " $)$	$=$	$-\tan\alpha$		$\tan($ " $)$	$=$	$+\tan\alpha$
e 30	$\cot($ " $)$	$=$	$-\cot\alpha$		$\cot($ " $)$	$=$	$+\cot\alpha$
e 31	$\sin(-\alpha)$	$=$	$-\sin\alpha$		$\sin(\alpha \pm n\times360°)$	$=$	$+\sin\alpha$
e 32	$\cos($ " $)$	$=$	$+\cos\alpha$		$\cos($ " $)$	$=$	$+\cos\alpha$
e 33	$\tan($ " $)$	$=$	$-\tan\alpha$		$\tan(\alpha \pm n\times180°)$	$=$	$+\tan\alpha$
e 34	$\cot($ " $)$	$=$	$-\cot\alpha$		$\cot($ " $)$	$=$	$+\cot\alpha$

Basic identities

e 35
$$\sin^2\alpha + \cos^2\alpha = 1 \qquad \tan\alpha \quad \cot\alpha = 1$$

e 36
$$1 + \tan^2\alpha = \frac{1}{\cos^2\alpha} \qquad 1 + \cot^2\alpha = \frac{1}{\sin^2\alpha}$$

Sum and difference of angles

e 37
$$\sin(\alpha \pm \beta) = \sin\alpha \ \cos\beta \pm \cos\alpha \ \sin\beta$$

e 38
$$\cos(\alpha \pm \beta) = \cos\alpha \ \cos\beta \mp \sin\alpha \ \sin\beta$$

e 39
$$\tan(\alpha \pm \beta) = \frac{\tan\alpha \pm \tan\beta}{1 \mp \tan\alpha \ \tan\beta}; \quad \cot(\alpha \pm \beta) = \frac{\cot\alpha \ \cot\beta \mp 1}{\pm \cot\alpha + \cot\beta}$$

Sum and difference of functions of angles

e 40
$$\sin\alpha + \sin\beta = 2 \sin\frac{\alpha - \beta}{2} \ \cos\frac{\alpha - \beta}{2}$$

e 41
$$\sin\alpha - \sin\beta = 2 \cos\frac{\alpha + \beta}{2} \ \sin\frac{\alpha - \beta}{2}$$

e 42
$$\cos\alpha + \cos\beta = 2 \cos\frac{\alpha + \beta}{2} \ \cos\frac{\alpha - \beta}{2}$$

e 43
$$\cos\alpha - \cos\beta = -2 \sin\frac{\alpha + \beta}{2} \ \sin\frac{\alpha - \beta}{2}$$

e 44
$$\tan\alpha \pm \tan\beta = \frac{\sin(\alpha \pm \beta)}{\cos\alpha \ \cos\beta}$$

e 45
$$\cot\alpha \pm \cot\beta = \frac{\sin(\beta \pm \alpha)}{\sin\alpha \ \sin\beta}$$

e 46
$$\sin\alpha \quad \cos\beta = \frac{1}{2}\sin(\alpha + \beta) + \frac{1}{2}\sin(\alpha - \beta)$$

e 47
$$\cos\alpha \quad \cos\beta = \frac{1}{2}\cos(\alpha + \beta) + \frac{1}{2}\cos(\alpha - \beta)$$

e 48
$$\sin\alpha \quad \sin\beta = \frac{1}{2}\cos(\alpha - \beta) - \frac{1}{2}\cos(\alpha + \beta)$$

e 49
$$\tan\alpha \quad \tan\beta = \frac{\tan\alpha + \tan\beta}{\cot\alpha + \cot\beta} = -\frac{\tan\alpha - \tan\beta}{\cot\alpha - \cot\beta}$$

e 50
$$\cot\alpha \quad \cot\beta = \frac{\cot\alpha + \cot\beta}{\tan\alpha + \tan\beta} = -\frac{\cot\alpha - \cot\beta}{\tan\alpha - \tan\beta}$$

e 51
$$\cot\alpha \quad \tan\beta = \frac{\cot\alpha + \tan\beta}{\tan\alpha + \cot\beta} = -\frac{\cot\alpha - \tan\beta}{\tan\alpha - \cot\beta}$$

Sum of 2 harmonic oscillations of the same frequency

e 52
$$a \sin(\omega t + \varphi_1) + b \cos(\omega t + \varphi_2) = \sqrt{c^2 + d^2} \ \sin(\omega t + \varphi)$$

with $c = a \sin\varphi_1 + b \cos\varphi_2$; $d = a \cos\varphi_1 - b \sin\varphi_2$

$\varphi = \arctan\dfrac{c}{d}$ and $\varphi = \arcsin\dfrac{c}{\sqrt{c^2 + d^2}}$ $\left\{ \begin{array}{l} \text{both conditions} \\ \text{must be satisfied} \end{array} \right.$

Ratios
between simple, double and half angles

	$\sin \alpha =$	$\cos \alpha =$	$\tan \alpha =$	$\cot \alpha =$
e 53	$\cos(90° - \alpha)$	$\sin(90° - \alpha)$	$\cot(90° - \alpha)$	$\tan(90° - \alpha)$
e 54	$\sqrt{1 - \cos^2\alpha}$	$\sqrt{1 - \sin^2\alpha}$	$\dfrac{1}{\cot \alpha}$	$\dfrac{1}{\tan \alpha}$
e 55	$2\sin\dfrac{\alpha}{2}\cos\dfrac{\alpha}{2}$	$\cos^2\dfrac{\alpha}{2} - \sin^2\dfrac{\alpha}{2}$	$\dfrac{\sin \alpha}{\cos \alpha}$	$\dfrac{\cos \alpha}{\sin \alpha}$
e 56	$\dfrac{\tan \alpha}{\sqrt{1 + \tan^2\alpha}}$	$\dfrac{\cot \alpha}{\sqrt{1 + \cot^2\alpha}}$	$\dfrac{\sin \alpha}{\sqrt{1 - \sin^2\alpha}}$	$\dfrac{\cos \alpha}{\sqrt{1 - \cos^2\alpha}}$
e 57	$\sqrt{\cos^2\alpha - \cos 2\alpha}$	$1 - 2\sin^2\dfrac{\alpha}{2}$	$\sqrt{\dfrac{1}{\cos^2\alpha} - 1}$	$\sqrt{\dfrac{1}{\sin^2\alpha} - 1}$
e 58	$\sqrt{\dfrac{1 - \cos 2\alpha}{2}}$	$\sqrt{\dfrac{1 + \cos 2\alpha}{2}}$	$\dfrac{\sqrt{1 - \cos^2\alpha}}{\cos \alpha}$	$\dfrac{\sqrt{1 - \sin^2\alpha}}{\sin \alpha}$
e 59	$\dfrac{1}{\sqrt{1 + \cot^2\alpha}}$	$\dfrac{1}{\sqrt{1 + \tan^2\alpha}}$		
e 60	$\dfrac{2\tan\dfrac{\alpha}{2}}{1 + \tan^2\dfrac{\alpha}{2}}$	$\dfrac{1 - \tan^2\dfrac{\alpha}{2}}{1 + \tan^2\dfrac{\alpha}{2}}$	$\dfrac{2\tan\dfrac{\alpha}{2}}{1 - \tan^2\dfrac{\alpha}{2}}$	$\dfrac{\cot^2\dfrac{\alpha}{2} - 1}{2\cot\dfrac{\alpha}{2}}$

	$\sin 2\alpha =$	$\cos 2\alpha =$	$\tan 2\alpha =$	$\cot 2\alpha =$
e 61	$2\sin \alpha \cos \alpha$	$\cos^2\alpha - \sin^2\alpha$	$\dfrac{2\tan \alpha}{1 - \tan^2\alpha}$	$\dfrac{\cot^2\alpha - 1}{2\cot \alpha}$
e 62		$2\cos^2\alpha - 1$	$\dfrac{2}{\cot \alpha - \tan \alpha}$	$\dfrac{1}{2}\cot\alpha - \dfrac{1}{2}\tan\alpha$
e 63		$1 - 2\sin^2\alpha$		

	$\sin\dfrac{\alpha}{2} =$	$\cos\dfrac{\alpha}{2} =$	$\tan\dfrac{\alpha}{2} =$	$\cot\dfrac{\alpha}{2} =$
e 64			$\dfrac{\sin \alpha}{1 + \cos \alpha}$	$\dfrac{\sin \alpha}{1 - \cos \alpha}$
e 65	$\sqrt{\dfrac{1 - \cos \alpha}{2}}$	$\sqrt{\dfrac{1 + \cos \alpha}{2}}$	$\dfrac{1 - \cos \alpha}{\sin \alpha}$	$\dfrac{1 + \cos \alpha}{\sin \alpha}$
e 66			$\sqrt{\dfrac{1 - \cos \alpha}{1 + \cos \alpha}}$	$\sqrt{\dfrac{1 + \cos \alpha}{1 - \cos \alpha}}$

Oblique angle triangle

Sine Rule

e 67
$$\sin \alpha : \sin \beta : \sin \gamma = a : b : c$$

e 68
$$a = \frac{b}{\sin \beta} \sin \alpha = \frac{c}{\sin \gamma} \sin \alpha$$

e 69
$$b = \frac{a}{\sin \alpha} \sin \beta = \frac{c}{\sin \gamma} \sin \beta$$

e 70
$$c = \frac{a}{\sin \alpha} \sin \gamma = \frac{b}{\sin \beta} \sin \gamma$$

Cosine Rule

e 71
$$a^2 = b^2 + c^2 - 2bc \cos \alpha$$

e 72
$$b^2 = c^2 + a^2 - 2ac \cos \beta$$

e 73
$$c^2 = a^2 + b^2 - 2ab \cos \gamma$$

(for obtuse angles the cosine is negative)

Tangent Rule

e 74
$$\frac{a+b}{a-b} = \frac{\tan \frac{\alpha+\beta}{2}}{\tan \frac{\alpha-\beta}{2}} \quad \bigg| \quad \frac{a+c}{a-c} = \frac{\tan \frac{\alpha+\gamma}{2}}{\tan \frac{\alpha-\gamma}{2}} \quad \bigg| \quad \frac{b+c}{b-c} = \frac{\tan \frac{\beta+\gamma}{2}}{\tan \frac{\beta-\gamma}{2}}$$

Half-angle Rule

e 75
$$\tan \frac{\alpha}{2} = \frac{\varrho}{s-a} \quad \bigg| \quad \tan \frac{\beta}{2} = \frac{\varrho}{s-b} \quad \bigg| \quad \tan \frac{\gamma}{2} = \frac{\varrho}{s-c}$$

Area, radius of incircle and circumcircle

e 76
$$A = \frac{1}{2} bc \sin \alpha = \frac{1}{2} ac \sin \beta = \frac{1}{2} cb \sin \gamma$$

e 77
$$A = \sqrt{s(s-a)(s-b)(s-c)} = \varrho s$$

e 78
$$\varrho = \sqrt{\frac{(s-a)(s-b)(s-c)}{s}}$$

e 79
$$r = \frac{1}{2} \frac{a}{\sin \alpha} = \frac{1}{2} \frac{b}{\sin \beta} = \frac{1}{2} \frac{c}{\sin \gamma}$$

e 80
$$s = \frac{a+b+c}{2}$$

Inverse circular functions

Definitions

		function $y =$			
		$\arcsin x$	$\arccos x$	$\arctan x$	$\text{arccot}\, x$
e 81	identical with	$x = \sin y$	$x = \cos y$	$x = \tan y$	$x = \cot y$
e 82	defined within	$-1 \leqq x \leqq +1$	$-1 \leqq x \leqq +1$	$-\infty < x < +\infty$	$-\infty < x < +\infty$
e 83	principal value	$-\frac{\pi}{2} \leqq y \leqq +\frac{\pi}{2}$	$\pi \geqq y \geqq 0$	$-\frac{\pi}{2} < y < +\frac{\pi}{2}$	$\pi > y > 0$

Basic properties

e 84
$$\arccos x = \frac{\pi}{2} - \arcsin x \qquad \text{arccot}\, x = \frac{\pi}{2} - \arctan x$$

Ratios between inverse circular functions

For $x \geqq 0$:

	$\arcsin x =$	$\arccos x =$	$\arctan x =$	$\text{arccot}\, x =$
e 85	$\arccos \sqrt{1-x^2}$	$\arcsin \sqrt{1-x^2}$	$\arcsin \frac{x}{\sqrt{1+x^2}}$	$\arcsin \frac{1}{\sqrt{1+x^2}}$
e 86	$\arctan \frac{x}{\sqrt{1-x^2}}$	$\arctan \frac{\sqrt{1-x^2}}{x}$	$\arccos \frac{1}{\sqrt{1+x^2}}$	$\arccos \frac{x}{\sqrt{1+x^2}}$
e 87	$\text{arccot} \frac{\sqrt{1-x^2}}{x}$	$\text{arccot} \frac{x}{\sqrt{1-x^2}}$	$\text{arccot} \frac{1}{x}$	$\arctan \frac{1}{x}$

For $x \leqq 0$:

e 88	$\arcsin(-x) = -\arcsin x$	$\arccos(-x) = \pi - \arccos x$
e 89	$\arctan(-x) = -\arctan x$	$\text{arccot}(-x) = \pi - \text{arccot}\, x$

Addition theorems

e 90	$\arcsin a \pm \arcsin b$	$=$	$\arcsin\left(a\sqrt{1-b^2} \pm b\sqrt{1-a^2}\right)$
e 91	$\arccos a \pm \arccos b$	$=$	$\arccos\left(a\,b \mp \sqrt{1-a^2}\,\sqrt{1-b^2}\right)$
e 92	$\arctan a \pm \arctan b$	$=$	$\arctan \frac{a \pm b}{1 \mp a\,b}$
e 93	$\text{arccot}\, a \pm \text{arccot}\, b$	$=$	$\text{arccot} \frac{a\,b \mp 1}{b \mp a}$

ANALYTICAL GEOMETRY
Straight line, Triangle

Straight line

f 1	**Equation**	$y = mx + b$
f 2	**Gradient**	$m = \dfrac{y_2 - y_1}{x_2 - x_1} = \tan a$

Interc. form for $a \neq 0; \ b \neq 0$

f 3
$$\frac{x}{a} + \frac{y}{b} - 1 = 0$$

Gradient m_l of perpendicular $\overline{AB}$

f 4
$$m_l = \frac{-1}{m}$$

Line joining two points $P_1 (x_1, y_1)$ and $P_2 (x_2, y_2)$

f 5
$$\frac{y - y_1}{x - x_1} = \frac{y_2 - y_1}{x_2 - x_1}$$

Line through one point $P_1 (x_1, y_1)$ and gradient m

f 6
$$y - y_1 = m(x - x_1)$$

f 7 **Distance between two points** $\qquad d = \sqrt{(x_2 - x_1)^2 + (y_2 - y_1)^2}$

Mid point of a line joining two points

f 8
$$x_m = \frac{x_1 + x_2}{2} \qquad \Big| \qquad y_m = \frac{y_1 + y_2}{2}$$

Point of intersection of two straight lines (see diagram triangle)

f 9
$$x_3 = \frac{b_2 - b_1}{m_1 - m_2} \qquad y_3 = m_1 x_3 + b_1 = m_2 x_3 + b_2$$

Angle of intersection φ of two straight lines

f10
$$\tan \varphi = \frac{m_2 - m_1}{1 + m_2 \, m_1} \quad \left(\begin{array}{c}\text{see} \\ \text{diagram-} \\ \text{triangle}\end{array}\right)$$

Triangle

f11	**Centroid** S	$x_S = \dfrac{x_1 + x_2 + x_3}{3}$
f12		$y_S = \dfrac{y_1 + y_2 + y_3}{3}$

Area

f13
$$A = \frac{(x_1 y_2 - x_2 y_1) + (x_2 y_3 - x_3 y_2) + (x_3 y_1 - x_1 y_3)}{2}$$

Where x and y have same dimension and are represented in equal scales (see also h 1).

Circle

Circle equation

	at the origin	centre elsewhere
f 14	$x^2 + y^2 = r^2$	$(x-x_0)^2 + (y-y_0)^2 = r^2$

Basic equation

f 15 $\quad x^2 + y^2 + ax + by + c = 0$

Radius of circle

f 16 $\quad r = \sqrt{x_0^2 + y_0^2 - c}$

Coordinates of the centre M

f 17 $\quad x_0 = -\dfrac{a}{2} \qquad\qquad y_0 = -\dfrac{b}{2}$

Tangent T at point $P_1 (x_1, y_1)$

f 18 $\quad y = \dfrac{r^2 - (x-x_0)(x_1-x_0)}{y_1 - y_0} + y_0$

Parabola

Parabola equation (by converting to this equation the vertex and parameter p may be ascertained)

	vertex at the origin	elsewhere	parabola open at	F: focus L: directrix
f 19	$x^2 = 2py$	$(x-x_0)^2 = 2p(y-y_0)$	top	S: tangent at
f 20	$x^2 = -2py$	$(x-x_0)^2 = -2p(y-y_0)$	bottom	the vertex

Basic equation

f 21 $\quad y = ax^2 + bx + c$

f 22 **Vertex radius** $\qquad r = p$

f 23 **Basic property** $\qquad \overline{PF} = \overline{PQ}$

Tangent T at point $P_1 (x_1, y_1)$

f 24 $\quad y = \dfrac{2(y_1-y_0)(x-x_1)}{x_1 - x_0} + y_1$

Hyperbola

Hyperbolic equation

	point of intersection of asymptotes	
	at the origin	elsewhere

f 25
$$\frac{x^2}{a^2} - \frac{y^2}{b^2} - 1 = 0 \qquad \frac{(x - x_0)^2}{a^2} - \frac{(y - y_0)^2}{b^2} - 1 = 0$$

Basic equation

f 26
$$ax^2 + by^2 + cx + dy + e = 0$$

Basic property

f 27
$$\overline{F_2 P} - \overline{F_1 P} = 2a$$

Eccentricity

f 28
$$e = \sqrt{a^2 + b^2} \qquad +)$$

Gradient of asymptotes

f 29
$$\tan \alpha = m = \pm \frac{b}{a} \qquad +)$$

Vertex radius $\qquad p = \dfrac{b^2}{a}$

Tangent T
at $P_1 (x_1, y_1)$

f 30
$$y = \frac{b^2}{a^2} \ \frac{(x_1 - x_0)(x - x_1)}{y_1 - y_0} + y_1$$

Rectangular hyperbola

Explanation in a rectangular hyperbola $\qquad a = b \qquad$ thus

Gradient of asymptotes

f 31
$$\tan \alpha^{+)} = m = \pm 1 \qquad (\alpha = 45°)$$

Equation (for asymptotes parallel to x and y axes):

	point of intersection of asymptotes	
	at the origin	elsewhere

f 32
$$x y = c^2 \qquad (x - x_0)(y - y_0) = c^2$$

Vertex radius

f 33
$$p = a \qquad \text{(parameter)}$$

+) Conditions according to note on page F 1

Ellipse

Ellipse equation

	point of intersection of axes	
	at the origin	elsewhere
f 34	$\dfrac{x^2}{a^2} + \dfrac{y^2}{b^2} - 1 = 0$	$\dfrac{(x - x_0)^2}{a^2} + \dfrac{(y - y_0)^2}{b^2} - 1 = 0$

Vertex radii

f 35 $\quad r_N = \dfrac{b^2}{a} \quad \Big| \quad r_H = \dfrac{a^2}{b}$

Eccentricity

f 36 $\quad e = \sqrt{a^2 - b^2}$

Basic property

f 37 $\quad \overline{F_1 P} + \overline{F_2 P} = 2\,a$

Tangent T at $P_1\,(x_1;\,y_1)$

f 38 $\quad y = -\dfrac{b^2}{a^2}\dfrac{(x_1 - x_0)(x - x_1)}{y_1 - y_0} + y_1$

Note: F_1 and F_2 are focal points

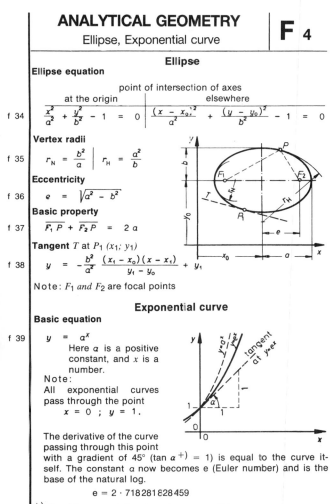

Exponential curve

Basic equation

f 39 $\quad y = a^x$

Here a is a positive constant, and x is a number.

Note:
All exponential curves pass through the point $x = 0$; $y = 1$.

The derivative of the curve passing through this point with a gradient of 45° ($\tan \alpha\,^{+)} = 1$) is equal to the curve itself. The constant a now becomes e (Euler number) and is the base of the natural log.

$$e = 2 \cdot 718\,281\,828\,459$$

+) Conditions according to note on page F 1

Hyperbolic functions

Definition

f 40 $\sinh x = \dfrac{e^x - e^{-x}}{2}$

f 41 $\cosh x = \dfrac{e^x + e^{-x}}{2}$

f 42 $\tanh x = \dfrac{e^x - e^{-x}}{e^x + e^{-x}} = \dfrac{e^{2x} - 1}{e^{2x} + 1}$

f 43 $\coth x = \dfrac{e^x + e^{-x}}{e^x - e^{-x}} = \dfrac{e^{2x} + 1}{e^{2x} - 1}$

Basic properties

f 44 $\cosh^2 x - \sinh^2 x = 1$

f 45 $\tanh x \times \coth x = 1$

f 46 $\tanh x = \dfrac{\sinh x}{\cosh x} \left| 1 - \tanh^2 x = \dfrac{1}{\cosh^2 x} \right| 1 - \coth^2 x = \dfrac{-1}{\sinh^2 x}$

Ratios between hyperbolic functions
where x is positive

	$\sinh x =$	$\cosh x =$	$\tanh x =$	$\coth x =$
f 47	$\sqrt{\cosh^2 x - 1}$	$\sqrt{\sinh^2 x + 1}$	$\dfrac{\sinh x}{\sqrt{\sinh^2 x + 1}}$	$\dfrac{\sqrt{\sinh^2 x + 1}}{\sinh x}$
f 48	$\dfrac{\tanh x}{\sqrt{1 - \tanh^2 x}}$	$\dfrac{1}{\sqrt{1 - \tanh^2 x}}$	$\dfrac{\sqrt{\cosh^2 x - 1}}{\cosh x}$	$\dfrac{\cosh x}{\sqrt{\cosh^2 x - 1}}$
f 49	$\dfrac{1}{\sqrt{\coth^2 x - 1}}$	$\dfrac{\coth x}{\sqrt{\coth^2 x - 1}}$	$\dfrac{1}{\coth x}$	$\dfrac{1}{\tanh x}$

f 50   For negative $\quad \| \sinh(-x) = -\sinh x \, | \, \cosh(-x) = +\cosh x$

f 51   argument $\quad\;\; \| \tanh(-x) = -\tanh x \, | \, \coth(-x) = -\coth x$

Addition theorems

f 52 $\sinh(a \pm b) = \sinh a \; \cosh b \pm \cosh a \; \sinh b$

f 53 $\cosh(a \pm b) = \cosh a \; \cosh b \pm \sinh a \; \sinh b$

f 54 $\tanh(a \pm b) = \dfrac{\tanh a \pm \tanh b}{1 \pm \tanh a \; \tanh b}$

f 55 $\coth(a \pm b) = \dfrac{\coth a \; \coth b \pm 1}{\coth a \pm \coth b}$

Inverse hyperbolic functions

Definition

		$\text{arsinh}\,x$	$\text{arcosh}\,x$	$\text{artanh}\,x$	$\text{arcoth}\,x$
			function $y =$		
f 56	identical with	$x = \sinh y$	$x = \cosh y$	$x = \tanh y$	$x = \coth y$
f 57	logarithmic equivalents	$= \ln(x+\sqrt{x^2+1})$	$= \ln(x+\sqrt{x^2-1})$	$= \frac{1}{2}\ln\frac{1+x}{1-x}$	$= \frac{1}{2}\ln\frac{x+1}{x-1}$
f 58	defined within	$-\infty < x < +\infty$	$1 \leqq x < +\infty$	$\|x\| < 1$	$\|x\| > 1$
f 59	primary value	$-\infty < y < +\infty$	$0 \leqq y < +\infty$	$-\infty < y < +\infty$	$-\infty < y < +\infty$

Ratios between inverse hyperbolic functions
where x is positive:

	$\text{arsinh}\,x =$	$\text{arcosh}\,x =$	$\text{artanh}\,x =$	$\text{arcoth}\,x =$
f 60	$\text{arcosh}\,\sqrt{1+x^2}$	$\text{arsinh}\,\sqrt{x^2-1}$	$\text{arsinh}\,\dfrac{x}{\sqrt{1-x^2}}$	$\text{arsinh}\,\dfrac{1}{\sqrt{x^2-1}}$
f 61	$\text{artanh}\,\dfrac{x}{\sqrt{1+x^2}}$	$\text{artanh}\,\dfrac{\sqrt{x^2-1}}{x}$	$\text{arcosh}\,\dfrac{1}{\sqrt{1-x^2}}$	$\text{arcosh}\,\dfrac{x}{\sqrt{x^2-1}}$
f 62	$\text{arcoth}\,\dfrac{\sqrt{1+x^2}}{x}$	$\text{arcoth}\,\dfrac{x}{\sqrt{x^2-1}}$	$\text{arcoth}\,\dfrac{1}{x}$	$\text{artanh}\,\dfrac{1}{x}$

For negative argument:

f 63	$\text{arsinh}(-x) = -\text{arsinh}\,x$		
f 64	$\text{artanh}(-x) = -\text{artanh}\,x$		$\text{arcoth}(-x) = -\text{arcoth}\,x$

Addition theorems

f 65	$\text{arsinh}\,a \pm \text{arsinh}\,b$	$=$	$\text{arsinh}\,(a\sqrt{b^2+1} \pm b\sqrt{a^2+1})$
f 66	$\text{arcosh}\,a \pm \text{arcosh}\,b$	$=$	$\text{arcosh}\left[ab \pm \sqrt{(a^2-1)(b^2-1)}\right]$
f 67	$\text{artanh}\,a \pm \text{artanh}\,b$	$=$	$\text{artanh}\,\dfrac{a \pm b}{1 \pm ab}$
f 68	$\text{arcoth}\,a \pm \text{arcoth}\,b$	$=$	$\text{arcoth}\,\dfrac{ab \pm 1}{a \pm b}$

Theoretical probability $P(A)$

g 1
If E is the set of outcomes of an experiment all of which are assumed to be equally likely and an event A is satisfied by a subset A of them, then $P(A) = n(A)/n(E)$.

Experimental probability $P(A)$

g 2
If an event A is satisfied by a certain outcome of an experiment and, when the experiment is repeated n times under exactly the same conditions, A occurs r times out of n, then
$$P(A) = \lim_{n \to \infty} (r/n)$$

Axioms to the probability

g 3
$P(A) \geqq 0$, event A has the probability $P(A)$

g 4
$$h(A) = \frac{\text{number of events in which } A \text{ occurs}}{\text{number of possible events}}$$
$$= \text{relative frequency}$$

g 5
$\sum_i P(A_i) = 1.0$. The sum of the probabilities of all possible events A_i taking place must be 1.0.

g 6
$P(A \cap B)^{*)} = P(A) + P(B) - P(A \cap B)^{*)}$.
If A and B cannot take place at once, then
$= P(A) + P(B)$ and the events are said to be disjoint.

g 7
$P(A/B) = P(A \cap B)/P(B)^*$ is called the probability of A conditional on B (the probability of the event A, given that the event B has happened).
If the events are independent (if the knowledge that one event has occurred has no effect on the probability of the other occurring) assuming $P(A)$ resp. $P(B) \neq 0$.

g 8

g 9
$P(A/B) = P(A)$, and $P(B/A) = P(B)$

g 10
$P(A \cap B) = P(A) \times P(B)$ if events are independent.

g 11
$P(A \cap \bar{A}) = P(A) \times P(\bar{A}) = 0$, as A and $\bar{A}$ are mutually exclusive.

*) Venn Diagrams

The rectangle   represents the sum of all events A
The large circle   represents the event A
The small circle   represents the event B
Hatched area shows the conjunction of the different cases.

$\bar{A}$	$A \cup B$	$A \cap B$	$\bar{A} \cap B$
("not" A)	(A "or" B)	(A "and" B)	(B "but not" A)

The random variable A

The random variable A is a measurable quantity which can take any number x_i or a range of values with a given probability distribution.

The cumulative distribution function $F(x)$

The cumulative distribution function $F(x)$ shows the probability of the random variable being less than a specified value x.

g 12
g 13
$F(x)$ varies between 0 and 1·0.
$F(-\infty) = 0$ and $F(x)$ increases with x.

The probability density function $f(x)$

The probability density function $f(x)$ shows the number of times one particular value p_i or range of values $f(x)$ of the random variable A occurs.

14/15
$$F(x) = \sum_{i < x} p_i \qquad F(x) = \int_{-\infty}^{x} f(x)\ dx$$

The hatched area under the probability density function curve shows the probability that the random variable A lies between x_1 and x_2.

g 16
$$P(x_1 \leqslant A < x_2) = \int_{x_1}^{x_2} f(x)\ dx$$
g 17
$$= F(x_2) - F(x_1) = P(A < x_2) - P(A < x_1)$$

STATISTICS
General terms

G 3

Mean value $\overline{x}$ or expected mean $E(x)$ or μ

Random variable A discrete	Random variable A continuous
g 18 $\overline{x} = x_1 p_1 + x_2 p_2 + \ldots + x_n p_n$	
g 19 $= \sum\limits_{i=1}^{n} x_i p_i$	g 20 $\mu = \int\limits_{-\infty}^{+\infty} x\, f(x)\ \mathrm{d}x$

where p_i and $f(x)$ are probability densities.

Variance σ^2

Random variable A discrete	Random variable A continuous
g 21 $\sigma^2 = (x_1-\overline{x})^2 \times p_1 + (x_2-\overline{x})^2\ p_2 +$	
g 22 $+ \ldots + (x_n-\overline{x})^2 \times p_n$	$\sigma^2 = \int\limits_{-\infty}^{+\infty}(x-\mu)^2 \times f(x)\ \mathrm{d}x$
g 23 $= \sum\limits_{i=1}^{n}(x_i-\overline{x})^2 \times p_i$	
g 24	
g 25 $= \sum\limits_{i=1}^{n} x_i^2 \times p_i - \overline{x}^2$	$= \int\limits_{-\infty}^{+\infty} x^2 \times f(x)\ \mathrm{d}x - \mu^2$

where p_i and $f(x)$ are probability densities and σ is called the "Standard Deviation".

Central limit theorem (addition law)

When two or more random distributions A with expected values μ and variances σ^2 are combined

g 26	the random variable	$A = \sum\limits_{i=1}^{n} A_i$	
g 27	the mean value	$\mu = \sum\limits_{i=1}^{n} \mu_i$	$\left(\overline{x} = \sum\limits_{i=1}^{n}\overline{x}_i\right)$
g 28	the variance	$\sigma^2 = \sum\limits_{i=1}^{n}\sigma_i^2\ ;$	

If the random variables have normal distributions, then

g 29
$$P(A \leqslant x) = \Phi\left(\frac{x-\mu}{\sigma}\right)$$

where Φ is the cumulative distribution function for the standard normal distribution.

g 30 Example: If 10 batches of components, each batch having a standard deviation of $0.03\,\mu m$, are mixed together, the standard deviation of the whole σ_t, is given by:

$$\sigma_t^2 = 10\,\sigma^2\ ; \qquad \sigma_t = \pm\sigma\sqrt{10} \approx \pm 0.095\ \mu m$$

STATISTICS
Special distributions

Kind of distrib.	Probability density-function	Distribution function	Expected mean μ, mean val. $\bar{x}$	Variance σ^2	Form of the density function	Remarks, Application-field
Definition equat.	$f(x)$ continuous	$F(x)=\int_{-\infty}^{x} f(t)\,dt$	$\int_{-\infty}^{\infty} x\,f(x)\,dx$	$\int_{-\infty}^{\infty} x^2 f(x)\,dx - \mu^2$		k : numbers of errors n : number in random sample x_i : discrete value of a random variable p : error probability
	p_i discrete	$F(x)=\sum_{i\le x} p_i$	$\sum_{i=1}^{n} x_i\,p_i$	$\sum_{i=1}^{n} x_i^2\, p_i - \mu^2$		
hyper-geometric	$P(k)=\dfrac{\binom{pN}{k}\binom{N(1-p)}{n-k}}{\binom{N}{n}}$	$F(x)=\sum_{k\le x}\dfrac{\binom{pN}{k}\binom{N(1-p)}{n-k}}{\binom{N}{n}}$	$n\,p$	$n\,p\,\dfrac{N-n}{N-1}(1-p)$		N : Size of the lot pN : Defect. parts within N Precise but expensive calculation. Without replacement.
	$P(k)$ means the probability that in n random samples from a lot N, exactly k are defective					
bino-mial	$P(k)=\binom{n}{k}p^{k}(1-p)^{n-k}$	$F(x)=\sum_{k\le x}\binom{n}{k}p^{k}(1-p)^{n-k}$	$n\,p$	$n\,p\,(1-p)$		Conditions: Lot size, ∞
	$P(k)$ means the probability that in n random samples exactly k errors occur.					
Poisson	$P(k)=\dfrac{(np)^{k}}{k!}\,e^{-np}$	$F(x)=\sum_{k\le x}\dfrac{(np)^{k}}{k!}\,e^{-np}$	$n\,p$	$n\,p$		Conditions: Large value of random sampling and small value of proportion defective. $n\cdot p=\text{const.}$ $n\to\infty$; $p\to 0$
	$P(k)$ means the probability that in n random samples k errors occur. Application: Curves for random sampling valuation (s. G11)					continued on G 5

| g 31 | g 32 | g 33 | g 34 | g 35 |

Kind of distrib.	Probability density-function	Distribution function	Expected mean μ / mean val. $\bar{x}$	Variance σ^2	Form of the density function	Remarks, Application-field
Defini-tion equat.	$f(x)$ continuous	$F(x) = \int_{-\infty}^{x} f(t)\,dt$	$\int_{-\infty}^{\infty} x f(x)\,dx$	$\int_{-\infty}^{\infty} x^2 f(x)\,dx - \mu^2$		n: number in random sample; x_i: discrete value of a random variable; p: error probability
	p_i discrete	$F(x) = \sum_{i<x} p_i$	$\sum_{i=1}^{n} x_i\, p_i$	$\sum_{i=1}^{n} x_i^2\, p_i - \mu^2$		
exponential	$f(x) = a\,e^{-ax}$ $\quad a > 0$ $\quad x > 0$	$1 - e^{-ax}$	$\dfrac{1}{a}$	$\dfrac{1}{a^2}$		Special case of the Poisson distribution for $x = 0$. Gives the probability without error. $n \to \infty$; $p \to 0$.
	Used for reliability calculations. Replacement of $a\,x$ by failure rate λ multiplied by control time t (see G 12).					
normal (Gaussian) or error	$f(x) = \dfrac{1}{\sigma\sqrt{2\pi}}\, e^{-\frac{(x-\mu)^2}{2\sigma^2}}$	$\int_{-\infty}^{x} \dfrac{1}{\sigma\sqrt{2\pi}}\, e^{\frac{-(t-\mu)^2}{2\sigma^2}}\, dt$	μ	σ^2		Special case of the Binomial distribution. $n \to \infty$, $p = 0.5 = $ const.
	Often obtained in practice, as measured values with bell-formed distribution occur around a mean value.					
uni-form	$f(x) = \dfrac{1}{b-a}$ for $a \le x \le b$ $= 0$ for x outside	$F(x) = 0$ for $-\infty < x < a$ $= \dfrac{x-a}{b-a}$ for $a \le x < b$	$\dfrac{a+b}{2}$	$\dfrac{(b-a)^2}{12}$		Random variable x is $\ne 0$ only within the interval a, b. There each value is of equal probability.
	Application when only maximum and minimum value and no other information about the distribution between is known.					

Determination of σ when discrete values are available

By calculation
Equation g 23 says.

g 41

$$\sigma^2 = \sum_{i=1}^{n} (x_i - \bar{x})^2 \, p_i \qquad \text{with} \qquad \bar{x} = \sum_{i=1}^{n} x_i \, p_i$$

g 42

$$= \sum_{i=1}^{n} x_i^2 \, p_i - \bar{x}^2$$

where x_i are measured values of the random variable A and
p_i are the frequencies of their occurrence.

By graphics
Standardise the distribution and choose four values of x_i spread across the range, say x_4, x_6, x_7 and x_9 shown in the drawing.

For each of these plot the cumulative frequency against the value of x_i e. g. 10% to value x_4, 38% to value x_6 and so on.

If a straight line can be drawn through these points, the distribution is proved to be normal. The values of the mean $\bar{x}$ and the standard deviation σ are obtained as shown in the diagram.

The mean value $\bar{x}$ is at 50%. The difference between the value A at 84% and the value A at 16% gives 2σ.

Normal curve for probability density $\varphi(\lambda)$

$\sigma^2 = 1$ and $\mu = 0$ in g 39 leads to the standardized probability density with mean value $\lambda = 0$.

g 43
$$\varphi(\lambda) = \frac{1}{\sqrt{2\pi}}\, e^{\frac{-\lambda^2}{2}}$$

$\varphi(\lambda)$ is given in tables Z 26 and Z 27 for $0 \leq \lambda \leq 1.99$, but can also be calculated from g 43.

The connection between standardized probability density $\varphi(\lambda)$ and the real probability density $f(x)$ for $\mu \neq 0$ and $\sigma^2 \neq 1$ is

g 44
$$f(x) = \frac{\varphi(\lambda)}{\sigma} = \frac{1}{\sigma\sqrt{2\pi}}\, e^{\frac{-(x-\mu)^2}{2\sigma^2}} \qquad \text{where} \quad \lambda = \frac{x-\mu}{\sigma}$$

To use the table, first find the value of the standardized probability density $\varphi(\lambda)$ corresponding to λ. Divide by σ to get the real value of the probability density $f(x)$ for the value of x (see g 44).

Normal probability curve (Probability distribution function)

$\sigma^2 = 1$ and $\mu = 0$ in g 39 leads to the standardized normal distribution

g 45
$$\bar{\Phi}(\lambda) = \int_{-\infty}^{\lambda} \varphi(t)\, dt = \frac{1}{\sqrt{2\pi}} \int_{-\infty}^{\lambda} e^{\frac{-t^2}{2}}\, dt$$

As limit $\Phi(\lambda) = 1$ for $\lambda \to \infty$ and $\varphi(t)$ is a symmetrical function means that:

g 46
$$\bar{\Phi}(-\lambda) = 1 - \bar{\Phi}(\lambda)$$

The relation between the standardized $\Phi(\lambda)$ distribution function and the real distribution for $\mu \neq 0$ and $\sigma^2 \neq 1$ is

47/48
$$F(x) = \frac{\bar{\Phi}(\lambda)}{\sigma} = \frac{1}{\sigma\sqrt{2\pi}} \int_{-\infty}^{x} e^{\frac{-(t-\mu)^2}{2\sigma^2}}\, dt \qquad \text{where} \quad \lambda = \frac{t-\mu}{\sigma}$$

Gaussian or Error curve

The curve is based on the standardized normal distribution using g 45 for $\sigma^2 = 1$ and $\mu = 0$. The area under the curve gives the value of the distribution function between $-x$ and $+x$ of the symmetrical density function $\varphi(t)$.

g 49
$$\bar{\Phi}_0(x) = \frac{2}{\sqrt{2\pi}} \int_0^x e^{\frac{-t^2}{2}} \, dt$$

Values of $\Phi_0(x)$ between $0 \le x \le 1.99$ are given in tables Z 26 and Z 27. For greater values of x look at the approximation in the next paragraph. The connection between $\Phi_c(x)$ and the error function is $\bar{\Phi}_0(x) = \text{erf}(x/\sqrt{2})$.

g 50

Error function

g 51
$$\text{erf}(x) = \bar{\Phi}_0(x\sqrt{2}) = \frac{2}{\sqrt{\pi}} \int_0^x e^{-t^2} \, dt$$

g 52
$$= \frac{2}{\sqrt{\pi}} e^{-x^2} \sum_{n=0}^{\infty} \frac{2^n}{1 \times 3 \times \dots \times (2n+1)} x^{2n+1}$$

Values of erf (x) between $0 \le x \le 1.99$ are given in tables Z 26 and Z 27. For $x \ge 2$ values of erf(x) can be found approximately using

g 53
$$\text{erf}(x) = 1 - \frac{a}{x \, e^{x^2}}$$

where $a = 0.515$ for $2 \le x \le 3$
$a = 0.535$ for $3 \le x \le 4$
$a = 0.545$ for $4 \le x \le 7$
$a = 0.56$ for $7 \le x \le \infty$

Area beneath the error curve when erf(x) is subtracted:

g 54
$$\text{erfc}(x) = 1 - \text{erf}(x) = \frac{2}{\sqrt{\pi}} \int_x^{\infty} e^{-t^2} \, dt$$

g 55
$\Phi_0(x)$ and $[1-\Phi_0(x)]$ in % relation to the whole area for special values

x	$\Phi_0(x)/\%$	$[1-\Phi_0(x)]/\%$
$\pm \sigma$	68.26	31.74
$\pm 2\sigma$	95.44	4.56
$\pm 2.58\sigma$	99	1
$\pm 3\sigma$	99.73	0.27
$\pm 3.29\sigma$	99.9	0.1

General: When testing each individual component is too expensive or not possible, test by random sampling is used. The samples must be chosen arbitrarily to give equal chances for all parts (i. e. good intermixing).

The aim of the test by random sampling is to predict the probability of the real failure rate of the whole lot on the basis of measured failure or error numbers in a sample.

Hypergeometric distribution: A hypergeometric distribution occurs when the sampling takes place without replacement. The probability $P(k)$ that in a lot of N using samples of n, without replacement, exactly k defective parts are found, when p is the assumed probability for a defective part (i. e. pN is the number of real defective parts in N and is a whole number).

g 56

$$P(k) = \frac{\binom{pN}{k}\binom{N(1-p)}{n-k}}{\binom{N}{n}}; \quad pN \text{ is a whole number}$$

The probability that not more than k defective parts are found is:

g 57

$$\sum_{x=0}^{k} P(k) = P(0) + P(1) + \dots + P(k)$$

g 58

$$= \sum_{x=0}^{k} \frac{\binom{pN}{x}\binom{N(1-p)}{n-x}}{\binom{N}{n}}; pN \text{ is a whole number}$$

Example:

In a batch of 100 screws, a maximum of 3 can be defective ($N = 100$, $pN = 3$). Random samples of $n = 20$ are taken. How many defective parts are allowed in the sample? — The probabilities $\sum P(x)$ are

x	$P(x)$	$\sum_{x=0}^{k} P(x)$
0	0·508	0·508
1	0·391	0·899
2	0·094	0·993
3	0·007	1·000

The table shows that for $\leq 90\%$ probability one part may be defective.

Further special distributions: Besides the hypergeometric distribution which takes much time for calculation there are other special distributions for defined assumptions and conditions. In tables G 4 and G 5 these are shown together with the hypergeometric distribution; special characteristics of these are explained.

The confidence statement $P(x > k)$

From a lot N, a random sample of n is taken and k defective parts are found in it. If the probability of finding a defective part in the lot is p, the probability of finding more than k defective parts in the sample n can be derived from g 57.

g 59 $$P(x > k) = P(k+1) + P(k+2) + \ldots + P(n) = \sum_{x=k+1}^{n} P(x)$$

If N is large which is true for most manufacturing processes, and $p < 0.1$ the Poisson distribution may be used:

g 60 $$P(x > k) = \sum_{x=k+1}^{x=n} \frac{(np)^x}{x!} e^{-np} = 1 - \sum_{x=0}^{x=k} \frac{(np)^x}{x!} e^{-np}$$

and if the size of the sample k is small, then

g 61 $$P(x > k) = 1 - \sum_{x=0}^{k} \frac{(np)^x}{x!} e^{-np} = 1 - e^{-np}\left[1 + \frac{np}{1!} + \frac{(np)^2}{2!} + \ldots + \frac{(np)^k}{k!}\right]$$

Using g 61, the confidence statement $P(x > k)$ for the proportion defective in a lot N can be determined when there are k defective parts found in the sample n, or g 61 may be used to find the size of the sample required if with an error probability of $p = k/n$, k defective parts are allowed for a given confidence statement $P(x > k)$.

The Operating Characteristic (OC)

A user needs to know whether a lot delivered by a producer meets his quality requirements. Assuming a proportion p defective in the whole batch $(p \leq p_0)$ he wants to know whether to accept or reject the whole lot if in a random sample of n parts, up to c are found to be defective. The probability that the lot will be accepted on the basis of the evidence of the sample is

g 62 $$L(p, c) \geq 1 - \alpha \qquad \text{where } \alpha \text{ is the producer risk or}$$

from g 57:

g 63 $$L(p, c) = P(0) + P(1) + \ldots + P(k = c)$$

or using the Poisson distribution:

g 64 $$L(p, c) = \sum_{k=0}^{c} \frac{(np)^k}{k!} e^{-np} = e^{-np}\left[1 + np + \frac{(np)^2}{2!} + \ldots + \frac{(np)^c}{c!}\right]$$

continued on G11

continued from G 10

Using equation g 64, the operating characteristics $L(p,c)$ may be plotted in two ways:

Type A	Type B
n = constant; c: parameter	c = constant; n: parameter
Example	Example

Note: The smaller the value of c becomes, the nearer the operating characteristic approaches $p = 0$.

c must be $\leq n$

Note: The bigger the value of n, the steeper is the operating characteristic; when $n = N$ the curve is parallel to the ordinate and every article is tested. The steeper the curve the more stringent is the control. n must be $\geq c$.

Acceptable Quality Level (A.Q.L.): Agreement between the producer and the user leads to the most important point on the operating characteristic, the AQL-value. The manufacturer needs to be assured that the method of sampling will accurately predict the quality of the lot. If this has a probability of 90%, then the producer risk from g 32 :

$$L(p,c) \geq 1 - \alpha = 1 - 0.9 = 10\%,$$

but the method of sampling may increase the producer risk. To overcome it, the producer may decide to hold his failure rate well below the agreed value of the AQL to say p_0 *) which gives a permitted failure of c_1, in the sample as shown in the graph of $L(p,c)$ against p, which is less than c_2, the value originally required. As a result the probability of success in the lot rises to 99%. In practice, the AQL has a value of about 0.65.

n : number in random samples
c : number of the maximum admissible defective parts

General definitions

g 65   Reliability
$$R(t) = \frac{n(t)}{n_0} = e^{-\int_0^t \lambda(\tau)\,d\tau}$$

g 66   Probability to failure
$$F(t) = 1 - R(t)$$

g 67   Failure density
$$f(t) = -\frac{dR}{dt}$$
$$= \lambda(t)\,e^{-\int_0^t \lambda(\tau)\,d\tau}$$

g 68   Failure rate
$$\lambda(t) = \frac{f(t)}{R(t)} = -\frac{1}{R(t)}\frac{dR}{dt}$$

MTTF (**m**ean **t**ime **t**o **f**ailure)

g 69
$$MTTF = \int_0^\infty f(t)\,t\,dt = \int_0^\infty R(t)\,dt$$

In systems which can be repaired, MTTF is replaced by the mean time between two errors, the mean failure distance m = MTBF (**m**ean **t**ime **b**etween **f**ailures). Values of MTTF and MTBF are equal.

g 70
$$MTTF = MTBF = m = \int_0^\infty R(t)\,dt$$

Product rule for the reliability R_s:
When $R_1 \ldots R_n$ are the reliabilities of the single elements $1 \ldots n$, the reliability of the whole system becomes:

g 71
$$R_S = R_1\,R_2\,\ldots.\,R_n = \prod_{i=1}^n R_i$$

g 72
$$= e^{-\int_0^t \left[\lambda_1(\tau) + \lambda_2(\tau) \ldots \lambda_n(\tau)\right]\,d\tau}$$

Note
Expressions for the reliability functions $R(t)$ are the distribution functions $F(x)$ in tables G 4 and G 5 (for calculation use g 66). The exponential distribution, simple to calculate, usually fulfills the requirements (λ = const).

$n(t)$: number of elements at the time t
n_0 : number of elements at the beginning

Exponential distribution used as reliability function

g 73	Reliability	$R(t) = e^{-\lambda t}$
g 74	Probability to failure	$F(t) = 1 - e^{-\lambda t}$
g 75	Failure density	$f(t) = \lambda\, e^{-\lambda t}$
g 76	Failure rate	$\lambda(t) = \dfrac{f(t)}{R(t)} = \lambda = \text{const.}$

(Dimension: 1/time)

g 77	Failure distance (MTBF)	$m = \displaystyle\int_0^\infty e^{-\lambda t}\,dt = \dfrac{1}{\lambda}$

Product rule for the reliability R_s:

g 78	$R_S = e^{-\lambda_1 t}\, e^{-\lambda_2 t} \cdot \ldots \, e^{-\lambda_n t}$
g 79	$\quad = e^{-(\lambda_1 + \lambda_2 + \ldots + \lambda_n) t}$
g 80	Cumulative failure rate $\quad \lambda_S = \lambda_1 + \lambda_2 + \ldots + \lambda_n = \dfrac{1}{\text{MTBF}}$

For small values the failure rate can be calculated approximately

g 81	$\lambda = \dfrac{\text{number of defectives}}{\text{number of elements at the beginning} \times \text{working time}}$

λ-values are mostly related to working hours

g 82	Unit: 1 fit = 1 failure/10^9 hours

Typical examples for failure rate λ in fit:

IC-digital bipolar (SSI)	15	Resistor-metal	1
IC-analog bipolar (OpAmp)	100	Resistor-wire wound	10
Transistor-Si-Universal	20	Small transformer	5
Transistor-Si-Power	200	HF-cool	1
Diode-Si	5	Quartz	10
Tantalum electrolyte capacitor (liquid / solid)	20 / 5	Light emitting diode ($\triangleq$ luminous intensity is reduced to 50%)	500
Alu-electrolytic capacitor	20	Soldered connection	0·5
Ceramic (multilayer) capacitor	10	Wrapped connection	0·0025
Paper capacitor	2	Crimped connection	0·26
Vulcanite capacitor	1	plug-in contact	0·3
Resistor-carbon $\geq$ 100 kΩ	5	plug-in socket per used contact	0·4
Resistor-carbon $\leq$ 100 kΩ	0·5	plug-in switch	5 ... 30

Note: Specifications for reliability are DIN 29500, page 1, DIN 40040 and DIN 41611.

Differential coefficients (or derivatives)

Gradient of a curve
The gradient of a curve $y = f(x)$ varies from point to point. By the gradient of a curve at point P we mean the gradient of the tangent at the point. If x and y have equal dimensions – which is not the case in most technical diagrams – and are presented at equal scales, the gradient may be expressed by the tangent of angle a between the tangent at point P and the horizontal axis:

$$m = \tan a$$

h 1 | Always applicable is gradient: $m = \dfrac{\Delta y}{\Delta x}$

Difference coefficient
The difference coefficient or mean gradient of the function $y = f(x)$ between PP_1 is:

h 2

$$\frac{\Delta y}{\Delta x} = \frac{f(x+\Delta x) - f(x)}{\Delta x}$$

Differential coefficient
Where Δx is infinitely small, i.e. where Δx approaches zero, the slope at P becomes the limiting value of the slope of one of the secants. This slope is the "derivative" or "differential coefficient" of the function at P.

h 3

$$y' = \frac{dy}{dx} = f'(x)$$

$$y' = \lim_{\Delta x \to 0} \frac{\Delta y}{\Delta x} = \lim_{\Delta x \to 0} \frac{f(x + \Delta x) - f(x)}{\Delta x} = \frac{dy}{dx} = f'(x)$$

Geometric meaning of derivative

Gradient of a curve

If, for each point x of a curve, we plot its corresponding gradient as an ordinate y', we obtain the first gradient curve $y' = f'(x)$ or the first derivative of the original curve $y = f(x)$. If we now take the derivative of the first gradient $y' = f'(x)$ we obtain $y'' = f''(x)$ or the second derivative of the original curve $y = f(x)$ etc.

Example: $\qquad y = Ax^3 + Bx^2 + Cx + D$

Radius of curvature ϱ at any point x

h 4
$$\varrho = \frac{\sqrt{(1 + y'^2)^3}}{y''}$$

M is below the curve where ϱ is $-$
M is above the curve where ϱ is $+$

Centre coordinates for radius ϱ

h 5
$$a = x - \frac{1 + y'^2}{y''} \, y'$$

h 6
$$b = y + \frac{1 + y'^2}{y''}$$

continued on H 3

Determination of minima, maxima and inflexions

Minima and maxima

The value $x = a$ obtained for $y' = 0$ is inserted in y''.

h 7	For $y''(a) > 0$ there is a minimum at $x = a$,
h 8	For $y''(a) < 0$ there is a maximum at $x = a$,
h 9	For $y''(a) = 0$ see h 19.

Inflexion

The value $x = a$ obtained for $y'' = 0$ is inserted in y'''.

h 10	For $y'''(a) \neq 0$ there is an inflexion at $x = a$.

Shape of the curve $y = f(x)$

Rise and fall

h 11	$y'(x) > 0$	$y(x)$	increases as x increases
h 12	$y'(x) < 0$	$y(x)$	decreases as x increases
h 13	$y'(x) = 0$	$y(x)$	is tangentially parallel the x-axis at x

Curve

h 14	$y''(x) < 0$	$y(x)$	is convex (viewed from above)
h 15	$y''(x) > 0$	$y(x)$	is concave (viewed from above)
h 16	$y''(x) = 0$	with	a change of sign	flexion
		without	$y'(x)$ at x has a	bottom point

Exceptional case

Where at a point $x = a$

h 17	$y'(a) = y''(a) = y'''(a) = \ldots \quad y^{(n-1)}(a) = 0$, but
h 18	$y^n(a) \neq 0$, one of the 4 conditions is present:

	n = even number		n = uneven number	
h 19	$y^{(n)}(a) > 0$	$y^{(n)}(a) < 0$	$y^{(n)}(a) > 0$	$y^{(n)}(a) < 0$

DIFFERENTIAL CALCULUS

Basic differentials

4

Derivatives

Basic rules

	function	derivative
h 21	$y = c\,x^n + C$	$y' = c\,n\,x^{n-1}$
h 22	$y = u(x) \pm v(x)$	$y' = u'(x) \pm v'(x)$
h 23	$y = u(x)\,v(x)$	$y' = u'v + u\,v'$
h 24	$y = \dfrac{u(x)}{v(x)}$	$y' = \dfrac{u'v - u\,v'}{v^2}$
h 25	$y = \sqrt{x}$	$y' = \dfrac{1}{2\sqrt{x}}$
h 26	$y = u(x)^{v(x)}$	$y' = u^v\left(\dfrac{u'\,v}{u} + v'\ln u\right)$

Derivative of a function of a function
(chain rule)

h 27	$y = f\left[u(x)\right]$	$y' = f'(u)\,u'(x)$
		$= \dfrac{dy}{dx} = \dfrac{dy}{du}\dfrac{du}{dx}$

Parametric form of derivative

h 28	$y = f(x)$	$\begin{cases} x = f(t) \\ y = f(t) \end{cases}$	$y' = \dfrac{dy}{dt}\dfrac{dt}{dx} = \dfrac{\dot y}{\dot x}$
h 29			$y'' = \dfrac{d^2 y}{dx^2} = \dfrac{\dot x \ddot y - \dot y \ddot x}{\dot x^3}$

Derivative of inverse functions
The equation $y = f(x)$ solved for x gives the inverse function $x = \varphi(y)$.

h 30	$x = \varphi(y)$	$f'(x) = \dfrac{1}{\varphi'(y)}$
	Example:	
h 31	$y = f(x) = \arccos x$	$f'(x) = \dfrac{1}{-\sin y} = -\dfrac{1}{\sqrt{1-x^2}}$
h 32	gives $x = \varphi(y) = \cos y$	

Derivatives

Exponential functions

	function	derivative
h 33	$y = e^x$	$y' = e^x = y'' = \ldots$
h 34	$y = e^{-x}$	$y' = -e^{-x}$
h 35	$y = e^{\alpha x}$	$y' = \alpha\, e^{\alpha x}$
h 36	$y = x\, e^x$	$y' = e^x(1+x)$
h 37	$y = \sqrt{e^x}$	$y' = \dfrac{\sqrt{e^x}}{2}$
h 38	$y = a^x$	$y' = a^x \ln a$
h 39	$y = a^{nx}$	$y' = n\, a^{nx} \ln a$
h 40	$y = a^{x^2}$	$y' = a^{x^2}\, 2x \ln a$

Trigonometrical functions

	function	derivative
h 41	$y = \sin x$	$y' = \cos x$
h 42	$y = \cos x$	$y' = -\sin x$
h 43	$y = \tan x$	$y' = \dfrac{1}{\cos^2 x} = 1 + \tan^2 x = \sec^2 x$
h 44	$y = \cot x$	$y' = \dfrac{-1}{\sin^2 x} = -(1 + \cot^2 x) = -\csc^2 x$
h 45	$y = a \sin(kx)$	$y' = a\, k \cos(kx)$
h 46	$y = a \cos(kx)$	$y' = -a\, k \sin(kx)$
h 47	$y = \sin^n x$	$y' = n \sin^{n-1} x \cos x$
h 48	$y = \cos^n x$	$y' = -n \cos^{n-1} x \sin x$
h 49	$y = \tan^n x$	$y' = n \tan^{n-1} x (1 + \tan^2 x)$
h 50	$y = \cot^n x$	$y' = -n \cot^{n-1} x (1 + \cot^2 x)$
h 51	$y = \dfrac{1}{\sin x}$	$y' = \dfrac{-\cos x}{\sin^2 x}$
h 52	$y = \dfrac{1}{\cos x}$	$y' = \dfrac{\sin x}{\cos^2 x}$

Derivatives

Logarithmic functions

	function	derivative
h 53	$y = \ln x$	$y' = \dfrac{1}{x}$
h 54	$y = {}^{a}\log x$	$y' = \dfrac{1}{x \ln a}$
h 55	$y = \ln(1 \pm x)$	$y' = \dfrac{\pm 1}{1 \pm x}$
h 56	$y = \ln x^n$	$y' = \dfrac{n}{x}$
h 57	$y = \ln \sqrt{x}$	$y' = \dfrac{1}{2x}$

Hyperbolic functions

	function	derivative
h 58	$y = \sinh x$	$y' = \cosh x$
h 59	$y = \cosh x$	$y' = \sinh x$
h 60	$y = \tanh x$	$y' = \dfrac{1}{\cosh^2 x}$
h 61	$y = \coth x$	$y' = \dfrac{-1}{\sinh^2 x}$

Inverse trigonometrical functions

	function	derivative
h 62	$y = \arcsin x$	$y' = \dfrac{1}{\sqrt{1 - x^2}}$
h 63	$y = \arccos x$	$y' = -\dfrac{1}{\sqrt{1 - x^2}}$
h 64	$y = \arctan x$	$y' = \dfrac{1}{1 + x^2}$
h 65	$y = \mathrm{arccot}\, x$	$y' = -\dfrac{1}{1 + x^2}$
h 66	$y = \mathrm{arsinh}\, x$	$y' = \dfrac{1}{\sqrt{x^2 + 1}}$
h 67	$y = \mathrm{arcosh}\, x$	$y' = \dfrac{1}{\sqrt{x^2 - 1}}$
h 68	$y = \mathrm{artanh}\, x$	$y' = \dfrac{1}{1 - x^2}$
h 69	$y = \mathrm{arcoth}\, x$	$y' = \dfrac{1}{1 - x^2}$

Integration

Integration reverse of differentiation

By integral calculus we mean the problem of finding a function $y = f(x)$, the derivative of $F(x)$ being equal to $f(x)$.
Thus

j 1
$$F'(x) = \frac{dF(x)}{dx} = f(x)$$

hence, by integration

the indefinite integral

j 2
$$\int f(x)\ dx = F(x) + C$$

Here C is unknown constant which disappears on differentiation, since the derivative of a constant equals zero.

Geometric meaning of the indefinite integral

As this figure shows, there are an infinite number of $y = F(x)$ curves with a gradient $y' = f(x)$. All $y = F(x)$ curves are the same shape, but intersect the x-axis at varying distances. The constant C, however, establishes a fixed curve. If the curve is to pass through the point x_0/y_0, then

j 3
$$C = y_0 - F(x_0)$$

The definite integral

The definite integral is represented by

j 4
$$\int_a^b f(x)\ dx = F(x)\Big|_a^b = F(b) - F(a)$$

Here integration takes place between the limits a und b, the second substitution resultant is subtracted from the first causing the constant C to disappear.

Integration

Basic formulae

j 5
$$\int x^n \, dx = \frac{x^{n+1}}{n+1} + C, \qquad \text{here} \qquad n \neq -1$$

j 6
$$\int \frac{dx}{x} = \ln x + C$$

j 7
$$\int \left[u(x) \pm v(x) \right] dx = \int u(x) \, dx \pm \int v(x) \, dx$$

j 8
$$\int \frac{u'(x)}{u(x)} \, dx = \ln u(x) + C$$

j 9
$$\int u(x) \, u'(x) \, dx = \frac{1}{2} \left[u(x) \right]^2 + C$$

Integration by parts

j10
$$\int u(x) \, v'(x) \, dx = u(x) \, v(x) - \int u'(x) \, v(x) \, dx$$

Integration by substitution

j11
$$\int f(x) \, dx = \int f \left[\varphi(z) \right] \varphi'(z) \, dz$$
$$\text{here} \qquad x = \varphi(z) \qquad \text{and} \qquad dx = \varphi'(z) \, dz$$

Example:

j12
$$F(x) = \int \sqrt{3x - 5} \, dx.$$

Where $3x - 5 = z$, the derivative is $z' = \frac{dz}{dx} = 3$.

Thus $dx = \frac{dz}{3}$ expressed in terms of z, the integral becomes

$F(x) = \frac{1}{3} \int \sqrt{z} \, dz = \frac{2}{9} z \sqrt{z} + C$. Insert value of z in above

expression: $\qquad F(x) = \frac{2}{9}(3x-5)\sqrt{3x-5} + C$

Integrals

(omitting integra constant C)

j 13 $\quad \int e^{ax}\, dx = \frac{1}{a}\, e^{ax} \qquad\qquad \int \ln x\, dx = x \cdot \ln x - x$

j 14 $\quad \int a^{bx}\, dx = \frac{1}{b} \cdot \frac{a^{bx}}{\ln a} \qquad\qquad \int \frac{dx}{x-a} = \ln(x-a)$

j 15 $\quad \int \frac{dx}{(x-a)(x-b)} = \frac{1}{a-b} \ln \frac{x-c}{x-t} \qquad (a \neq b)$

j 16 $\quad \int \frac{dx}{(x-a)^n} = -\frac{1}{(n-1)(x-a)^{n-1}} \qquad (n \neq 1)$

j 17 $\quad \int \frac{dx}{x^2 - a^2} = -\frac{1}{a} \operatorname{arcoth} \frac{x}{a} = \frac{1}{2a} \ln \frac{x-a}{x+a} \qquad (x > a)$

j 18 $\quad \int \frac{dx}{a^2 - x^2} = \frac{1}{a} \operatorname{artanh} \frac{x}{a} = \frac{1}{2a} \ln \frac{a+x}{a-x} \qquad (x < a)$

j 19 $\quad \int \frac{dx}{x^2 + a^2} = \frac{1}{a} \arctan \frac{x}{a} \qquad \int \frac{x \cdot dx}{x^2 + a^2} = \frac{1}{2} \ln(x^2 + a^2)$

j 20 $\quad \int \frac{dx}{(x^2 + a^2)^2} = \frac{x}{2a^2(x^2 + a^2)} + \frac{1}{2a^3} \arctan \frac{x}{a}$

j 21 $\quad \int \frac{dx}{(x^2 + a^2)^n} = \frac{x}{2a^2(n-1)(x^2 + a^2)^{n-1}} + \frac{2n-3}{2a^2(n-1)} \int \frac{dx}{(x^2 + a^2)^{n-1}} \qquad (n \neq 1)$

j 22 $\quad \int \sqrt{x}\, dx = \frac{2}{3} \sqrt{x^3} \qquad\qquad \int \frac{dx}{\sqrt{x}} = 2\sqrt{x}$

j 23 $\quad \int \frac{dx}{\sqrt{a^2 - x^2}} = \arcsin \frac{x}{a} \qquad \int \frac{dx}{\sqrt{ax+b}} = \frac{2}{a} \sqrt{ax+b}$

j 24 $\quad \int \frac{dx}{\sqrt{x^2 - a^2}} = \operatorname{arcosh} \frac{x}{a} = \ln(x + \sqrt{x^2 - a^2})$

j 25 $\quad \int \frac{dx}{\sqrt{x^2 + a^2}} = \operatorname{arsinh} \frac{x}{a} = \ln(x + \sqrt{x^2 + a^2})$

j 26 $\quad \int \sqrt{a^2 - x^2}\, dx = \frac{x}{2} \sqrt{a^2 - x^2} + \frac{a^2}{2} \arcsin \frac{x}{a}$

j 27 $\quad \int \sqrt{x^2 - a^2}\, dx = \frac{x}{2} \sqrt{x^2 - a^2} - \frac{a^2}{2} \operatorname{arcosh} \frac{x}{a}$

j 28 $\quad \int \sqrt{x^2 + a^2}\, dx = \frac{x}{2} \sqrt{x^2 + a^2} + \frac{a^2}{2} \operatorname{arsinh} \frac{x}{a}$

Integrals
(omitting integral constant C)

j 29 $\quad \int \sin x \, dx \quad = -\cos x$

j 30 $\quad \int \sin^2 x \, dx \quad = \dfrac{x}{2} - \dfrac{1}{4} \sin(2x)$

j 31 $\quad \int \sin^3 x \, dx \quad = -\cos x + \dfrac{1}{3} \cos^3 x = -\dfrac{3}{4} \cos x + \dfrac{1}{12} \cos 3x$

j 32 $\quad \int \sin^n x \, dx \quad = -\dfrac{1}{n} \cos x \, \sin^{n-1} x + \dfrac{n-1}{n} \int \sin^{n-2} x \, dx$

j 33 $\quad \int \sin(ax) \, dx = -\dfrac{1}{a} \cos(ax)$

j 34 $\quad \int \cos x \, dx \quad = \sin x$

j 35 $\quad \int \cos^2 x \, dx \quad = \dfrac{x}{2} + \dfrac{1}{4} \sin(2x)$

j 36 $\quad \int \cos^3 x \, dx \quad = \sin x - \dfrac{1}{3} \sin^3 x = \dfrac{3}{4} \sin x + \dfrac{1}{12} \sin 3x$

j 37 $\quad \int \cos^n x \, dx \quad = \dfrac{1}{n} \sin x \, \cos^{n-1} x + \dfrac{n-1}{n} \int \cos^{n-2} x \, dx$

j 38 $\quad \int \cos(ax) \, dx = \dfrac{1}{a} \sin(ax)$

j 39 $\quad \int \tan x \, dx \quad = -\ln \cos x \quad \bigg\| \quad \int \tan(ax) \, dx = -\dfrac{1}{a} \ln \cos(ax)$

j 40 $\quad \int \tan^2 x \, dx \quad = \tan x - x$

j 41 $\quad \int \tan^n x \, dx \quad = \dfrac{\tan^{n-1} x}{n-1} - \int \tan^{n-2} x \, dx \qquad (n \neq 1)$

j 42 $\quad \int \cot x \, dx \quad = \ln \sin x \quad \bigg\| \quad \int \cot(ax) \, dx = \dfrac{1}{a} \ln \sin(ax)$

j 43 $\quad \int \cot^2 x \, dx \quad = -x - \cot x$

j 44 $\quad \int \cot^n x \, dx \quad = -\dfrac{\cot^{n-1} x}{n-1} - \int \cot^{n-2} x \, dx \qquad (n \neq 1)$

j 45 $\quad \int \dfrac{dx}{\sin x} \quad = \ln \tan \dfrac{x}{2} \quad \bigg\| \quad \int \dfrac{dx}{\sin^2 x} = -\cot x$

j 46 $\quad \int \dfrac{dx}{\sin^n x} \quad = -\dfrac{1}{n-1} \dfrac{\cos x}{\sin^{n-1} x} + \dfrac{n-2}{n-1} \int \dfrac{dx}{\sin^{n-2} x} \qquad (n \neq 1)$

j 47 $\quad \int \dfrac{dx}{\cos x} \quad = \ln \tan\left(\dfrac{x}{2} + \dfrac{\pi}{4}\right) \quad \bigg\| \quad \int \dfrac{dx}{\cos^2 x} = \tan x$

j 48 $\quad \int \dfrac{dx}{\cos^n x} \quad = \dfrac{1}{n-1} \dfrac{\sin x}{\cos^{n-1} x} + \dfrac{n-2}{n-1} \int \dfrac{dx}{\cos^{n-2} x} \qquad (n \neq 1)$

Integrals
(omitting integral constant C)

j 49 $\quad \int \dfrac{dx}{1 + \sin x} = \tan\left(\dfrac{x}{2} - \dfrac{\pi}{4}\right)$ $\qquad \int \dfrac{dx}{1 - \sin x} = -\cot\left(\dfrac{x}{2} - \dfrac{\pi}{4}\right)$

j 50 $\quad \int \dfrac{dx}{1 + \cos x} = \tan \dfrac{x}{2}$ $\qquad \int \dfrac{dx}{1 - \cos x} = -\cot \dfrac{x}{2}$

j 51 $\quad \int \sin(ax)\sin(bx)\,dx = -\dfrac{\sin(ax+bx)}{2(a+b)} + \dfrac{\sin(ax-bx)}{2(a-b)} \quad (|a| \neq |b|)$

j 52 $\quad \int \sin(ax)\cos(bx)\,dx = -\dfrac{\cos(ax+bx)}{2(a+b)} - \dfrac{\cos(ax-bx)}{2(a-b)} \quad (|a| \neq |b|)$

j 53 $\quad \int \cos(ax)\cos(bx)\,dx = \dfrac{\sin(ax+bx)}{2(a+b)} + \dfrac{\sin(ax-bx)}{2(a-b)} \quad (|a| \neq |b|)$

j 54 $\quad \int x^n \sin(ax)\,dx = -\dfrac{x^n}{a}\cos(ax) + \dfrac{n}{a}\int x^{n-1}\cos(ax)\,dx$

j 55 $\quad \int x^n \cos(ax)\,dx = \dfrac{x^n}{a}\sin(ax) - \dfrac{n}{a}\int x^{n-1}\sin(ax)\,dx$

j 56 $\quad \int \arcsin x\,dx \;=\; x\arcsin x + \sqrt{1 - x^2}$

j 57 $\quad \int \arccos x\,dx \;=\; x\arccos x - \sqrt{1 - x^2}$

j 58 $\quad \int \arctan x\,dx \;=\; x\arctan x - \dfrac{1}{2}\ln(1 + x^2)$

j 59 $\quad \int \operatorname{arccot} x\,dx \;=\; x\operatorname{arccot} x + \dfrac{1}{2}\ln(1 + x^2)$

j 60 $\quad \int \sinh x\,dx = \cosh x$

j 61 $\quad \int \sinh^2 x\,dx = \dfrac{1}{4}\sinh(2x) - \dfrac{x}{2}$

j 62 $\quad \int \sinh^n x\,dx = \dfrac{1}{n}\cosh x\,\sinh^{n-1} x - \dfrac{n-1}{n}\int \sinh^{n-2} x\,dx$

j 63 $\quad \int \sinh(ax)\,dx = \dfrac{1}{a}\cosh(ax)$

j 64 $\quad \int \cosh x\,dx = \sinh x$

j 65 $\quad \int \cosh^2 x\,dx = \dfrac{1}{4}\sinh(2x) + \dfrac{x}{2}$

j 66 $\quad \int \cosh^n x\,dx = \dfrac{1}{n}\sinh x\,\cosh^{n-1} x + \dfrac{n-1}{n}\int \cosh^{n-2} x\,dx$

j 67 $\quad \int \cosh(ax)\,dx = \dfrac{1}{a}\sinh(ax)$

Integrals
(omitting integral constant C)

j 68	$\int \tanh x \, dx$	$=$	$\ln \cosh x$
j 69	$\int \tanh^2 x \, dx$	$=$	$x - \tanh x$
j 70	$\int \tanh^n x \, dx$	$=$	$-\dfrac{1}{n-1}\tanh^{n-1} x + \int \tanh^{n-2} x \, dx \quad (n \neq 1)$
j 71	$\int \tanh(ax) \, dx$	$=$	$\dfrac{1}{a} \ln \cosh(ax)$

j 72	$\int \coth x \, dx$	$=$	$\ln \sinh x$
j 73	$\int \coth^2 x \, dx$	$=$	$x - \coth x$
j 74	$\int \coth^n x \, dx$	$=$	$-\dfrac{1}{n-1}\coth^{n-1} x + \int \coth^{n-2} x \, dx \quad (n \neq 1)$
j 75	$\int \coth(ax) \, dx$	$=$	$\dfrac{1}{a} \ln \sinh(ax)$

j 76	$\int \dfrac{dx}{\sinh x}$	$=$	$\ln \tanh \dfrac{x}{2}$
j 77	$\int \dfrac{dx}{\sinh^2 x}$	$=$	$-\coth x$
j 78	$\int \dfrac{dx}{\cosh x}$	$=$	$2 \arctan e^x$
j 79	$\int \dfrac{dx}{\cosh^2 x}$	$=$	$\tanh x$

j 80	$\int \operatorname{arsinh} x \, dx$	$=$	$x \operatorname{arsinh} x - \sqrt{x^2 + 1}$
j 81	$\int \operatorname{arcosh} x \, dx$	$=$	$x \operatorname{arcosh} x - \sqrt{x^2 - 1}$
j 82	$\int \operatorname{artanh} x \, dx$	$=$	$x \operatorname{artanh} x + \dfrac{1}{2} \ln(1 - x^2)$
j 83	$\int \operatorname{arcoth} x \, dx$	$=$	$x \operatorname{arcoth} x + \dfrac{1}{2} \ln(x^2 - 1)$

j 84	$\int \sin^m x \, \cos^n x \, dx$	$=$	$\dfrac{1}{m+n} \sin^{m+1} x \, \cos^{n-1} x +$
			$\dfrac{n-1}{m+n} \int \sin^m x \, \cos^{n-2} x \, dx$

Where n is an uneven number the residual integral is:

j 85	$\int \sin^m x \, \cos x \, dx$	$=$	$\dfrac{\sin^{n+1} x}{m+1}$

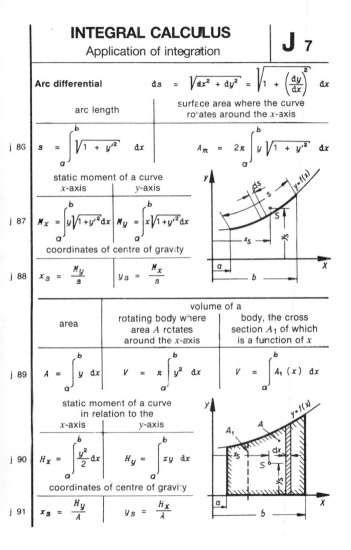

Arc differential $\quad ds = \sqrt{dx^2 + dy^2} = \sqrt{1 + \left(\dfrac{dy}{dx}\right)^2}\ dx$

arc length	surface area where the curve rotates around the x-axis

j 86
$$s = \int_a^b \sqrt{1 + y'^2}\ dx \qquad\qquad A_m = 2\pi \int_a^b y\sqrt{1 + y'^2}\ dx$$

static moment of a curve	
x-axis	y-axis

j 87
$$M_x = \int_a^b y\sqrt{1+y'^2}\,dx \qquad M_y = \int_a^b x\sqrt{1+y'^2}\,dx$$

coordinates of centre of gravity

j 88
$$x_s = \frac{M_y}{s} \qquad\qquad y_s = \frac{M_x}{s}$$

area	volume of a	
	rotating body where area A rotates around the x-axis	body, the cross section A_1 of which is a function of x

j 89
$$A = \int_a^b y\ dx \qquad V = \pi \int_a^b y^2\ dx \qquad V = \int_a^b A_1(x)\ dx$$

static moment of a curve in relation to the	
x-axis	y-axis

j 90
$$H_x = \int_a^b \frac{y^2}{2}\,dx \qquad H_y = \int_a^b xy\ dx$$

coordinates of centre of gravity

j 91
$$x_s = \frac{H_y}{A} \qquad\qquad y_s = \frac{H_x}{A}$$

INTEGRAL CALCULUS

Application of integration

J 8

Static moment of a body
(in relation to the y–z plane)

j 92
$$M_{yz} = \pi \int_a^b x \; y^2 \; dx$$

Coordinates of centre of gravity

j 93
$$x_S = \frac{M_{yz}}{V}$$

Pappus theorems

Surface area of a revolving body

j 94 A_m = arc length s times the distance covered by the centre
of gravity
$= 2 \pi s y_s$ (see also formulae j 86 and j 88)

Volume of a revolving body

j 95 V = area A times the distance covered by the centre of
gravity
$= 2 \pi A y_s$ (see also formulae j 89 and j 91)

Numerical integration

Division of area into an even
number n of strips of equal

j 96   width $h = \dfrac{b_1 - b_0}{n}$.

Then, according to the

Trapezium rule

j 97
$$A = \frac{b}{2} (y_0 + 2y_1 + 2y_2 + \ldots + y_n)$$

Simpson's rule for three ordinates:

j 98
$$A_1 = \frac{b}{3} (y_0 + 4y_1 + y_2)$$

Simpson's rule for more than three ordinates:

j 99
$$A = \frac{b}{3}\left[y_0 + y_n + 2(y_2 + y_4 + \ldots + y_{n-2}) + 4(y_1 + y_3 + \ldots + y_{n-1})\right]$$

Moment of inertia
(Second moment of area)

General

By moment of inertia in relation to an axis x or a point 0, we mean the sum of the products of line-, area-, volume- or mass-elements and the squares of their distances form the x-axis or point 0:

	Moment of inertia	Second moment of area
j 100	$I = \int x^2 \, dm \quad$ kg m^2	$I = \int x^2 \, dA \quad$ m^4

Steiner's theorem (Parallel axis theorem)

For every mass moment of inertia, both axial and polar, the following equation will apply:

j 101

$$I_{xx} = I_{yy} + m \, l_s^2 \quad \text{kg m}^2$$

Similar equations will apply for line, area and volume moments of inertia:

$$I_{xx} = I_{yy} + A \, l_s^2 \quad \text{m}^4$$

Moment of inertia of plane curves

	in relation to the	
	x-axis	y-axis
j 102	$I_{ox} = \int_a^b y^2 \sqrt{1+y'^2} \, dx$	$I_{oy} = \int_a^b x^2 \sqrt{1+y'^2} \, dx$

I_{xx} : moment of inertia about a general axis xx
I : moment of inertia about the centre of gravity
m, A : total length, area, volume, or mass
l_s : distance of centre of gravity from axis or point

INTEGRAL CALCULUS

Application of integration

Moments of inertia, centrif. moments of plane surfaces

By **axial second moment of area** of a plane surface in relation to an axis x or y within the plane we mean the sum of the products of the area-elements dA and the squares of their distances from axis x or y, respectively:

j 103
$$I_x = \int y^2 \, dA \; ; \quad I_y = \int x^2 \, dA$$

A given function $y = f(x)$ yields:

x-axis	y-axis
j 104 $\quad I_x = \int_a^b \dfrac{y^3}{3} \, dx$	$I_y = \int_a^b x^2 y \, dx$

By **polar second moment of area** of a plane surface in relation to a point O within the plane we mean the sum of the products of the area-elements dA and the squares of their distances r from point O.

j 105
$$I_p = \int r^2 \, dA$$

Where the relative axes of I_x and I_y are perpendicular to each other, the polar second moment of area in relation to the pole (intersection O of axis x and y) is:

j 106
$$I_p = \int r^2 \, dA = \int (y^2 + x^2) \, dA = I_x + I_y$$

By **centrifugal moment** (product of inertia) of a plane surface in relation to 2 axes within the plane we mean the sum of the products of the area-elements dA and the products of their distances x and y from the two axes:

j 107
$$I_{xy} = \int x y \, dA \; \gtreqless \; 0$$

One of the relative axes being an axis of symmetry of the plane surface results in $I_{xy} = 0$.

Conversion to an inclined axis x': Where moments I_x, I_y, and I_{xy} in relation to two perpendicular axes x and y are known, the second moment of area I_α in relation to an axis inclined x' by an angle α with respect to the x-axis can be calculated by:

j 108
$$I_\alpha = I_x \cos^2 \alpha + I_y \sin^2 \alpha - I_{xy} \sin 2\alpha$$

Examples in conjunction to second moments of area on page J 10

Rectangle

j 109 $\quad I_x = \int_0^h y^2 b \; dy \quad = b\left[\dfrac{y^3}{3}\right]_0^h = \dfrac{b h^3}{3}$

j 110 $\quad I_{x'} = I_x - A\left(\dfrac{h}{2}\right)^2 \quad = \dfrac{b h^3}{12}$

j 111 $\quad I_y = \dfrac{b^3 h}{3} \; ; \quad I_{y'} = \dfrac{b^3 h}{12}$

j 112 $\quad I_{po} = I_x + I_y = \dfrac{b h^3}{3} + \dfrac{b^3 h}{3} = \dfrac{b h}{3}(b^2 + h^2) \; ; \quad I_{DS} = \dfrac{b h}{12}(b^2 + h^2)$

j 113 $\quad I_{xy} = I_{x'y'} + \dfrac{b}{2} \times \dfrac{h}{2} A .$

As x' and/or y' are axes of symmetry, $I_{x'y'}$ is zero. Hence:

j 114 $\quad I_{xy} = \dfrac{b}{2} \times \dfrac{h}{2}(b h) = \left(\dfrac{b h}{2}\right)^2$

Circle

j 115 $\quad I_p = \int_0^R r^2 \, dA \quad = \int_0^R r^2 \, 2 \pi r \; dr$

j 116 $\quad = 2\pi\left[\dfrac{r^4}{4}\right]_0^R \quad = \dfrac{\pi R^4}{2}$

j 117 $\quad I_x = I_y = \dfrac{I_p}{2} = \dfrac{\pi R^4}{4} = \dfrac{\pi D^4}{64}$

j 118 $\quad I_{xy} = 0$, as x and y are axes of symmetry.

Semicircle

j 119 $\quad I_x = \int_0^R y^2 \; dA \quad = \int_0^R y^2 \, 2 x \; dy$

j 120 $\quad = 2\int_0^R y^2 \sqrt{R^2 - y^2} \; dy = \dfrac{\pi R^4}{3} = I_y$

j 121 $\quad I_p = 2 \dfrac{\pi R^4}{8} = \dfrac{\pi R^4}{4} \; ; \quad I_{xy} = 0$, as y is axis of symmetry.

Regular polygon

j 122 $\quad I_x = I_y = \dfrac{I_p}{2} = \dfrac{n \, a \, r}{2 \times 48}(12 r^2 + a^2) = \dfrac{n \, a \, R}{2 \times 24}(6 R^2 - a^2) \; ; \quad I_{xy} = 0$

r : radius of inscribed circle | a : length of side
R : radius of circumscribed circle | n : number of sides

Second moment of volume of a solid

'Moment of inertia' of a cuboid

Where $\left(\dfrac{b\,h^3}{12} + \dfrac{b^3\,h}{12}\right)$ is the polar moment of inertia of a rectangle (see J 11), the equation for the z-axis:

j 123
$$I_{v,zz} = \int_{0}^{a}\left(\frac{bh^3}{12} + \frac{b^3 h}{12}\right)\,dz = \frac{abh}{12}(b^2 + h^2)$$

'Moment of inertia' of a circular cylinder

for the axis zz:

j 124
$$I_{v,zz} = \int_{-\frac{h}{2}}^{+\frac{h}{2}} \frac{\pi\,r^4}{2}\,dz = \frac{\pi\,r^4\,h}{2}$$

for the axis xx:

j 125
$$I_{v,xx} = \int_{-\frac{h}{2}}^{+\frac{h}{2}}\left(\frac{\pi\,r^4}{4} + \pi\,r^2\,z^2\right)\,dz = \frac{\pi\,r^2\,h}{12}(3r^2 + h^2)$$

Dynamic moment of inertia (mass moment of inertia)

The mass moment of inertia I about a particular axis is the product of the second moment of volume I_v about that axis and the density ϱ.

j 126
$$I = I_v \times \varrho \qquad \text{kg m}^2,\ \text{kgf m s}^2,\ \text{lb ft}^2$$

j 127
where
$$\varrho = \frac{m}{V} \qquad \text{kg m}^{-3},\ \text{kg dm}^{-3},\ \text{lb ft}^{-3}$$

e. g. for a cylinder about the axis zz:

j 128
$$I_{zz} = I_{v,zz} \times \frac{m}{V} = \frac{\pi\,r^4\,h}{2} \times \frac{m}{r^2\,\pi\,h} = \frac{m\,r^2}{2}$$

For other mass moments of inertia see M 3

General

Statics deals with the theory of equilibrium and with the determination of external forces acting on stationary solid bodies (e. g. support reactions). The contents of page K1 ... K14 are applicable only to forces acting in one plane.

The most important quantities of statics and their units

Length l
Is a base quantity, see preface.
Units: m; cm; km

Force F (see explanation on M 1)
Being a vector a force is defined by its magnitude, direction, and point of application (P).

Gravitational force G
definition: force of earth's attraction
point of application: centre of grav. S
line of action: vertical line intersecting centre of gravity
direction: downwards (towards earth's centre)
magnitude: determined by spring balance.

Support reaction F_A
force applied to body by support A.

Resultant force F_R
force representing the total action of several external forces.

Moment M **of a force** F **about a point** O
The perpendicular distance from point O to the line of action of force F is called lever arm l.

F_1 and F_2 form a pair of forces. The moment may be represented by a vector.

k 1
k 2

$$F_1 = F \; ; \quad F_2 = -F_1$$
moment $\quad M = \pm F\,l$

Moment theorem: The moment of the resultant force is equal to the sum of the moments of the individual forces.

Graphical composition of forces

diagram of forces	force polygon

Two forces

k 4

A number of forces and a common point of application

k 5

Parallel forces

k 6

link polygon link beam pole pole beam

A number of forces and any random point of application

k 7

Construction of the link polygon

Draw force polygon and determine pole O so as to avoid any link rays running parallel. Draw pole rays. Construct link polygon such that link rays run parallel to corresponding pole rays. Thereby each point of intersection in the link polygon corresponds to a triangle in the force polygon (e.g. triangle F_1-1-2 of force polygon corresponds to point of intersection F_1-1-2 of link polygon).

STATICS

Forces composition

Mathematical composition of forces

Resolution of a force

k 8 $F_x = F \times \cos \alpha$ | $F_y = F \times \sin \alpha$

k 9 $F = +\sqrt{F_x^2 + F_y^2}$ | $\tan \alpha = \dfrac{F_y}{F_x}$

(for signs of trigonometrical functions of α see table k 16 to k 19)

Moment M_O of a force about a point O

k 10 $M_O = +F \times l = F_y\, x - F_x\, y$

(for signs of trigonometrical functions of α see table k 16 to k 19)

Resultant force F_R of any random given forces

k 11 components $F_{Rx} = \Sigma F_x$ | $F_{Ry} = \Sigma F_y$

k 12 magnitude $F_R = +\sqrt{F_{Rx}^2 + F_{Ry}^2}$

k 13 angle of direction α_{FR} $\tan \alpha_R = \dfrac{F_{Ry}}{F_{Rx}}$; $\sin \alpha_R = \dfrac{F_{Ry}}{F_R}$; $\cos \alpha_R = \dfrac{F_{Rx}}{F_R}$

k 14 distance $l_R = \dfrac{|\Sigma M_O|}{|F_R|}$ (moment theorem)

k 15 sign of $F_R \times l_R$ = sign of ΣM_O

Signs of trigonometrical functions of x, y; F_x, F_y; F_{Rx}, F_{Ry}

	quadrant	α, α_R	$\cos \alpha$	$\sin \alpha$	$\tan \alpha$	x, F_x, F_{Rx}	y, F_y, F_{Ry}
k 16	I	$0 \ldots 90°$	+	+	+	+	+
k 17	II	$90 \ldots 180°$	−	+	−	−	+
k 18	III	$180 \ldots 270°$	−	−	+	−	−
k 19	IV	$270 \ldots 360°$	+	−	−	+	−

F_x, F_y : components of F parallel to x-axis and y-axis
F_{Rx}, F_{Ry} : components of F_R parallel to x-axis and y-axis
x, y : coordinates of F
α, α_R : angles of F and F_R
l, l_R : distances of F and F_R from reference point

Conditions of equilibrium

A body is said to be in equilibrium when both the resultant force and the sum of the moments of all external forces about any random point are equal to zero.

	forces	graphical	mathematical
k 20	with common point of application	closed force polygon	$\Sigma F_x = 0$; $\Sigma F_y = 0$;
k 21	parallel to vertical axis	force polygon and link	$\Sigma F_y = 0$; $\Sigma M = 0$
k 22	arbitrary	polygon closed	$\Sigma F_x = 0$; $\Sigma F_y = 0$; $\Sigma M = 0$

Simply supported beam with point loads W_1 and W_2

Find reactions R_A and R_B:

Graph. solution:

$$M(x) = y^* m_L H m_F \qquad \text{kNm, Ncm, Nmm}$$

| k 23 | m_L : scale of lengths | = | true length/diagram length |
| k 24 | m_F : scale of forces | = | force/diagram length |

H : pole spacing $\qquad y^*$: vertical distance between closing line s and link polygon.

| k 25 | Mathem. solution: $R_A = W_1\, l_1/l + W_2\, l_2/l$; $\quad R_B = (W_1 + W_2) - R_A$ |

Distributed loads are divided into small sections and considered as corresponding point forces acting through the centres of mass of the sections.

Wall mounted crane (3 forces): Find reactions F_A, F_B.

problem   solution

point of intersection of the 3 lines of action

$$F_{Ax} = F_B = \frac{a}{b} F_L ; \qquad F_{Ay} = F_L$$

Mathematical determination of member loads

(Ritter method – Method of Sections)

O : upper boom
U : lower boom
D : diagonal member

k 26

Determine the support reactions from K 4 (girder on two sup-ports). Draw a line $X \ldots X$ through the framework to the bar in question, but intersecting no more than 3 bars. Take tensile forces as positive, so that compressive forces are negative.

Establish the equation of moments $\Sigma M = 0$ with moments of ex-ternal and internal forces taken about the point of inter-section of two unknown forces.

Rule for moment signs

Where turning moment is counter-clockwise the sign is positive.

Where turning moment is clockwise the sign is negative.

Example (from the above girder)

problem: to find force F_{U2} in bar U_2.
solution:
Draw a line $X \ldots X$ through $O_2 - D_2 - U_2$. Since the lines O_2 and D_2 meet at C, this is the relative point of inter-section selected so that the moment O_2 and D_2 may equal zero.

Proceed as follows:

$$\Sigma M_C = 0$$

$$+ a\, F_{U_2} + b\, F_2 - c(F_A - F_1) = 0$$

$$F_{U_2} = \frac{-b\, F_2 + c(F_A - F_1)}{a}$$

Graphical determination of forces in members

(Cremona method
– Bow diagramm)

k 27

Basic principles

Each bar is confined by two adjacent joints. The external forces only act through the joints.

Procedure

Establish a scale of forces and determine the support reactions. Since each force polygon must not contain more than two unknown forces, start at joint A. Establish identical order of forces (cw or ccw) for all joints(e.g. $F_A - F_1 - F_{S1} - F_{S2}$).

Joint A: Force polygon $a - b - c - d - a$. Keep a record of forces being tensile or compressional.
Joint C: Force polygon $d - c - e - f - d$.

etc.

Check

Forces acting through a single joint in the framework form a polygon in the Bow diagram.

Forces acting through a single point in the diagram of forces form a triangle in the framework.

Arc of circle

k 28 $\quad y = \dfrac{r \sin \alpha \, 180^{\circ}}{\pi \, \alpha} = \dfrac{r \, s}{b}$

k 29 $\quad y = 0 \cdot 6366 \, r \quad$ at $\quad 2\alpha = 180^{\circ}$

k 30 $\quad y = 0 \cdot 9003 \, r \quad$ at $\quad 2\alpha = 90^{\circ}$

k 31 $\quad y = 0 \cdot 9549 \, r \quad$ at $\quad 2\alpha = 60^{\circ}$

Triangle

k 31 $\quad y = \dfrac{1}{3} \, h$

S is the point of intersection of the medians

Sector of a circle

k 32 $\quad y = \dfrac{2r \sin \alpha \, 180^{\circ}}{3 \, \pi \, \alpha} = \dfrac{2r \, s}{3b}$

k 33 $\quad y = 0 \cdot 4244 \, r \quad$ at $\quad 2\alpha = 180^{\circ}$

k 34 $\quad y = 0 \cdot 6002 \, r \quad$ at $\quad 2\alpha = 90^{\circ}$

k 35 $\quad y = 0 \cdot 6366 \, r \quad$ at $\quad 2\alpha = 60^{\circ}$

Trapezium

k 36 $\quad y = \dfrac{h}{3} \times \dfrac{a + 2b}{a + b}$

Sector of an annulus

k 37 $\quad y = \dfrac{2}{3} \times \dfrac{R^3 - r^3}{R^2 - r^2} \times \dfrac{\sin \alpha}{\text{arc } \alpha}$

k 38 $\quad\quad = \dfrac{2}{3} \times \dfrac{R^3 - r^3}{R^2 - r^2} \times \dfrac{s}{b}$

Segment of a circle

k 39 $\quad y = \dfrac{s^3}{12 \, A}$

for area A see B 3

For determination of centre of gravity S, see also J 7

Determination of centre of gravity of any random surface area

Graphical solution

Subdivide the total area A into partial areas A_1, $A_2 \ldots A_n$ the centres of gravity of which are known. The size of each partial area is represented as a force applied to the centre of area of each partial area. Use the force polygon (see K 2) to determine the mean forces A_{Rx} and A_{Ry} operating in any two directions (preferably at right angles). The point of intersection of the lines of application will indicate the position of the centre of area A.

k 40

Mathematical solution

Subdivide the above total area A into partial areas A_1, $A_2 \ldots A_n$; we now get

distance	in general	in the above example
k 41 $x_s=$	$\dfrac{\sum_{i=1}^{n} A_i \; x_i}{A}$	$\dfrac{A_1 \; x_1 \; + \; A_2 \; x_2 \; + \; A_3 \; x_3}{A}$
k 42 $y_s=$	$\dfrac{\sum_{i=1}^{n} A_i \; y_i}{A}$	$\dfrac{A_1 \; y_1 \; + \; A_2 \; y_2 \; + \; A_3 \; y_3}{A}$

Note: In the above example the distances x_1, y_2 and y_3 each equal zero.

Force acting parallel to a sliding plane

	static friction	limiting friction	sliding friction

| k 43 | $v = 0$ | $v = 0$ | $\longrightarrow v > 0$ |

k 44	$F_{W_1} = -F_{Z_1} = G\,\tan\varrho_1$	$F_{W_0} = -F_{Z_0} = G\,\tan\varrho_0$	$F_W = -F_Z = G\,\tan\varrho$
k 45	$F_N = -G$	$F_N = -G$	$F_N = -G$
k 46		$\mu_0 = \tan\varrho_0 > \mu$	$\mu = \tan\varrho < \mu_0$
k 47	$0 < \varrho_1$ (variable) $< \varrho_0$	$\varrho_0 = $ const. $> \varrho$	$\varrho = $ const. $< \varrho_0$

A force F_{Z1} gradually increasing from zero is compensated by an increasing F_{W1} without causing the body to move, until F_{Z1} reaches the value

$F_{Z_1}; F_{Z_0}; F_Z$

| k 48 | $F_{Z_0} = G\,\mu_0$. |

As soon as this happens, the body starts sliding, whereby F_Z drops to $G\,\mu$. Any excessive force will now accelerate the body.

rest | motion

F_{W_0}

static friction | limit friction | sliding friction

F_W

force acting

Force applied obliquely

The force F needed to set in motion a body, weight G:

| k 49 | $F = G\,\dfrac{\mu_0}{\sin\alpha - \mu_c \cos\alpha} = G\,\dfrac{\sin\varrho_0}{\sin(\alpha - \varrho_0)}$ |

The force needed to maintain the motion is ascertained by replacing μ_0 by μ. No motion possible when result of F is negative.

F_{W_1}, F_{W_0}, F_W : friction coefficient	$-$, μ_0 , μ : friction force	see
F_{Z_1}, F_{Z_0}, F_Z : angle of friction	ϱ_1, ϱ_0, ϱ : traction force	Z 7

Inclined plane

General

The angle α at which a body will move easily down an inclined plane is the angle of friction ϱ.

k 50
$$\tan \alpha = \tan \varrho = \mu$$

Application in the experimental determination of the angle of friction or the friction coefficient:

$$\alpha = \tan \varrho$$

inclined plane

G

base (horizontal)

k 51 **Condition of automatic locking:** $\alpha < \varrho$

Friction properties

	constant velocity maintained by tractive force F parallel to	
motion	inclined plane	base
upwards $0 < \alpha < \alpha^{*}$ k 52	$F = G \dfrac{\sin(\alpha + \varrho)}{\cos \varrho}$	$F = G \tan(\alpha + \varrho)$
downwards $0 < \alpha < \varrho$ k 53	$F = G \dfrac{\sin(\varrho - \alpha)}{\cos \varrho}$	$F = G \tan(\varrho - \alpha)$
downwards $\varrho < \alpha < \alpha^{*}$ k 54	$F = G \dfrac{\sin(\alpha - \varrho)}{\cos \varrho}$	$F = G \tan(\alpha - \varrho)$

Note: For static friction replace μ by μ_{o} and ϱ by ϱ_{o}.

α^{*}: Tilting angle of body

Wedges

k 55	driving in	$F_1 = F \dfrac{\tan(\alpha_1+\varrho_1)+\tan(\alpha_2+\varrho_2)}{1-\tan\varrho_3\times\tan(\alpha_2+\varrho_2)}$	$F_1 = F\times\tan(\alpha+2\varrho)$
k 56	loos-ening	$F_2 = F \dfrac{\tan(\alpha_1-\varrho_1)+\tan(\alpha_2-\varrho_2)}{1+\tan\varrho_3\times\tan(\alpha_2-\varrho_2)}$	$F_2 = F\times\tan(\alpha-2\varrho)$
k 57	automatic locking	$\alpha_1 + \alpha_2 \leqq \varrho_{0_1} + \varrho_{0_2}$	$\alpha \leqq 2\varrho_0$

Screws

k 58	turning moment when	raising	$M_1 = F\times r\times\tan(\alpha+\varrho)$	$M_1 = F\times r\times\tan(\alpha+\varrho')$
k 59		lowering	$M_2 = F\times r\times\tan(\alpha-\varrho)$	$M_2 = F\times r\times\tan(\alpha-\varrho')$
k 60	conditions of automatic locking when lowering		$\alpha < \varrho$	$\alpha < \varrho'$
k 61	efficiency of screw when	raised	$\eta = \dfrac{\tan\alpha}{\tan(\alpha+\varrho)}$	$\eta = \dfrac{\tan\alpha}{\tan(\alpha+\varrho')}$
k 62		lowered	$\eta = \dfrac{\tan(\alpha-\varrho)}{\tan\alpha}$	$\eta = \dfrac{\tan(\alpha-\varrho')}{\tan\alpha}$

	M_1 :	raising moment	N m, [kgf m]
	M_2 :	lowering moment	N m, [kgf m]
k 63	α :	lead of thread $\quad(\tan\alpha = \dfrac{h}{2\pi r})$	
k 64	ϱ :	angle of friction $\quad(\tan\varrho = \mu)$	
	ϱ' :	angle of friction $\quad(\tan\varrho' = \dfrac{\mu}{\cos\beta/2})$	
k 65	r :	mean radius of thread	m, mm

Bearing friction

	radial bearing	longitudinal bearing

k 66

$$M_R = \mu_q \, r \, F \qquad\qquad M_R = \mu_L \, \frac{r_1 - r_2}{2} \, F$$

M_R : moment of friction

| μ_q : | coefficient of | radial | bearing (not |
| μ_L : | friction of a | longitudinal | constant values) |

Note: μ_q and μ_L are determined experimentally as a function of bearing condition, bearing clearance, and lubrication. For run in condition: $\mu_0 \approx \mu_L \approx \mu_q$. Always use $r_1 > 0$ to allow for lubrication.

k 67
k 68

Rolling resistance

Rolling of a cylinder

k 69

$$F = \frac{f}{r} \, F_N \approx \frac{f}{r} \, G$$

k 70

Rolling condition: $F_W < \mu_0 \, F_N$

F_W: force of rolling resistance

f : lever arm of rolling resistance – value on Z 7 (caused by deformation of cylinder and support)

μ_0: coefficient of static friction between cylinder and support

Displacement of a plate supported by cylinders

k 71

$$F = \frac{(f_1 + f_2) \, G_1 + n \, f_2 \, G_2}{2 \, r}$$

k 72

where $f_1 = f_2 = f$ and $n \, G_2 < G_1$:

k 73

$$F = \frac{f}{r} \, G_1$$

G_1 , G_2 : weight of plate and one cylinder

f_1 , f_2 : lever arms of force of rolling resistance

F : tractive force

r : radius of cylinder

n : number of cylinders

Rope friction

	traction force and friction force for	
	raising load	lowering load
k 75	$F_1 = e^{\mu\hat{a}}\, G$	$F_2 = e^{-\mu\hat{a}}\, G$
k 76	$F_R = (e^{\mu\hat{a}} - 1)G$	$F_R = (1 - e^{-\mu\hat{a}})G$

Formulae apply where cylinder is stationary and rope is moving at constant velocity, or where rope is stationary and cylinder is rotating at constant angular velocity.

k 77	**Condition of equilibrium:** $\quad F_2 < F < F_1 \quad \bigg| \quad G\, e^{-\mu\hat{a}} < F < G\, e^{\mu\hat{a}}$

(F : force without friction)

Belt drive

k 78	$F_U = \dfrac{M_a}{r}$
k 79	$F_U = F_R$

forces	in motion	at rest
k 80 — F_0	$F_0 = \dfrac{F_U}{e^{\mu\hat{a}} - 1}$	$F_0 = F_1 = \dfrac{F_z}{2}\dfrac{(e^{\mu\hat{a}} + 1)}{e^{\mu\hat{a}} - 1}$
k 81 — F_1	$F_1 = F_U\dfrac{e^{\mu\hat{a}}}{e^{\mu\hat{a}} - 1}$	
k 82 — F_z	$F_z = F_U\dfrac{e^{\mu\hat{a}} + 1}{e^{\mu\hat{a}} - 1}$	

F_U : tangential force of driving wheel
F_R : frictional force of rope
M_a : driving torque
$\hat{a}$: angle of contact (radians). Always introduce lowest value into formula
μ : coefficient of sliding friction (value of experience for leather belt on steel drum: $\mu = 0\cdot22 + 0\cdot012\, v$ s/m
v : belt velocity
k 83
$e = 2\cdot71828183\ldots$ (base of natural logs)

Rope operated machines

The following figures deal solely with rope rigidity, disregarding bearing friction.

	unknown quantity	fixed sheave	free sheave	pulley block ordinary	pulley block differential
k 84	$F_1 =$	$\varepsilon\, G$	$\dfrac{\varepsilon}{1 + \varepsilon}\, G$	$\dfrac{\varepsilon^n(\varepsilon - 1)}{\varepsilon^n - 1}\, G$	$\dfrac{\varepsilon^2 - \dfrac{d}{D}}{\varepsilon + 1}\, G$
k 85	$F_0 =$	$\dfrac{1}{\varepsilon}\, G$	$\dfrac{1}{1 + \varepsilon}\, G$	$\dfrac{\dfrac{1}{\varepsilon^n}\left(\dfrac{1}{\varepsilon} - 1\right)}{\dfrac{1}{\varepsilon^n} - 1}\, G$	$\dfrac{\varepsilon}{1 + \varepsilon}\left(\dfrac{1}{\varepsilon^2} - \dfrac{d}{D}\right) G$
k 86	$F =$	G	$\dfrac{1}{2}\, G$	$\dfrac{1}{n}\, G$	$\dfrac{1}{2}\left(1 - \dfrac{d}{D}\right) G$
k 87	$s =$	h	$2\,h$	$n\,h$	$\dfrac{2}{1 - \dfrac{d}{D}}\, h$
k 88		mechanical advantage		$= \dfrac{\text{force}}{\text{effort}} = \dfrac{F}{G} = \dfrac{h}{s}$	

F_1 : force required to raise load, disregarding bearing friction
F_0 : force required to lower load, disregarding bearing friction
F : force, disregarding both rope rigidity and bearing friction

k 89 $\varepsilon = \dfrac{1}{\eta}$: loss factor for rope rigidity (for wire ropes and chains $\approx 1\cdot05$)

η : efficiency h : path of load
n : number of sheaves s : path of force

General

Kinematics deals with motions of bodies as a function of time.

The most important quantities of kinematics and their units

Length l, see K 1
Units: m; km

Rotational angle φ
Unit: rad

Time t
Is a base quantity, see preface.
Units: s; min; h

Frequency f
The frequency of a harmonic or sinusoidal oscillation is the ratio of the number of periods (full cycles) and the corresponding time.

I 1
$$f = \frac{\text{number of oscillations}}{\text{corresponding time}}$$

Units: Hz (Hertz) = 1/s = cycle/s; 1/min

Period T
The period T is the time required for one full cycle. It is the reciprocal of the frequency f.

I 2
$$T = \frac{1}{f}$$

Units: s; min; h

Rotational speed n
Where an oscillation is tightly coupled with the rotation of a shaft, and one revolution of the shaft corresponds exactly to one full cycle of the oscillation, the rotational speed n of the shaft is equal to the frequency f of the oscillation.

I 3
$$n = f \;;\quad f = \frac{n \text{ min}}{60 \text{ s}}$$

Units: revolutions/second (1/s)
rev./min. r.p.m. (1/min)

continued on L 2

continued from L 1

Velocity v

The velocity v is the first derivative of the distance s with respect to the time t:

I 4
$$v = \frac{ds}{dt} = \dot{s}$$

Where the velocity is constant, the following relation applies:

I 5
$$v = \frac{s}{t}$$

Units: m/s; km/h

Angular velocity ω, angular frequency ω

The angular velocity ω is the first derivative of the angle turned through φ, with respect to the time t:

I 6
$$\omega = \frac{d\varphi}{dt} = \dot{\varphi}$$

Hence, for constant angular velocity:

I 7
$$\omega = \frac{\varphi}{t}$$

Where $f = n$ (see I 3), the angular velocity ω is equal to the angular frequency ω.

I 8
$$\omega = 2\pi f = 2\pi n = \dot{\varphi}$$

Units: 1/s; rad/s; 1°/s

Acceleration a

The acceleration a is the first derivative of the velocity v with respect to the time t:

I 9
$$a = \frac{dv}{dt} = \dot{v} = \frac{d^2s}{dt^2} = \ddot{s}$$

Units: m/s²; km/h²

Angular acceleration α

The angular acceleration α is the first derivative of the angular velocity ω with respect to the time t:

I 10
$$\alpha = \frac{d\omega}{dt} = \dot{\omega} = \frac{d^2\varphi}{dt^2} = \ddot{\varphi}$$

Units: 1/s²; rad/s²; 1°/s²

Distance, velocity, and acceleration of mass point in motion

Distance-time curve

An s–t curve is recorded for the motion. The first derivative of this curve is the instantaneous velocity v:

I 11
$$v = \frac{ds}{dt} = \dot{s}$$

It is the slope dt the tangent to the s–t curve.

Velocity-time curve

The velocity-time history is expressed as a v–t curve. The first derivative of this curve is the instantaneous acceleration a. Hence the acceleration is the second derivative of the distance-time curve.

I 12
$$a = \frac{dv}{dt} = \dot{v} = \ddot{s}$$

It is the slope dt the tangent to the v–t curve.

The shaded area represents the distance travelled $s\,(t)$.

Acceleration-time curve

The acceleration-time history is shown as an a–t curve, which enables peak accelerations to be determined.

I 13
$a > 0$: acceleration
(increasing velocity)

I 14
$a < 0$: retardation
(decreasing velocity)

Note to diagrams

The letters in brackets apply to rotations (for explanation see L 5 and L 6).

Linear motion

Paths are straight lines. All points of a body cover congruent paths.

Special linear motions	
uniform	uniform accelerated
motion	
$v = v_o = $ const.	$a = a_o = $ constant

I 15

Rotational motion

Paths are circles about the axis. Angle turned through $\widehat{\varphi}$, angular velocity ω, and angular acceleration α are identical for all points of the body.

Special rotational motions	
uniform	uniform accelerated
motion	
$\omega = \omega_o = $ const.	$\alpha = \alpha_o = $ constant

I 16

Distance s, velocity v, and tangential acceleration a_t are proportional to the radius:

I 17

$$s = r\widehat{\varphi} \; ; \quad v = r\omega \; ; \quad a = r\alpha = a_t$$

I 18

centripetal acceleration $\qquad a_n = \omega^2 r = \dfrac{v^2}{r}$

Harmonic oscillation

Paths are straight lines or circles. The body moves back and forth about a position of rest. The maximum deflection from this position is called "amplitude".

Instantaneous position, velocity, and acceleration are harmonic functions of time.

Uniform and uniform accelerated linear motion

unknown parameter	uniform $a = 0$ $v = $ const.	uniform $a = $ constant $v_0 = 0$	$\begin{cases} \text{accelerated} & (a > 0) \\ \text{retarded} & (a < 0) \end{cases}$ $v_0 > 0$	EU
I 19 $s =$	$v\,t$	$\dfrac{v\,t}{2} = \dfrac{a\,t^2}{2} = \dfrac{v^2}{2\,a}$	$\dfrac{t}{2}(v_0 + v) = v_0 t + \dfrac{1}{2}a\,t^2$	m cm km
I 20 $v =$	$\dfrac{s}{t}$	$\sqrt{2as} = \dfrac{2\,s}{t} = a\,t$	$v_0 + a\,t = \sqrt{v_0^2 + 2as}$	m/s cm/s km/h
I 21 $v_0 =$	constant	0	$v - a\,t = \sqrt{v^2 - 2as}$	
I 22 $a =$	0	$\dfrac{v}{t} = \dfrac{2s}{t^2} = \dfrac{v^2}{2s}$	$\dfrac{v - v_0}{t} = \dfrac{v^2 - v_0^2}{2s}$	m/s^2 cm/h^2 km/h^2
I 23 $t =$	$\dfrac{s}{v}$	$\sqrt{\dfrac{2\,s}{a}} = \dfrac{v}{a} = \dfrac{2\,s}{v}$	$\dfrac{v - v_0}{a} = \dfrac{2s}{v_0 + v}$	s min h

Note

The shaded areas represent the distance s covered during the time period t.

The tangent β represents the linear acceleration a

KINEMATICS
Rotational motion

L 6

Uniform and uniform accelerated rotation about a fixed axis

	unknown parameter	uniform $a = 0$ $\omega = $ const.	uniform $\begin{cases} \text{accelerated} \quad (a > 0) \\ \text{retarded} \quad (a < 0) \end{cases}$ $a = $ constant $\omega_0 = 0$	$\omega_0 > 0$	EU
I 24	$\varphi =$	ωt	$\dfrac{\omega t}{2} = \dfrac{a t^2}{2} = \dfrac{\omega^2}{2a}$	$\dfrac{t}{2}(\omega_0 + \omega) = \omega_0 t + \dfrac{1}{2} a t^2$	– rad
I 25	$\omega =$	$\dfrac{\varphi}{t}$	$\sqrt{2a\varphi} = \dfrac{2\varphi}{t} = at$	$\omega_0 + at = \sqrt{\omega_0^2 + 2a\varphi}$	1/s m/m s rad/s
I 26	$\omega_0 =$	constant	0	$\omega - at = \sqrt{\omega^2 - 2a\varphi}$	
I 27	$a =$	0	$\dfrac{\omega}{t} = \dfrac{2\varphi}{t^2} = \dfrac{\omega^2}{2\varphi}$	$\dfrac{\omega - \omega_0}{t} = \dfrac{\omega^2 - \omega_0^2}{2\varphi}$	1/s² m/m s² rad/s²
I 23	$t =$	$\dfrac{\varphi}{\omega}$	$\sqrt{\dfrac{2\varphi}{a}} = \dfrac{\omega}{a} = \dfrac{2\varphi}{\omega}$	$\dfrac{\omega - \omega_0}{a} = \dfrac{2\varphi}{\omega_0 + \omega}$	s min h

Note

The shaded areas represent the angle of rotation φ covered during a time period t.
(Angle of rotation φ = $2\pi \times$ number of rotations respective $360° \times$ number of rotations).
The tangent β represents the angular acceleration a.

KINEMATICS

Oscillations

L 7

Linear simple harmonic motion

A body supported by a spring performs a linear harmonic oscillation. For this kind of motion, quantities s, v, and a as functions of time are equal to the projections $\underline{s}$, $\underline{v}$, and $\underline{a_n}$ of a uniform rotation of a point.

uniform rotation	path (project.)	simple harmonic motion
position		**position-time curve**
I 29 — $\varphi = \omega t + \varphi_0;\; b = r(\omega t + \varphi_0)$		$s = A\,\sin(\omega t + \varphi_0)$
velocity		**velocity-time curve**
I 30 — $v = r\,\omega$		$v = \dfrac{ds}{dt} = A\omega\,\cos(\omega t + \varphi_0)$
acceleration		**acceleration-time curve**
I 31 — $a = 0;\; a_n = \dfrac{v^2}{r} = r\omega^2$		$a = \dfrac{dv}{dt} = -A\omega^2\,\sin(\omega t + \varphi_0)$

Differential equation of simple harmonic motion

I 32

$$a = \frac{d^2 s}{dt^2} = -\omega^2 s$$

φ_0	angular	at time $t = 0$	s: displacement
φ	position	at time t	A: amplitude (max. displacement)
a_n: centripetal acceleration			r: radius of circle

$\underline{r}$: radius vector (origin: centre of circle; head: position of body)
$\underline{B}, \underline{C}$: extreme positions of oscillating point

Free fall and vertical projection

un-known param.	free fall $v_0 = 0$	vertical project.	upwards $(v_0 > 0)$ downwards $(v_0 < 0)$	EU
	o ─ initial height ─ +h	+h ↑ ─ initial height ─ o		
I 33 $h =$	$\dfrac{g}{2}t^2 = \dfrac{v}{2}t = \dfrac{v^2}{2g}$	$v_0 t - \dfrac{g}{2}t^2$	$= \dfrac{v_0 + v}{2}t$	m cm
I 34 $v =$	$g\,t = \dfrac{2h}{t} = \sqrt{2gh}$	$v_0 - g\,t$	$= \sqrt{v_0^2 - 2gh}$	m/s km/h
I 35 $t =$	$\dfrac{v}{g} = \dfrac{2h}{v} = \sqrt{\dfrac{2h}{g}}$	$\dfrac{v_0 - v}{g}$	$= \dfrac{2h}{v_0 + v}$	s min

Horizontal and angled projection

un-known param.	horizontal projection $v_0 > 0$	angled project.	upwards $(a > 0)$ downwards $(a < 0)$ $v_0 > 0$	EU
	o ─ v_0 ─ s ; h	h ↑ v_0 ... v upwards ... s ; downwards ... L		
I 36 $s =$	$v_0 t = v_0\sqrt{\dfrac{2h}{g}}$	$v_0 t\cos a$		m cm
I 37 $h =$	$\dfrac{g}{2}t^2$	$v_0 t\sin a - \dfrac{g}{2}t^2$		m cm
I 38 $v =$	$\sqrt{v_0^2 + g^2 t^2}$	$\sqrt{v_0^2 - 2gh}$		m/s km/s

Range L and max. height H for an angled upwards projection

				EU
I 39	general	$L = \dfrac{v_0^2}{g}\sin 2a$	$H = \dfrac{v_0^2}{2g}\sin^2 a$	m cm
I 40		$t_L = \dfrac{2v_0}{g}\sin a$	$t_H = \dfrac{v_0}{g}\sin a$	s min
		at $a = 45°$	at $a = 90°$	
I 41	maxima	$L_{max} = \dfrac{v_0^2}{g}$	$H_{max} = \dfrac{v_0^2}{2g}$	m cm
I 42		$t_{L\,max} = \dfrac{v_0\sqrt{2}}{g}$	$t_{H\,max} = \dfrac{v_0}{g}$	s min

a : angle of projection with respect to horizontal plane
t_H : time for height H t_L : time for distance L

Sliding motion on an inclined plane

	un-known param.	excluding friction $\mu = 0$	including friction $\mu > 0$
I 43	$a =$	$g \sin \alpha$	$g(\sin \alpha - \mu \cos \alpha)$
I 44			otherwise $g \dfrac{\sin(\alpha - \varrho)}{\cos \varrho}$
I 45	$v =$	$a\,t \quad = \dfrac{2s}{t} \quad = \sqrt{2as}$	
I 46	$s =$	$\dfrac{t^2}{2} \quad = \dfrac{vt}{2} \quad = \dfrac{v^2}{2a}$	
	α	$0 \ldots a^{*}$	$\varrho_0 \ldots a^{*}$

Rolling motion on an inclined plane

	un-known param.	excluding friction $f = 0$	including friction $f > 0$
I 47	$a =$	$\dfrac{g\,r^2}{r^2 + k^2} \sin \alpha$	$g r^2 \dfrac{\sin \alpha - \dfrac{f}{r} \cos \alpha}{r^2 + k^2}$
I 48	$v =$	see above I 45	
I 49	$s =$	see above I 46	
I 50	α	$0 \ldots a_{max}$	$\alpha_{min}: \quad \tan \alpha_{min} = \dfrac{f}{r}$
I 51		$\tan \alpha = \mu_0 \dfrac{r^2 + k^2}{k^2}$	$\alpha_{max}: \quad \tan \alpha_{max} = \mu_0 \dfrac{r^2 + k^2 + f\,r}{k^2}$

		ball	solid cylinder	pipe with low wall thickness
I 52		$k^2 = \dfrac{2}{5} r^2$	$k^2 = \dfrac{r^2}{2}$	$k^2 = \dfrac{r_1^2 + r_2^2}{2} \approx r^2$

a^{*} : tilting angle, where centre of gravity S vertically above tilting edge
μ : coefficient of sliding friction (see Z 7)
μ_o : coefficient of static friction (see Z 7)

I 53 ϱ : angle of sliding friction ($\mu = \tan \varrho$)
I 54 ϱ_o : angle of static friction ($\mu_o = \tan \varrho_o$)
     f : lever arm of rolling resistance (see k 70 and Z 7)
     k : radius of gyration

KINEMATICS
Mechanism

L 10

Simple Conn-Rod mechanism

I 55 $s = r(1 - \cos\varphi) + \dfrac{\lambda}{2} r \sin^2\varphi$

I 56 $v = \omega r \sin\varphi(1 + \lambda \cos\varphi)$

I 57 $a = \omega^2 r(\cos\varphi + \lambda \cos 2\varphi)$

I 58 $\lambda = \dfrac{r}{l} = \dfrac{1}{4} \cdots \dfrac{1}{6}$

I 59 $\varphi = \omega t = 2\pi n t$

(λ is called the crank ratio)

Scotch-Yoke mechanism

I 60 $s = r \sin(\omega t)$

I 61 $v = \omega r \cos(\omega t)$

I 62 $a = -\omega^2 r \sin(\omega t)$

I 63 $\omega = 2\pi n$

(motion is simple harmonic)

Cardan joint

For uniform drive the off-drive will be

non-uniform	uniform due to auxiliary shaft H

uniform drive
φ_1
ω_1
off-drive
ω_2

For all shafts being located in one plane the following relations apply:

I 64	$\tan\varphi_2 = \tan\varphi_1 \times \cos\beta$	$\tan\varphi_3 = \tan\varphi_1$	$\tan\varphi_3 = \tan\varphi_1$
I 65	$\omega_2 = \omega_1 \dfrac{\cos\beta}{1 - \sin^2\beta \times \sin^2\varphi_1}$	$\omega_3 = \omega_1$	$\omega_3 = \omega_1$
I 66	$a_2 = \omega_1^2 \dfrac{\sin^2\beta \times \cos\beta \times \sin 2\varphi_1}{(1 - \sin^2\beta \times \sin^2\varphi_1)^2}$		

Both axes A of the auxiliary shaft joints must be parallel to each other.

The more the angle of inclination β increases, the more the max. acceleration α and the accelerating moment M_α become; therefore, in practice $\beta \leq 45°$.

General

Dynamics deals with the forces acting on bodies in motion and with the terms "work, energy, and power".

The most important quantities of dynamics and their units

Mass m (is a base quantity, see preface)

Units: kg; Mg = t; g

1 kg is the mass of the international standard. A mass is measured by means of a steelyard.

Force (gravitational force) F

The force F is the product of mass m and acceleration a.

$$F = m\, a$$

The gravitational force W is the force acting on a mass m due to the earth's acceleration g:

$$W = m\, g$$

Being a gravitational force the weight W is measured by means of a spring balance.

Units: N; [kgf; lbf]

1 N is the force that, when acting on a body of a mass $m = 1$ kg for 1 s, accelerates this body to a final velocity of 1 m s^{-1} (i. e. accelerates this body at 1 m s^{-2}). $9 \cdot 81$ N [= 1 kgf] is the gravitational force acting on a mass of 1 kg due to the earth's attraction.

Work W

The mechanical work is the product of force F and distance s, where the constant force F acts on a body in linear motion in a direction parallel to the distance s covered ($W = F\, s$).

Units: N m = Joule = J = W s; [kgf m; ft lbf]

Where a force of 1 N acts over a distance of 1 m, it produces the work (energy) of 1 N m (J).

Power P

The power P is the derivative of work with respect to time. Where work (energy) increases or decreases linearly with time, power is the quotient of work and time ($P = W/t$).

Units: W (Watt); [kgf m s^{-1}; H. P.]

Where for a period of 1 s an energy of 1 J is converted at a constant rate, the corresponding power is 1 W.

$$1 \text{ W} = 1 \text{ J/s}$$

m 1

m 2

Definition of the mass moment of inertia I

The mass moment of inertia of a body about an axis has been defined as the sum of the products of mass-elements and the squares of their distance from the axis.

m 3
$$I = \sum r^2 \Delta m = \int r^2 \, dm \qquad \text{kg m}^2$$

Steiner's Theorem (Parallel axis theorem) (see also J 9)

Where the mass moment of inertia of a body of mass m about an axis through its centre of gravity S–S is I_{ss}, the mass moment of inertia about a parallel axis O–O at a distance l_s will be:

m 4
$$I_{OO} = I_{SS} + m \, l_s^2 \qquad \text{kg m}^2$$

Radius of gyration k

The radius of gyration of a body of mass m and mass moment of inertia I is the radius of an imaginary cylinder of infinitely small wall thickness having the same mass and the same mass moment of inertia as the body in question.

m 5
$$\text{hence} \quad k = \sqrt{\dfrac{I}{m}} \qquad \text{m, cm, mm}$$

Flywheel effect

m 6
Flywheel effect
$$W \, k^2 = m \, g \, k^2 = g \, I \qquad \text{kg cm}^3 \text{ s}^{-2}, \text{N m}^2$$
$$(k^2 \text{ formulae see M 3})$$

Equivalent mass (for rolling bodies)

m 8
$$m_{eq} = \dfrac{I}{k^2} \qquad \text{kg}$$

Basic formulae

	linear motion formulae	units	rotational motion formulae	units
m 9	$F_a = m \, a$	N , [kgf]	$M_a = I \, \alpha$	N m, [kgf m]
m 10	$W = F \, s$ ($F=$ const.)	N m, [kgf m]	$W = M \, \varphi$ ($M=$ const.)	N m, [kgf m]
m 11	$W_K = \frac{1}{2} m \, v^2$	J , [kgf m]	$W_K = \frac{1}{2} I \, \omega^2$	J , [kgf m]
m 12	$W_P = m \, g \, h$	J , [kgf m]	$\omega = 2 \, \pi \, n$	s^{-1} , min^{-1}
m 13	$W_F = \frac{1}{2} F \, \Delta l$	J , [kgf m]	$W_F = \frac{1}{2} M \, \Delta \beta$	W s , [kgf m]
m 14	$P = \dfrac{dW}{dt} = F \, v$	W , kW	$P = \dfrac{dW}{dt} = M \, \omega$	W , kW

For explanation of symbols see M 4

	Mass moment of inertia about		type of body
	axis $a-a$ (turning axis)	axis $b-b$ passing through centre of gravity S	
			circular hoop
m 15	$I = m\,r^2$	$I = \frac{1}{2}\,m\,r^2$	
m 16	$k^2 = r^2$	$k^2 = \frac{1}{2}\,r^2$	
			cylinder
m 17	$I = \frac{1}{2}\,m\,r^2$	$I = \frac{m}{12}\,(3\,r^2 + h^2)$	
m 18	$k^2 = \frac{1}{2}\,r^2$	$k^2 = \frac{1}{12}\,(3r^2 + h^2)$	
			hollow cylinder
m 19	$I = \frac{1}{2}\,m\,(R^2 + r^2)$	$I = \frac{m}{12}\,(3R^2 + 3r^2 + h^2)$	
m 20	$k^2 = \frac{1}{2}\,(R^2 + r^2)$	$k^2 = \frac{1}{12}\,(3R^2 + 3r^2 + h^2)$	
			cone
m 21	$I = \frac{3}{10}\,m\,r^2$	$I = \frac{3}{80}\,m\,(4\,r^2 + h^2)$	
m 22	$k^2 = \frac{3}{10}\,r^2$	$k^2 = \frac{3}{80}\,(4r^2 + h^2)$	
			sphere
m 23	$I = \frac{2}{5}\,m\,r^2$	$I = \frac{2}{5}\,m\,r^2$	
m 24	$k^2 = \frac{2}{5}\,r^2$	$k^2 = \frac{2}{5}\,r^2$	
			torus
m 25	$I = m\,(R^2 + \frac{3}{4}\,r^2)$	$I = m\,\dfrac{4R^2 + 5r^2}{8}$	
m 26	$k^2 = R^2 + \frac{3}{4}\,r^2$	$k^2 = \frac{1}{8}\,(4R^2 + 5r^2)$	
			bar
m 27	$I = \frac{1}{3}\,m\,l^2$	$I = \frac{m}{12}\,(d^2 + c^2)$	
m 28	$k^2 = \frac{1}{3}\,l^2$	$k^2 = \frac{1}{12}\,(d^2 + c^2)$	

Total kinetic energy of a body

m 29
$$W_K = \frac{1}{2} m v_s^2 + \frac{1}{2} I_s \omega^2$$

J, [kgf m]

Kinetic energy of a rolling body – no sliding

m 30
$$W_K = \frac{1}{2} (m + m_{eq}) v_s^2$$

J, [kgf m]

m 31
$$v_s = \omega r$$

m/s, km/h

Rotational torque

m 32
$$M = \frac{P}{\omega} = \frac{P}{2 \pi n}$$

N m, [kgf m]

Transmission ratios

Transmission ratio

m 33
$$i = \frac{d_2}{d_1} = \frac{z_2}{z_1} = \frac{n_1}{n_2} = \frac{\omega_1}{\omega_2}$$

driving

Torque ratio

m 34
$$\frac{moment\ of\ force}{moment\ of\ load} = \frac{M_F}{M_L} = \frac{1}{i\ \eta}$$

Efficiency

m 35
$$\eta = \frac{work\ produced}{work\ applied} = \frac{output}{input}$$

driven

Overall efficiency for a series of transmissions

m 36
$$\eta = \eta_1 \times \eta_2 \times \eta_3 \times \ldots$$

m_{eq} : see m 8
v_s : velocity of linear motion of centre of gravity
F_a : accelerating force — N, [kgf]
M_a : accelerating moment — N m, [kgf m]
W_K : kinetic energy — J, [kgf m]
W_P : potential energy — J, [kgf m]
W_F : energy of helical spring under tension — J, [kgf m]
Δl : extension of helical spring
$\Delta \hat{\beta}$: angular deflection of spiral spring (in radians)

Centrifugal force

m 37 $\quad F_z = m \omega^2 r = \dfrac{m \, v^2}{r}$ $\qquad$ N, [kgf]

m 38 $\qquad = 4 \pi^2 m \, n^2 \, r$ $\qquad$ N [kgf]

m 39 $\quad v = 2 \pi \, r \, n$ $\qquad$ m/s, km/h

m 40 $\quad \omega = 2 \pi \, n$ $\qquad$ 1/s, 1/min

Stresses in rotation bodies (appr. formulae)

Disc

m 41 $\quad \sigma_z = \dfrac{\omega^2 r^2 \rho}{3} = \dfrac{v^2 \rho}{3}$

$\qquad$ N/m², [kgf/cm²]

Ring

m 42 $\quad \sigma_z = \dfrac{\omega^2 \rho}{3} (r_1^2 + r_1 \, r_2 + r_2^2)$

$\qquad$ N/m², [kgf cm²]

l_s :	distance from centre of gravity	m, cm, mm
e :	maximum pendulum swing	m, cm, mm
f :	instantaneous pendulum swing	m, cm, mm
F_z :	centrifugal force	N, [kgf, gf]
I_0 :	mass moment of inertia about O	kg m², [kgf m s²]
I_S :	mass moment of inertia about S	kg m², [kgf m s²]
M_1 :	moment required to deflect spiral spring	
	by 1 rad = $57 \cdot 3°$	N m, [kgf cm]
σ_z :	tensile stress	N/m², kgf/cm², [kgf/mm²]
T :	period of oscillation	
	(B to B' and back)	s, min
v_E :	velocity at E	m/s, cm/s, km/h
v_F :	velocity at F	m/s, cm/s, km/h
W_{KE}:	kinetic energy at E	N m, [kgf m]

Mechanical oscillation

General

m 43 | period | $T = 2\pi\sqrt{\dfrac{m}{c}}$ | s, min

m 44 | stiffness | $c = \dfrac{G}{\Delta l}$ | N/m, [kgf/cm]

m 45 | frequency | $f = \dfrac{1}{T}$ | (see L 1) s^{-1}, min^{-1}

m 46 | angular velocity | $\omega = 2\pi f = \sqrt{\dfrac{c}{m}}$ | s^{-1}, min^{-1}

Critical speed n_c of shaft

m 47
$$n_c = \frac{1}{2\pi}\sqrt{\frac{c_q}{m}}$$

m 48
$$= 300\sqrt{\frac{10\ c_q\ mm}{9\cdot 81\ N}\times\frac{kg}{m}}\quad min^{-1}$$

stiffness c_q of

2-bearing shaft, load		overhung (cantilever) shaft
symmetrical	asymmetrical	
$c_q = \dfrac{48\ E\ I}{l^3}$	$c_q = \dfrac{3\ E\ I\ l}{a^2\ b^2}$	$c_q = \dfrac{3\ E\ I}{l^3}$

m 49 (row label for the $c_q$ formulas)

Δl : deflection or elongation

I : second moment of area of shaft cross section

m : mass. When calculating the critical speed the mass m (e.g. of a belt disc) is assumed to be concentrated at a single point. The mass of the shaft should be allowed for by a slight increase

c_q : stiffness for transverse oscillations

Pendulum
(Explanations see L 4)

Conical pendulum

m 50 $T = 2\pi\sqrt{\dfrac{h}{g}} = 2\pi\sqrt{\dfrac{l\cos\alpha}{g}}$ s, min

m 51 $\tan\alpha = \dfrac{r\omega^2}{g} = \dfrac{r}{h}$

m 52 $\omega = \sqrt{\dfrac{g}{h}}$ $\bigg|$ $h = \dfrac{g}{\omega^2}$ m, cm

Simple pendulum

The arm of a pendulum has no mass, the total mass is represented as a point.

m 53 $T = 2\pi\sqrt{\dfrac{l}{g}}$ s, min

m 54 $v_E = e\sqrt{\dfrac{g}{l}}$ $\bigg|$ $v_F = \sqrt{\dfrac{g}{l}(e^2 - f^2)}$ m/s, km/h

m 55 $W_{KE} = m\,g\,\dfrac{e^2}{2\,l}$ J, N m, [kgf cm]

Compound pendulum

m 56 $T = 2\pi\sqrt{\dfrac{I_0}{m\,g\,l_S}} = 2\pi\sqrt{\dfrac{k_0^2}{g}}$ s, min

m 57 $I_0 = I_S + m\,l_S^2$ N m s², [kgf cm s²]

m 58 $I_S = m\,g\,l_S\left(\dfrac{T^2}{4\pi^2} - \dfrac{l_S}{g}\right)$ N m s², [kgf cm s²]

If a body with centre of gravity S is suspended from O, distant l_S from S, and the period of swing determined the mass moment of inertia about O can be calculated using m 58.

Torsional pendulum

m 59 $T = 2\pi\sqrt{\dfrac{I}{M_1}}$ s, min

For explanation of symbols see M 5

Impact

m 60 When two bodies of mass m_1 and m_2 and velocities v_{11} and v_{21} collide, the total momentum $p = m \, v$ will remain constant over the whole impact period (velocities become v_{12} and v_{22}):

m 61
$$p = m_1 \, v_{11} + m_2 \, v_{21} = m_1 \, v_{12} + m_2 \, v_{22}$$

Impact-direction

direct and concentric impact	velocities parallel to normal to surfaces at point of impact	normal to surfaces at point of impact through centre of gravity of both bodies
oblique and concentric impact	any random velocities	
oblique and excentric impact		any random normal to surfaces at point of impact

Types of impact

	elastic impact[+]	plastic impact
relative velocity	equal, before and after impact	equals zero after impact
velocity after direct and concentric impact	$v_{12} = \dfrac{v_{11}(m_1 - m_2) + 2m_2\,v_{21}}{m_1 + m_2}$ $v_{22} = \dfrac{v_{21}(m_2 - m_1) + 2m_1\,v_{11}}{m_1 + m_2}$	$v_{02} = \dfrac{m_1\,v_{11} + m_2\,v_{21}}{m_1 + m_2}$
coeff. of restitution	$\varepsilon = 1$	$\varepsilon = 0$

m 62
m 63
m 64

m 65

Coefficient of restitution ε

This indicates by what factor the relative velocities will vary before (v_{r1}) and after (v_{r2}) impact:

m 66
$$\varepsilon = \frac{v_{r2}}{v_{r1}} \, , \qquad\qquad \text{here} \quad 0 \leqq \varepsilon \leqq 1$$

[+] For an oblique, concentric, elastic impact the velocity vector v is split into a normal and a tangential component. The normal component v_n produces a direct impact (see above), the tangential component v_t has no effect on the impact.

normal to surfaces at point of impact

General

Hydraulics deals with the behaviour of liquids. With good approximation, liquids may be considered incompressible, which means that the influence of pressure changes on their densities is negligibly small.

Quantities

Pressure p see O 1

Density ϱ see O 1

Dynamic viscosity η

$$\left(\text{EU: Pascal-second Pa s} = \frac{\text{kg}}{\text{m s}} = \frac{\text{N s}}{\text{m}^2} \; [= 10 \text{ P}] \right)$$

The dynamic viscosity is a material constant, which is a function of pressure and temperature:

n 1
$$\eta = f(p, t)$$

The dependence on pressure can often be neglected. Hence

n 2
$$\eta = f(t) \qquad \text{(for figures see Z 14)}$$

Kinematic viscosity ν (EU: m²/s [= 10^4 St = 10^6 cSt])

The kinematic viscosity is the quotient of dynamic viscosity η and density ϱ:

n 3
$$\nu = \frac{\eta}{\varrho}$$

Hydrostatics

Pressure distribution in a fluid

n 4
$$p_1 = p_0 + g \varrho h_1$$

n 5
$$p_2 = p_1 + g \varrho (h_2 - h_1)$$
$$= p_1 + g \varrho \, \Delta h$$

continued on N 2

Hydrostatic forces on plane surfaces

Hydrostatic force is the component acting on the surface which is caused by the weight of the fluid alone, i.e. without taking into account the atmospheric pressure p_o.

n 6
$$F = g \varrho \, y_s A \cos a = g \varrho \, h_s A$$

n 7
$$y_D = \frac{I_x}{y_s A} = y_s + \frac{I_s}{y_s A} \; ; \qquad x_D = \frac{I_{xy}}{y_s A}$$
m, mm

Hydrostatic forces on curved surfaces

The hydrostatic force acting on the curved surface 1, 2, is resolved into the horizontal component F_H and the vertical component F_V.

F_V is equal to the weight of the fluid in (a) or the equivalent weight of fluid (b), above the surface 1,2. The line of action runs through the centre of gravity of the volume V.

n 8
$$|F_V| = g \varrho \, V$$
N, kN

F_H is equal to the hydrostatic pressure force acting on the projection of the considered surface 1,2 on the plane perpendicular to F_H. Calculation is accomplished by n 6 and n 7.

S : centre of gravity of area A
D : centre of pressure = point of action of force F
I_x : second moment of area A in relation to axis x
I_s : second moment of area A in relation to an axis running parallel to axis x through the centre of gravity (see J 10 and P 10)
I_{xy} : centrifugal moment of area A in relation to axes x and y (see J 10).

Buoyancy

The buoyancy F_A is equal to the weight of the displaced fluids of densities ϱ and ϱ'.

n 9 $\quad F_A = g\,\varrho\,V + g\,\varrho'\,V' \qquad$ N, kN

If the fluid of density ϱ' is a gas, the following formula is valid:

n 10 $\quad F_A \approx g\,\varrho\,V \qquad\qquad\qquad$ N, kN

With ϱ_k being the density of the body,

n 11 $\quad \varrho > \varrho_k$ the body will float
n 12 $\quad \varrho = \varrho_k$ " " " remain suspended $\Big\}$ in the heavier fluid
n 13 $\quad \varrho < \varrho_k$ " " " sink

Determination of density ϱ of solid and liquid bodies

Solid body of greater / smaller density than the fluid used		For fluids first determine F_1 and m of a deliberate body in a fluid of known density ϱ_b. This yields:
n 14, n 15, n 16 $\quad \varrho = \varrho_F \dfrac{1}{1 - \dfrac{F}{m\,g}}$	$\varrho = \varrho_F \dfrac{1}{1 + \dfrac{F_H - F}{m\,g}}$	$\varrho = \varrho_b \dfrac{1 - \dfrac{F}{m\,g}}{1 - \dfrac{F_1}{m\,g}}$

m : mass of the body remaining suspended in the fluid
F : equilibrium force necessary
F_H : equilibrium force necessary in the preliminary trial for the auxiliary body alone
ϱ_F : density of the fluid used

Hydrodynamics
(of a steady flow)

Continuity equation

Rule of conservation of mass:

n 17
$$A_1 \, v_1 \, \varrho_1 \; = \; A \, v \, \varrho \; = \; A_2 \, v_2 \, \varrho_2$$

n 18
$$= \; \dot{m} \; = \; \dot{V} \, \varrho \qquad \frac{g}{s} \; , \; \frac{kg}{s}$$

Rule of conservation of volume:

n 19
$$\dot{V} \; = \; A \, v \qquad \frac{m^3}{s} \; , \; \frac{cm^3}{s} \qquad v \perp A$$

Bernoulli's equation (Rule of conservation of energy)

No friction (ideal fluid):

n 20
$$\frac{p_1}{\varrho} + g \, z_1 + \frac{v_1^2}{2} = \frac{p}{\varrho} + g \, z + \frac{v^2}{2} = \frac{p_2}{\varrho} + g \, z_2 + \frac{v_2^2}{2} \qquad \frac{J}{kg}$$

$\dfrac{p}{\varrho}$: pressure energy per unit mass

$g \, z$: potential energy per unit mass

$\dfrac{v^2}{2}$: kinetic energy per unit mass

Including losses (real fluid):

n 21
$$\frac{p_1}{\varrho} + g \, z_1 + \frac{v_1^2}{2} = \frac{p_2}{\varrho} + g \, z_2 + \frac{v_2^2}{2} + w_{R\,1,2} \qquad \frac{J}{kg}$$

v : velocity
$w_{R\,1,2}$: resistance losses along path from 1 to 2   (per unit mass)

Power P of an hydraulic machine

n 22
$$P = \dot{m}\, w_{t\,1,2} \qquad \text{kW, W}$$

technical work per unit mass:

n 23
$$w_{t\,1,2} = \frac{1}{\rho}(p_2 - p_1) + g(z_2 - z_1) + \frac{1}{2}(v_2^2 - v_1^2) - w_{F\,1,2} \qquad \frac{J}{kg}$$

n 24
$$\text{for hydraulic machines:} \qquad w_{t\,1,2} < 0$$

n 25
$$\text{for pumps:} \qquad w_{t\,1,2} > 0$$

Momentum equation

For a fluid flowing through a stationary reference volume the following vector equation is valid:

n 26
$$\sum \vec{F} = \dot{m}(\vec{v_2} - \vec{v_1}) \qquad \text{N, kN}$$

$\sum \vec{F}$ is the vector sum of the forces acting on the fluid contained in the reference volume. These can be:

> volume forces (e. g. weight)
> pressure forces
> friction forces.

$\vec{v_2}$ is the exit velocity of the fluid leaving the reference volume

$\vec{v_1}$ is the entrance velocity of the fluid entering the reference volume.

Angular-momentum equation

In a steady state rotational flow a torque M is exerted on the fluid flowing through the reference volume, given by:

n 27
$$M = \dot{m}(v_{2,u} \times r_2 - v_{1,u} \times r_1) \qquad \text{N m}$$

$v_{2,u}$ and $v_{1,u}$ are the circumferential components of exit velocity out of and entrance velocity into the reference volume.

r_2 and r_1 are the radii associated with v_2 and v_1.

Friction losses in pipe flow

n 28	Friction loss per unit mass	$w_{R\,1,2} = \Sigma(\zeta\,a\,\dfrac{v^2}{2})$, hence
n 29	Pressure loss	$\Delta p_V = \varrho\,w_{R\,1,2}$

Determination of coefficient of resistance ζ and coefficient of shape a:

	circular pipes	non circular pipes
n 30	$Re = \dfrac{v\,d\,\varrho}{\eta}$	$Re = \dfrac{v\,d_h\,\varrho}{\eta}$

n 31 Where $Re < 2000$, the flow is laminar.
n 32 Where $Re > 3000$, the flow is turbulent.
Where $Re = 2000 \ldots 3000$, the flow can be either laminar or turbulent.

	Flow		Flow	
	laminar	turbulent*)	laminar	turbulent*)
n 33	$\zeta = \dfrac{64}{Re}$	$\zeta = f(Re, \dfrac{k}{d})$	$\zeta = \varphi\dfrac{64}{Re}$	$\zeta = f(Re, \dfrac{k}{d_h})$
n 34	$a = \dfrac{l}{d}$ for straight pipes		$a = \dfrac{l}{d_h}$ for straight pipes	
n 35	$a = 1$ for fittings, unions and valves.			

Determination of coefficient φ

n 36 For annular cross sections:

D/d	1	3	5	7	10	30	50	70	100	∞
φ	1·50	1·47	1·44	1·42	1·40	1·32	1·29	1·27	1·25	1·00

n 37 For rectangular cross sections:

a/b	0	0·1	0·2	0·3	0·4	0·5	0·6	0·7	0·8	1·0
φ	1·50	1·34	1·20	1·10	1·02	0·97	0·94	0·92	0·90	0·89

n 38

d : internal diameter of pipe $\qquad$ l : length of pipe
$d_h = 4\,A/U$: hydraulic diameter
A : cross section perpendicular to fluid flow
U : wetted circumference
k/d and k/d_h : relative roughness
k : mean roughness (see Z 9)
η : dynamic viscosity
*)ζ is taken from diagram Z 8

Flow of liquids from containers

Base apertures

n 39 $v = C_v \sqrt{2 g H}$

n 40 $Q = C_d A \sqrt{2 g H}$

Small lateral apertures

n 41 $v = C_v \sqrt{2 g H}$

n 42 $s = 2 \sqrt{H h}$

n 43 $Q = C_d A \sqrt{2 g H}$

n 44 $F = \varrho Q v$

Large lateral apertures

n 45 $Q = \dfrac{2}{3} C_d b \sqrt{2 g} \left(H_2^{\frac{3}{2}} - H_1^{\frac{3}{2}} \right)$

Excess pressure on surface of liquid

n 46 $v = C_v \sqrt{2 \left(g H + \dfrac{p_{ex}}{\varrho} \right)}$

n 47 $Q = C_d A \sqrt{2 \left(g H + \dfrac{p_{ex}}{\varrho} \right)}$

Excess pressure applied to an outlet point

n 48 $v = C_v \sqrt{2 \dfrac{p_{ex}}{\varrho}}$

n 49 $Q = C_d A \sqrt{2 \dfrac{p_{ex}}{\varrho}}$

v : outlet velocity		m/s, km/h
p_{ex}: pressure in excess of atmosphere pressure		N/m², kgf/cm²
C_d : discharge coefficient	$(C_d = C_c \times C_v)$	
C_c : contraction coefficient	$(C_c = 0 \cdot 62$ for sharp edge aperture$)$	
	$(C_c = 0 \cdot 97$ for well rounded aperture$)$	
C_v : velocity coefficient (for water $C_v = 0 \cdot 97$)		
b : width of aperture		m, cm
F : reaction force		N, kgf
Q : volume of outlet flow		m³/s, m³/h

Thermal variables of state are pressure p, temperature t, and density ϱ or volume per unit mass (specific volume), respectively.

Pressure p (EU: N/m² = Pa, bar)

o 1
Pressure is the quotient of force F and area A:

$$p = \frac{F}{A}$$

The absolute pressure can be interpreted as the total result of the impacts of the molecules on the wall. The pressure measured with a pressure gauge is the pressure differential Δp in relation to the ambient pressure p_u. A state of pressure means $\Delta p > 0$, vacuum means $\Delta p < 0$. Thus, the absolute pressure p can be expressed by:

o 2
$$p = p_u + \Delta p$$

Temperature T, t (Base quantity) see explanations at front of book.

The unit of temperature T is the Kelvin K, defined by equation

o 3
$$1 \text{ K} = \frac{T_{TR}}{273 \cdot 16}$$

where T_{TR} is the temperature of pure water at the triple point. In addition to the Kelvin scale the centigrade scale is also used. The temperature of this scale has been internationally defined by:

o 4
$$t = \left(\frac{T}{K} - 273 \cdot 15\right) {}^\circ C \; ; \quad T = \left(\frac{t}{{}^\circ C} + 273 \cdot 15\right) K$$

Density ϱ (EU: kg/m³)

Density is the quotient of mass m and volume V:

o 5
$$\varrho = \frac{m}{V}$$

Volume per unit mass (specific volume) v (EU: m³/kg)

Specific volume is the quotient of the volume V and the mass m:

o 6
$$v = \frac{V}{m} = \frac{1}{\varrho}$$

Molecular volume V_m (EU: m³/mol)

Molecular volume is the quotient of volume V and number of moles contained in the volume:

o 7
$$V_m = \frac{V}{n}$$

Amount of substance n (Base quantity) see explanations at front of book.

Heating of solid and liquid bodies

Heat (thermal energy) Q (EU: J)

Heat is energy exchanged between systems of different temperatures, where these systems interact with each other through diathermal walls.

Heat per unit mass q (EU: J/kg)

The heat per unit mass is the quotient of heat Q and mass m:

o 8

$$q = \frac{Q}{m}$$

Specific heat c EU: J/(kg K)

The specific heat c denotes the amount of heat Q to be supplied to or extracted from a substance of mass m to change its temperature by a difference Δt:

o 9

$$c = \frac{Q}{m \, \Delta t} = \frac{q}{\Delta t}$$

The specific heat is a function of temperature. For figures see Z 1 ... Z 5.

Latent heats per unit mass l (EU: J/kg) Values see Z 10

The supply or extraction of latent heat causes a body to change its state without changing its temperature. The following latent heats exist:

o 10	l_f	fusion	solid body of the fusing temperature into a fluid	
o 11	l_d	latent heat of — vapourisation — is the heat necessary to convert a	fluid of the boiling temperature (dependent on pressure) into dry saturated vapour	of the same temperature
o 12	l_s	sublimation	solid body of a temperature below its triple temperature at the sublimation temperature (dependent on pressure) directly into dry saturated vapour	

Expansion of solid bodies

A solid body changes its dimensions due to temperature changes. With α being the coefficient of linear expansion (for figures see Z 11) the following formulae are valid for:

o 13 Length: $\quad l_2 = l_1 \left[1 + \alpha (t_2 - t_1) \right]$

o 14 $\qquad \Delta l = l_2 - l_1 \approx l_1 \alpha (t_2 - t_1)$

o 15 Area: $\quad A_2 \approx A_1 \left[1 + 2\alpha (t_2 - t_1) \right]$

o 16 $\qquad \Delta A = A_2 - A_1 \approx A_1 2\alpha (t_2 - t_1)$

o 17 Volume: $\quad V_2 \approx V_1 \left[1 + 3\alpha (t_2 - t_1) \right]$

o 18 $\qquad \Delta V = V_2 - V_1 \approx V_1 3\alpha (t_2 - t_1)$

Expansion of liquid bodies

With β being the coefficient of volume expansion (for figures see Z 11) the following formulae apply:

o 19 $\qquad V_2 = V_1 \left[1 + \beta (t_2 - t_1) \right]$

o 20 $\qquad \Delta V = V_2 - V_1 = V_1 \beta (t_2 - t_1)$

Bending due to heat A

Bimetallic strips are subject to bending due to heat. Bending occurs towards the side of the metal with the lower coefficient of expansion. With α_b being the "specific thermal bending" the bending due to heat can be calculating by (α_b approx. 14×10^{-6}/K, for exact values see manufacturers catalogues):

o 21 $$A = \frac{\alpha_b L^2 \Delta t}{s}$$

l_1 : length at $t = t_1$		A_1 : area at $t = t_1$	
l_2 : length at $t = t_2$		A_2 : area at $t = t_2$	
V_1 : volume at $t = t_1$		t_1 temper- prior to	heating
V_2 : volume at $t = t_2$		t_2 ature after	
s : thickness		Δt : temperature difference	

General equation of state of ideal gases

The state of ideal gas is determined by two thermal variables of state. Thus, the third variable can be calculated using the general equation of state. With R being the characteristic gas constant (different values for different gases, see Z 12) the equation reads as follows:

o 22

$$p\,v = R\,T \qquad \text{or} \qquad p\,V = n\,R\,T \qquad \text{or} \qquad p = \varrho\,R\,T$$

If the gas constant is related to the mole volume, the equation reads

o 23

$$p\,V_m = R_m T$$

where $R_m = 8314 \cdot 3$ J/(kmol K) is the universal gas constant (valid for all ideal gases). R and R_m are related by

o 24

$$R_m = M\,R$$

where M is the molecular mass (see Z 12).

Thermal state of real (non ideal) gases and vapours

The thermal state of real gases and vapours is calculated using special equations or diagrams.

Changes of state

Changes of state are caused by interactions of the system with the surroundings. These interactions are calculated using the 1st and the 2nd law:

	1st law for		2nd law for all systems
	closed systems	open systems	

o 25
o 26
o 27

$$q_{1,2} + w_{1,2} = u_2 - u_1 \quad \bigg| \quad q_{1,2} + w_{t\,1,2} = h_2 - h_1 + \Delta e \quad \bigg| \quad q_{1,2} = \int_1^2 T\,ds$$

In these formulae, energy input is positive (i. e. $q_{1,2}$, $w_{1,2}$, $w_{t\,1,2}$) and energy output negative.

h : enthalpy per unit mass

s : entropy per unit mass

u : internal energy per unit mass

$w_{1,2}$: external work done per unit mass (see 0 7)

$w_{t\,1,2}$: continuous external work done per unit mass (see 0 7)

Δe : changes in kinetic or potential energies

Changes of state of ideal gases

The table on page 0 6 shows the relations for different changes of state, which have been developed from formulae o 25 to o 27. The following explanations apply:

Each change of state, may be represented by an equation

o 28
$$p \, v^n = \text{const}$$

The various exponents n are given in column 1.

c_{pm} and c_{vm} are the mean specific heats for constant pressure and constant volume, respectively, in the temperature range between t_1 and t_2. There, the following relations apply (values for c_{pm} see Z 13):

o 29
$$c_{pm} = c_{pm}\Big|_{t_1}^{t_2} = \frac{c_{pm}\Big|_{c}^{t_2} \, t_2 - c_{pm}\Big|_{0}^{t_1} \, t_1}{t_2 - t_1}$$

o 30
$$c_{vm} = c_{vm}\Big|_{t_1}^{t_2} = c_{pm}\Big|_{t_1}^{t_2} - R$$

o 31
$$\gamma = \gamma_m = \gamma_m\Big|_{t_1}^{t_2} = c_{pm}\Big|_{t_1}^{t_2} \Big/ c_{v}\Big|_{t_1}^{t_2}$$

The change of entropy occurring during the change of state is given by:

o 32
$$s_2 - s_1 = c_{pm}\ln\left(\frac{T_2}{T_1}\right) - R \ln\left(\frac{p_2}{p_1}\right) = c_{vm} \ln\left(\frac{T_2}{T_1}\right) + R \ln\left(\frac{v_2}{v_1}\right)$$

Changes of state of real gases and vapours

The table below shows the relations for different changes of state, which have been developed from formulae o 25 to o 27. The thermal variables of state, p, v, T as well as the properties, u, h, s are generally taken from appropriate diagrams.

	change of state, const. quantity	external work $w_{1,2} = -\int_1^2 p \, dv$	continuous external work $w_{t1,2} = \int_1^2 v \, dp$	heat per unit mass $q_{1,2}$
o 33	isochoric, $v = $ const.	0	$v(p_2 - p_1)$	$u_2 - u_1 = (h_2 - h_1) - v(p_2 - p_1)$
o 34	isobaric, $p = $ const.	$p(v_1 - v_2)$	0	$h_2 - h_1$
o 35	isothermal, $T = $ const.	$(u_2 - u_1) - T(s_2 - s_1) = (h_2 - h_1) - T(s_2 - s_1) - (p_2 v_2 - p_1 v_1)$	$(h_2 - h_1) - T(s_2 - s_1)$	$T(s_2 - s_1)$
o 36	isentropic, $s = $ const.	$u_2 - u_1 = (h_2 - h_1) - (p_2 v_2 - p_1 v_1)$	$h_2 - h_1$	0

process details, exponent	relation between state 1 and state 2	closed system, reversible $w_{1,2} = -\int_1^2 p\,dv$	open system, reversible $w_{t1,2} = \int_1^2 v\,dp$	heat transfer per unit mass $q_{1,2}$	p–v diagram	T–s diagram
isochoric v = const. $n = \infty$ (o 37)	$\dfrac{p_2}{p_1} = \dfrac{T_2}{T_1}$	0	$v(p_2 - p_1)$ $= R(T_2 - T_1)$	$c_{vm}(T_2 - T_1)$		
isobaric p = const. $n = 0$ (o 38)	$\dfrac{v_2}{v_1} = \dfrac{T_2}{T_1}$	$p(v_1 - v_2)$ $= R(T_1 - T_2)$	0	$c_{pm}(T_2 - T_1)$		
isothermal T = const. $n = 1$ (o 39)	$\dfrac{p_2}{p_1} = \dfrac{v_1}{v_2}$	$RT \ln\left(\dfrac{v_1}{v_2}\right)$ $= RT \ln\left(\dfrac{p_2}{p_1}\right)$	$w_{1,2}$	$-w_{1,2}$		
isentropic s = const. $n = \gamma$ (o 40)	$\dfrac{p_2}{p_1} = \left(\dfrac{v_1}{v_2}\right)^{\gamma}$ $\dfrac{p_2}{p_1} = \left(\dfrac{T_2}{T_1}\right)^{\frac{\gamma}{\gamma-1}}$ $\dfrac{v_1}{v_2} = \left(\dfrac{T_1}{T_2}\right)^{\frac{1}{\gamma-1}}$	$u_2 - u_1 = c_{vm}(T_2 - T_1)$ $= \dfrac{1}{\gamma-1}RT_1\left[\left(\dfrac{p_2}{p_1}\right)^{\frac{\gamma-1}{\gamma}} - 1\right]$	$h_2 - h_1 = c_{pm}(T_2 - T_1)$ $= c_{pm}T_1\left[\left(\dfrac{p_2}{p_1}\right)^{\frac{\gamma-1}{\gamma}} - 1\right]$ $= \dfrac{\gamma}{\gamma-1}RT_1\left[\left(\dfrac{p_2}{p_1}\right)^{\frac{\gamma-1}{\gamma}} - 1\right]$	0		
polytropic process n = const. (o 41)	$\dfrac{p_2}{p_1} = \left(\dfrac{v_1}{v_2}\right)^{n}$ $\dfrac{p_2}{p_1} = \left(\dfrac{T_2}{T_1}\right)^{\frac{n}{n-1}}$ $\dfrac{v_2}{v_1} = \left(\dfrac{T_1}{T_2}\right)^{\frac{1}{n-1}}$	$\dfrac{1}{n-1}R(T_2 - T_1)$ $= \dfrac{1}{n-1}RT_1\left[\left(\dfrac{p_2}{p_1}\right)^{\frac{n-1}{n}} - 1\right]$	$\dfrac{n}{n-1}R(T_2 - T_1)$ $= \dfrac{n}{n-1}RT_1\left[\left(\dfrac{p_2}{p_1}\right)^{\frac{n-1}{n}} - 1\right]$	$c_{vm}\dfrac{n-\gamma}{n-1}(T_2 - T_1)$		

p–v diagram and T–s diagram: drawn to fit existing process

$p-v$ diagram

For reversible processes the area between the curve of the variation of state and the v-axis represents the external work per unit mass, the area between the curve and the p-axis represents the continuous external work per unit mass.

$T-s$ diagram

For reversible processes the area between the curve and the s-axis represents the heat transfer per unit mass.

Total transfer of heat

The heat added to or removed from a closed system during a single variation of state is:

o 42
$$Q_{1,2} = m\, q_{1,2} \qquad \text{J}$$

The heat flow continuously added to or removed from an open system is:

o 43
$$\Phi_{1,2} = \dot{Q}_{1,2} = \dot{m}\, q_{1,2} \qquad \text{W}$$

where $\dot{m}$ is the mass flow (EU: kg/s).

Total transfer of work

The external work added to or done by a closed system during a single variation of state is:

o 44
$$W_{1,2} = m\, w_{1,2} \qquad \text{J}$$

The external power continuously added to or done by an open system is given by:

o 45
$$P_{1,2} = \dot{m}\, w_{t1,2} \qquad \text{W}$$

Mass m of a mixture of components m_1, m_2, ...

o 46
$$m = m_1 + m_2 + \ldots + m_n = \sum_{i=1}^{i=n} m_i$$

Mass fractions ξ_i of a mixture

o 47
$$\xi_i = \frac{m_i}{m} \qquad \text{and} \qquad \sum_{i=1}^{i=n} \xi_i = 1$$

Number of moles n of a mixture of components n_1, n_2, ...

o 48
$$n = n_1 + n_2 + \ldots + n_n = \sum_{i=1}^{i=n} n_i$$

Mole fractions ψ_i of a mixture

o 49
$$\psi_i = \frac{n_i}{n} \qquad \text{and} \qquad \sum_{i=1}^{i=n} \psi_i = 1$$

Equivalent molecular mass M of a mixture
For the molecular mass the following formulae apply:

o 50
$$M_i = \frac{m_i}{n} \qquad \text{and} \qquad M = \frac{m}{n}$$

where the equivalent molecular mass M of the mixture can be calculated as follows:

o 51
$$M = \sum_{i=1}^{i=n} (M_i \times \psi_i) \quad \text{and} \quad \frac{1}{M} = \sum_{i=1}^{i=n} \left(\frac{\xi_i}{M_i} \right)$$

Conversion between mass- and mole-fractions

o 52
$$\xi_i = \frac{M_i}{M} \psi_i$$

Pressure p of the mixture and partial pressures p_i of the components

o 53
$$p = \sum_{i=1}^{i=n} p_i \qquad \text{where} \qquad p_i = \psi_i \times p$$

continued on page O 9

Continuation of page O 8

Volume fractions r_i of a mixture

o 54
$$r = \frac{V_i}{V} = \psi_i \quad \text{and} \quad \sum_{i=1}^{i=n} r_i = 1$$

Here, by partial volume V_i we mean the volume the component would occupy at the temperature T and the total pressure p of the mixture. For ideal gases the following formulae apply:

o 55
$$V_i = \frac{m_i R_i T}{p} = \frac{n_i R_m T}{p} \quad \text{and} \quad \sum_{i=1}^{i=n} V_i = V$$

Internal energy u and enthalpy h of a mixture

o 56
$$u = \sum_{i=1}^{i=n} (\xi_i \times u_i) \quad ; \quad h = \sum_{i=1}^{i=n} (\xi_i \times h_i)$$

Using these formulae, the temperature of the mixture can be determined, for real gases and vapours by using diagrams, and for ideal gases as follows:

o 57
internal energy
$$t = \frac{c_{v_{m1}} \times t_1 \, m_1 + c_{v_{m2}} \times t_2 \, m_2 + \ldots + c_{v_{mn}} \times t_n \, m_n}{c_{v_m} \times m}$$

o 58
enthalpy
$$t = \frac{c_{p_{m1}} \times t_1 \, m_1 + c_{p_m} \times t_2 \, m_2 + \ldots + c_{p_{mn}} \times t_n \, m_n}{c_{p_m} \times m}$$

where the specific heats of the mixture are determined as follows:

o 59
$$c_{v_m} = c_{p_m} - R$$

o 60
$$c_{p_m} = \sum_{i=1}^{i=n} (\xi_i \times c_{p_{mi}})$$

Due to the temperature difference between two points heat flows from the point of higher temperature towards the point of lower temperature. The following kinds of heat transmission must be distinguished:

Conduction

o 61 in a plane wall: $\qquad \Phi = \dot{Q} = \lambda A \dfrac{t_{w_1} - t_{w_2}}{s}$

o 62 in the wall of a pipe: $\quad \Phi = \dot{Q} = \lambda A_m \dfrac{t_{w_1} - t_{w_2}}{s}$

The mean logarithmic area is

o 63 $A_m = \pi\, d_m\, L$; where $d_m = \dfrac{d_\alpha - d_i}{\ln\left(\dfrac{d_\alpha}{d_i}\right)}$

--- plane wall
— pipe

L : length of the pipe

Convection

By heat convection we mean the heat transfer in a fluid. Due to their flow the molecules as carriers of the mass are also the carriers of the heat.

Where the flow originates by itself, the convection is called natural convection. The convection taking place in a flow is called forced convection.

o 64 $\qquad\qquad \Phi = \dot{Q} = \alpha A (t - t_w)$

Radiation

This kind of heat transmission does not require mass as a carrier (e. g. the radiation of the sun through space). For calculations formula o 64 is used.

Heat transfer

By heat transfer we mean the combined result of the different processes contributing to the heat transmission:

o 65 $\qquad \Phi = \dot{Q} = k A (t_1 - t_2)$

The heat transfer coefficient k is given by (for approx. values see Z 11):

o 66 plane wall: $\quad \dfrac{1}{k} = \dfrac{1}{\alpha_1} + \sum\limits_{i=1}^{i=n}\left(\dfrac{s}{\lambda}\right)_i + \dfrac{1}{\alpha_2}$

o 67 pipe: $\qquad \dfrac{1}{k A} = \dfrac{1}{\alpha_1 A_1} + \sum\limits_{i=1}^{i=n}\left(\dfrac{s}{\lambda A_m}\right)_i + \dfrac{1}{\alpha_2 A_2}$

λ : thermal conductivity (for values see Z 1 ... Z 5)
α : heat transfer coefficient (for calculation see O 12)

Heat exchanger

A heat exchanger transmits heat from one fluid to another. The heat flow may be calculated by:

o 68
$$\Phi = \dot{Q} = k\,A\,\Delta t_m$$

Here, Δt_m is the logarithmic mean temperature difference. The following formula applies for both parallel-flow and counter-flow heat exchangers:

o 69
$$\Delta t_m = (\Delta t_{great} - \Delta t_{small}) \Big/ \ln \frac{\Delta t_{great}}{\Delta t_{small}}$$

parallel-flow *counterflow*

In counterflow operation Δt_{great} and Δt_{small}, can occur on the opposite ends of the exchanger, to that shown in the figure.

Symbols used on page O 12

A_1 : surface of the smaller body
A_2 : surface of the bigger body
d : inside diameter of pipe
D : outer diameter of pipe
Gr : Grashof'number
H : height of plate
L : length of plate
υ : velocity

C_1 and C_2 : radiation constants of the surfaces exchanging radiation
(for values see Z 12)
$C_s = 5 \cdot 67 \times 10^{-8}$ W/(m² K⁴): radiation constant of the black body

o 70
Pr : Prandtl-Number; $Pr = (\eta\,c_p)/\lambda$
$\Delta t = |\,t_w - t_\infty\,|$ absolute temperature difference between wall and fluid in the not affected region
t_∞ : ambient temperature
ν : kinematic viscosity ($\nu = \eta/\varrho$)
η : dynamic viscosity
η_{Fl} : dynamic viscosity at mean temperature of fluid
η_W : dynamic viscosity at wall temperature
λ : thermal conductivity of fluid (for values see Z 5, Z 6)
β : volume expansion coefficient (see Z 11 and o 77)
β^* : temperature factor

Calculation of heat transfer coefficient α [1]

For free convection (according to Grigull)

o 71
o 72
o 73

	on a vertical plate	$\alpha = \dfrac{Nu\,\lambda}{H}$	$Nu = 0 \cdot 55 \sqrt[4]{Gr\,Pr}$, for $1700 < Gr\,Pr < 10^8$
			$Nu = 0 \cdot 13 \sqrt[3]{Gr\,Pr}$, for $Gr\,Pr > 10^8$
			$Gr = \dfrac{g\,\beta\,\Delta t\,H^3}{\nu^2} = \dfrac{g\,\beta\,\Delta t\,\varrho^2\,h^3}{\eta^2}$

o 74
o 75

	on a horizontal plate	$\alpha = \dfrac{Nu\,\lambda}{D}$	$Nu = 0 \cdot 41 \sqrt[4]{Gr\,Pr}$, for $Gr\,Pr > 10^5$
			$Gr = \dfrac{g\,\beta\,\Delta t\,D^3}{\nu^2} = \dfrac{g\,\beta\,\Delta t\,\varrho^2\,D^3}{\eta^2}$

o 76 Fluid properties must be related to reference temperature $t_B = \dfrac{t_w + t_\infty}{2}$

o 77 The expansion coefficient of gases is: $\quad\quad \beta_{gas} = 1/T_\infty$

For forced convection inside pipes (according to Hausen)

o 79
$$\alpha = Nu\,\lambda/d$$

o 80

	laminar $Re < 2000$	$Nu = \left[3 \cdot 65 + \dfrac{0 \cdot 0668 \left(Re\,Pr\,\dfrac{d}{L} \right)}{1 + 0 \cdot 045 \left(Re\,Pr\,\dfrac{d}{L} \right)^{2/3}} \right] \left(\dfrac{\eta_{Fl}}{\eta_W} \right)^{0,14}$

o 81

flow		if $\quad 10^4 > Re\,Pr\,\dfrac{d}{L} > 10^{-1}$, where $Re = \dfrac{\upsilon\,d\,\varrho}{\eta}$
	turbulent $Re > 3000$	$Nu = 0 \cdot 116 (Re^{2/3} - 125) Pr^{1/3} \left[1 + \left(\dfrac{d}{L} \right)^{2/3} \right] \left(\dfrac{\eta_{Fl}}{\eta_W} \right)^{0,14}$
		if $\quad 2320 < Re < 10^6$; $\quad 0 \cdot 6 < Pr < 500$; $1 > L/d < \infty$

With the exception of η_W all material values are related to the mean temperature of the fluid.

For gases factor $(\eta_{Fl}/\eta_W)^{0.14}$ must be omitted.

For radiation (heat transfer coefficient: α_{Str})

o 82
$$\alpha_{Str} = \beta^* \, C_{1,2}$$

o 83
o 84
o 85

	parallel	surfaces	$\beta^* = \dfrac{T_1^* - T_2^4}{T_1 - T_2}$	$C_{1,2} = \dfrac{1}{\dfrac{1}{C_1} + \dfrac{1}{C_2} - \dfrac{1}{C_s}}$
between	enveloping			$C_{1,2} \approx \dfrac{1}{\dfrac{1}{C_1} + \dfrac{A_1}{A_2} \left(\dfrac{1}{C_2} - \dfrac{1}{C_s} \right)}$

[1] α in J/(m^2 s K) or W/(m^2 K)

For explanation of symbols see O 11

Stress

Stress is the ratio of applied force F and cross section A.

Tensile and compressive stresses occur at right angles to the cross section.

p 1
$$\sigma \text{ or } f = \frac{F}{A} \qquad \text{N/mm}^2$$

In calculations | tensile / compressive | stresses are usually | positive / negative

In calculations	tensile	stresses are	positive
	compressive	usually	negative

Shear stresses act along to the cross section.

p 2
$$\tau \text{ or } q = \frac{F}{A} \qquad \text{N/mm}^2$$

Stress-strain diagrams (tensile test)

Materials with

yield point (e.g. mild steel) | plastic yield (e.g. aluminium alloy)

Notation: The standard symbols are from BS 18 and DIN 50145.

p 3
$$R_m = \frac{F}{S_0} \; ; \; \left[\sigma_B = \frac{F}{A_0} \right] \; : \text{ tensile stress, where}$$
F : tensile force
S_0 ; $[A_0]$: original cross section (of unloaded specimen)

p 4
$$\varepsilon = \frac{\Delta L}{L_0} \times 100\% ; \; \left[\varepsilon = \frac{\Delta l}{l_0} \times 100\% \right] \; : \text{ strain, where}$$
L_0 ; $[l_0]$: original length (of unloaded specimen)
ΔL ; $[\Delta l]$: change in length of loaded specimen

continued on P 2

continued from P 1 (stress-strain diagram)

R_p ; $[\sigma_p]$: Proof stress or yield strength (offset)
The limit of proportionality is sometimes known as the elastic limit.

$$\varepsilon_p \doteq 0 \cdot 01\% \Longrightarrow R_{p\,0\cdot01} ; [\sigma_p]$$

Yield point (ferrous metals)

R_{eH} ; $[\sigma_{So}]$: upper yield stress or upper yield point

R_{eL} ; $[\sigma_{Su}]$: lower yield stress or lower yield point.

Proof stress (non-ferrous metals)

$$\varepsilon_p \doteq 0 \cdot 2\% \Longrightarrow R_{0\,0\cdot2} ; [\sigma_{p\,0\cdot2}]$$

p 5

$$R_m = \frac{F_m}{S_o} ; \left[\sigma_B = \frac{F_{max}}{A_o}\right] : \text{tensile strength}$$

p 6

$$A = \frac{\Delta L}{L_o} \times 100\% ; \left[\delta = \frac{\Delta l_{max}}{l_o} \times 100\%\right] : \text{percentage elongation after fracture.}$$

For specimens with circular cross sections, percentage elongations may be quoted, based on gauge lengths, e.g. A_5; $[\delta_5]$ is based

on a gauge length of $\qquad 5 \times \sqrt{\dfrac{4\,S_o}{\pi}}$ mm .

Permissible stress (allowable stress)
Must be below the elastic limit R_p, thus

the permissible stress is: $\quad p_t = \dfrac{R_m}{\nu}$

R_m : yield strength of material
ν : safety factor, always greater than 1.

Ultimate safety factor against fracture)	Proof safety factor (against yield or 0·2 proof)
$\nu = 2 \dots 3 \dots 4$	$\nu = 1 \cdot 2 \dots 1 \cdot 5 \dots 2$

Loads

type	nature of stress	load diagram
I	dead	
II	undulating	
III	alternating	

STRENGTH
Tension, Compression

Modulus of elasticity E: The relationship between σ and ε (Hooke's law) is applicable to the elastic range, i.e. below the elastic limit (see Z 16/17 for values of E). E is known as "Young's modulus".

p 7
$$\sigma = E \times \varepsilon = E \times \angle l/l_0 ; \qquad E = \sigma/\varepsilon = \sigma \times l_0/\Delta l$$

Tensile and compressive stresses σ_t and σ_c

p 8
$$\sigma_t = \frac{F_t}{A} \leqslant p_t ; \qquad \sigma_c = \frac{F_c}{A} \leqslant p_c$$

Strain ε **under tension**

p 9
$$\varepsilon = \frac{\Delta l}{l_0} = \frac{l - l_0}{l_0} = \frac{\sigma_t}{E} = \frac{F_t}{E \times A}$$

Compressive strain ε_c **under compression**

p10
$$\varepsilon_c = \frac{\Delta l}{l_0} = \frac{l_0 - l}{l_0} = \frac{\sigma_c}{E} = \frac{F_c}{E \times A} \quad \begin{vmatrix} E \times A = \text{tensile or compres-} \\ \text{sive stiffness} \end{vmatrix}$$

Transverse contraction under tension (Poisson's ratio)
For circular cross section

p11
$$\mu = \frac{\varepsilon_{cross}}{\varepsilon_{along}} ; \qquad \text{where} \quad \varepsilon_{along} = \frac{l - l_0}{l_0} \quad \text{and} \quad \varepsilon_{cross} = \frac{d_0 - d}{d_0}$$

For most metals Poisson's ratio can be assumed to be $\mu = 0 \cdot 3$

Thermal stresses: Tensile or compressive stress is caused by restricting thermal expansion (see also o 13/14):

p12
$$\sigma_{th} = E \times \varepsilon_{th} = E \times a \times \Delta t \qquad (\varepsilon_{th} = a \times \Delta t)$$

Δt is the temperature difference between the unstressed original state and the state considered.
$\Delta t > 0$ tensile stress, positive.
$\Delta t < 0$ compressive stress, negative.
For prestressed members subjected to thermal stress the total strain comprises:

p13
$$\varepsilon_{tot} = \varepsilon_{el} + \varepsilon_{th} = F/(E \times A) + a \, \Delta t ; \qquad \varepsilon_{el} = F/(E \times A)$$

Tensile and compressive stresses in thin-wall cylinders
(boiler formula):

Hoop stress	$\sigma = p \, d/(2 \, s)$	

p14
p15

Tensile stress	$\sigma = p_i \, d_i /(2 \, s)$	
Compressive stress	$\sigma = -p_a \, d_a /(2 \, s)$	

valid for $\dfrac{d_a}{d_i} \leqslant 1 \cdot 2$

p_i and p_a : internal and external pressures
d_i and d_a : inside and outside diameters
$s = 0 \cdot 5 (d_a - d_i)$: wall thickness

Tensile stresses in rotating bodies: see M 5.

Tensile stress in a shrunk-on ring (approximate formulae)

Shrunk-on ring on a rotating shaft:
The shrinkage force F_H of the ring
must be at least twice the centripetal force F_C.

p 16

$$F_H \geqslant 2\, F_C$$

p 17

$$F_C = m\, y_s\, \omega^2 = 4\, \pi^2\, m\, y_s\, n^2$$

p 18

$$y_s = \frac{4}{3\,\pi} \times \frac{R^3 - r^3}{R^2 - r^2}$$

p 19

Cross section $\qquad A = \dfrac{F_H}{2\, p_t}$

p 20

Shrinkage allowance $\qquad \lambda = \dfrac{1}{E}\, D_m \times p_t$

(λ = outside diameter of shaft – inside diameter of ring)

Shrunk-on ring for clamping

Split, rotating clamped parts.

F_C comprises:
Centripetal force F_{CR} for ring
Centripetal force F_{CM} for clamped parts,

Clamped parts

Ring

p 21

or $\qquad F_H \geqslant 2\left(F_{CR} + F_{CM}\right)$; $\qquad$ then as p 19 and p 20

Energy of deformation U (Strain energy)
The energy stored in a deformed component is:

p 22

$$U = w\, V \text{ ; where}$$

p 23

$$w = \frac{1}{2}\, \sigma\, \varepsilon = \frac{1}{2}\, E\, \varepsilon^2 = \frac{\sigma^2}{2\, E} \quad ; \quad V : \text{volume of component}$$

Limit cross section for similar types of stress
Where a tension (or compression) force is applied at a point
within the dotted core area, only tension (or compression)
forces will occur over the whole cross section. If applied at
any other point, bending stress, i.e. simultaneous tension
and compression stress will occur.

p 24

$$x = \frac{a}{6} \qquad u = \frac{b}{6} \; ; \; v = \frac{h}{6} \qquad r = \frac{D}{8} \qquad r = \frac{D}{8}\left[1 + \left(\frac{d}{D}\right)^2\right]$$

S : centre of mass of half ring (see K 7)
D_m : mean diameter ($D_m = R + r$)

STRENGTH
Loads in beams

Explanation

All external loads on a beam (including support reactions and its own weight) produce internal forces and moments which stress the material. By taking a section through the beam at a point x it is possible to show the internal loads: Vertical shear forces V and bending moments M.

End loads P and torsion T are considered separately.

Referring to the x–y **plane** (z axis is at right angles):

Forces in direction of	x-axis		end loads	P
	y-axis	produce	shear forces	V
Moments about the	z-axis		bending moments	M
	x-axis		torsion	T

Always consider the left-hand side of the section.

In each part of the beam there must be equilibrium between all external and internal forces and moments:

Considered separately:

*5/26
$$V + \sum_{i=1}^{n} V_i = 0 \qquad\qquad P + \sum_{i=1}^{n} P_i = 0$$

*7/28
$$M + \sum_{i=1}^{n} M_i = 0 \qquad\qquad T + \sum_{i=1}^{n} T_i = 0$$

Method of calculation

1. Calculate the reactions.
2. Section the beam at the following places:
    2.1 Points of action of point loads W and beginning and end of distributed loads w.
    2.2 Points where the beam axis changes direction or the cross section changes.
    2.3 Any other convenient places.

continued on P 6

continued from P 5

3. Find the forces and moments on the left hand side of the section as in p 25 ... p 28
4. Plot shear force and bending moment diagrams.

Relations between w V **and** M **at any point** x

29/30

$$\frac{dM}{dx} = V \qquad \Big| \qquad \frac{dV}{dx} = -w$$

Rules:

M is a maximum when $\qquad V = 0$

In sections with no loads $\qquad V = $ constant.

Example: Simply supported beam with end load. (Fixed at A)
The reactions are:

$$R_A = 2 \cdot 5 \text{kN}; \qquad P_A = 3 \text{ kN}; \qquad R_B = 1 \cdot 5 \text{ kN}$$

Calculations see P 7

continued from P 6

0 < x < 1 m from equation p...				1 m < x < 4 m from equation p...				4 m < x < 6 m from equation p...			
27	26	29	25	27	26	29	25	27	26	29	25
*)				*)				**)		*)	**)

0 < x < 1 m (column 27):

$$M - R_A \times x = 0 \; ; \quad M = R_A \times x = 2.5 \text{ kN} \times x$$
$$V - R_A = 0 \; ; \quad V = R_A = 2.5 \text{ kN} = \text{const.}$$
$$\text{or } V = \frac{d}{dx}(2.5 \text{ kN} \times x) = 2.5 \text{ kN} = \text{const.}$$
$$P + P_A = 0 \; ; \quad P = -P_A = -3 \text{ kN}$$

1 m < x < 4 m (column 27):

$$M - R_A \times x + W(x - 1\text{m}) + P_1 \times 1\text{m} = 0 \; ; \quad M = 0.5 \text{ kN } x - 1 \text{ kN m}$$
$$V - R_A + W = 0 \; ; \quad V = R_A - W = 2.5 \text{ kN} - 2 \text{ kN} = 0.5 \text{ kN} = \text{const.}$$
$$\text{or } V = \frac{d}{dx}(0.5 \text{ kN} \times x - 1 \text{ kN m}) = 0.5 \text{ kN} = \text{const.}$$
$$P + P_A - P_1 = 0 \; ; \quad P = P_1 - P_A = 3 \text{ kN} - 3 \text{ kN} = 0$$

4 m < x < 6 m (column 27):

$$M - R_A \times x + W(x - 1\text{m}) + P_1 \times 1\text{m} + w\frac{(x - 4\text{m})^2}{2} = 0$$
$$M = -9 \text{ kNm} + 4.5 \text{ kN} \times x - 0.5 \frac{\text{kN}}{\text{m}} \times x^2$$
$$V - R_A + W + w(x - 4\text{m}) = 0 \; ; \quad V = R_A - W - w(x - 4\text{m}) = 2.5 \text{ kN} - 2 \text{ kN} - 1\frac{\text{kN}}{\text{m}}(x - 4\text{m}) = 4.5 \text{ kN} - 1\frac{\text{kN}}{\text{m}} x$$
$$\text{or } V = \frac{d}{dx}\left(-9 \text{ kNm} + 4.5 \text{ kN } x - 0.5 \frac{\text{kN}}{\text{m}} x^2\right) = 4.5 \text{ kN} - 1 \frac{\text{kN}}{\text{m}} x$$
$$P + P_A - P_1 = 0 \; ; \quad P = P_1 - P_A = 3 \text{ kN} - 3 \text{ kN} = 0$$

*) Straight line
**) Parabola

continued on P 8

continued from P 7

Example:
Curved cantilever beam
(r = const.)

The limits are: $0 \leqslant \varphi \leqslant 90°$
        or: $0 \leqslant s \leqslant r\,\dfrac{\pi}{2}$

Bending moment:

p 31 $M + F_1\,r(1-\cos\varphi) + F_2\,r\sin\varphi = 0$

p 32 $M = -F_1\,r + F_1\,r\cos\varphi - F_2\,r\sin\varphi$

At the section φ, F_1 and F_2
are resolved into tangential
and radial components.

Shear force (radial):

p 33 $F_q + F_1\sin\varphi + F_2\cos\varphi = 0$

p 34 $F_q = -F_1\sin\varphi - F_2\cos\varphi;$ or from p 30:

p 35 $F_q = \dfrac{dM}{ds} = \dfrac{1}{r}\times\dfrac{dM}{d\varphi}$ (because $s = r\,\varphi$; $ds = r\,d\varphi$)

p 36 $= \dfrac{1}{r}\times\dfrac{d(-F_1\,r + F_1\,r\cos\varphi - F_2\,r\sin\varphi)}{d\varphi} = -F_1\sin\varphi - F_2\cos\varphi$

Normal force (tangential):

p 37 $F_n - F_1\times\cos\varphi + F_2\times\sin\varphi = 0$

p 38 $F_n = F_1\times\cos\varphi - F_2\times\sin\varphi$

For a graphical method of determining bending moment see K 4.

STRENGTH

Bending

P 9

Maximum bending stress

p 39

$$\sigma_{bt\,max} = \frac{M\,y_{max}}{I_{xx}}$$

p 40

$$= \frac{M}{Z_{min}} \leqslant p_b$$

Values for p_b see Z 16/17

$$\left.\begin{array}{l} +y_{max}\ \text{(tension)} \\[6pt] -y_{max}\ \text{(compression)} \end{array}\right\}\ \begin{array}{l}\text{distance from surface fibre to the }x\text{-axis pass-}\\ \text{ing through the centroid }S\text{ or neutral axis}\end{array}$$

I_{xx} : Second moment of area about axis S_z or about plane of neutral axis.

Bending stress at distance y from the neutral axis

p 41

$$\sigma_b = \frac{M}{I}\,y$$

Section modulus Z_{min}

p 42

$$Z_{min} = \frac{I}{y_{max}}$$

Second moments of area

Axial second moment of area see J 10 and table P 10
Polar second moment of area see J 10
Product moment   see J 10

Principal second moments of area and principal axes

The principal second moments of area
$I_1 = I_{max}$ and $I_2 = I_{min}$ are applicable
to asymmetric sections, when the
principal axes are rotated through
the angle φ_o.

p 43

$$I_1 = I_{\substack{max\\min}} = \frac{1}{2}(I_y + I_x) \pm \frac{1}{2}\sqrt{(I_y - I_x)^2 + 4 I_{xy}^2}$$

p 44

$$\tan 2\varphi_o = \frac{2 I_{xy}}{I_y - I_x}$$

For calculations of I_{xy} see J 10/11.
The principal axes are always perpendicular to each other.
The axis of symmetry of a symmetrical section is one principal
axis e.g. $I_1 = I_x$.

Values of I and Z for some common sections

(see p 41 and p 42)

For position of centroid S (or neutral axis) see K 7

	I_x and I_y	Z_x and Z_y	Cross section A
p 45	$I_x = \dfrac{b\,d^3}{12}$	$Z_x = \dfrac{b\,h^2}{6}$	
p 46	$I_y = \dfrac{d\,b^3}{12}$	$Z_y = \dfrac{h\,b^2}{6}$	
p 47	$I_x = I_y = \dfrac{\pi\,D^4}{64}$	$Z_x = Z_y = \dfrac{\pi\,D^3}{32} \simeq \dfrac{D^3}{10}$	
p 48	$I_x = I_y = \dfrac{\pi}{64}(D^4 - d^4)$	$Z_x = Z_y$ $= \dfrac{\pi}{32} \times \dfrac{D^4 - d^4}{D} \simeq \dfrac{D^4 - d^4}{10D}$	
p 49 p 50 p 51 p 52	$I_x = I_y = 0{\cdot}06014\ s^4$ $= 0{\cdot}5412\ R^4$	$Z_x = Z_y$ $= 0{\cdot}1203\ s^3$ $= 0{\cdot}6250\ R^3$ $Z_y = 0{\cdot}1042\ s^3$ $= 0{\cdot}5413\ R^3$	
p 53 p 54	$I_x = \dfrac{\pi\,a\,b^3}{4}$ $I_y = \dfrac{\pi\,a^3\,b}{4}$	$Z_x = \dfrac{\pi\,a\,b^2}{4}$ $Z_y = \dfrac{\pi\,a^2\,b}{4}$	
p 55 p 56	$I_x = \dfrac{b\,h^3}{36}$ $I_y = \dfrac{b^3\,h}{48}$	$Z_x = \dfrac{b\,h^2}{24}$ $Z_y = \dfrac{b^2\,h}{24}$	
p 57 p 58 p 59	$I_x = \dfrac{h^3}{36} \times \dfrac{(a+b)^2 + 2ab}{a+b}$ $y_{max} = \dfrac{h}{3} \times \dfrac{2a+b}{a+b}$ $y_{min} = \dfrac{h}{3} \times \dfrac{a+2b}{a+b}$	$Z_x = \dfrac{h^2}{12} \times \dfrac{(a+b)^2 + 2ab}{2a+b}$	

Steiner's theorem

(Parallel axis theorem for second moments of area).

centroid axis

p 60	$I_{B\text{-}B} = I_x + A\,a^2$	

Beams of uniform cross section

Equation of the elastic curve

The following apply to each section of the beam (see P 5, Method of calculation, Item 2):

p 61
$$\frac{d^2y}{dx^2} = y'' = -\frac{M}{E\,I} = -\frac{1}{R}$$

p 62
$$E \times I \times y'' = -M$$

p 63
$$E \times I\, \frac{dy}{dx} = E \times I \times y' = -\int M\,dx + C_1$$

p 64
$$E \times I \times y = -\int\!\!\int M\,dx \times dx + C_1 \times x + C_2$$

R : radius of curvature of the elastic curve at point x.

p 65
$y' = \tan \varphi$: inclination of the tangent to the elastic curve at point x.

y = deflection of beam at point x.

C_1 and C_2 are constants of integration and are determined from known factors.

e.g. $y = 0$ at the support.

$y_i = y_{i+1}$ at junction between sections i and $(i + 1)$.

$y' = 0$ at the support of a cantilever beam and at the centre of a beam with symmetrical loading.

$y'_i = y'_{i+1}$ at the junction between sections i and $(i + 1)$.

Strain energy due to bending U:

For a beam of length l:

p 66
$$U = \frac{1}{2}\int_0^l \frac{M^2}{E\,I}\,dx$$

A beam with discontinuous loads may be divided into n length:

p 67
$$U_{\text{tot}} = \frac{1}{2\,E}\left(\int_{x_1=0}^{x_1=l_1} \frac{M^2}{I_1}\,dx_1 + \ldots + \int_{x_n=0}^{x_n=l_n} \frac{M^2}{I_n}\,dx_n\right)$$

STRENGTH

Deflection of beams in bending

P 12

	Deflection at C, y_c / Max. y_m (p 68)	Deflection, y / Slope, $y' = \tan\varphi$ (p 69)	M_{max} at point (...) (p 70)	Support reactions (p 71)	Loading
Case 1	$y_m = \dfrac{W l^3}{3EI}$	$y = \dfrac{W l^3}{6EI}\left(2 - 3\dfrac{x}{l} + \dfrac{x^3}{l^3}\right)$; $\tan\varphi_B = -\dfrac{W l^2}{2EI}$	$W l$ (A)	$R_A = W$; $M_A = W l$	
Case 2	$y_c = \dfrac{W l^3}{3EI}\dfrac{a^2}{l^2}\dfrac{b^2}{l^2}$; Max $y_m = v_1\dfrac{l+b}{3h}\sqrt{\dfrac{l+b}{3a}}$ at point $x_1 = a\sqrt{\dfrac{l+b}{3a}}$	$y_1 = \dfrac{W l^3}{6EI}\dfrac{a}{l}\dfrac{b^2}{l^2}\dfrac{x_1}{l}\left(1 + \dfrac{l}{b} - \dfrac{x_1^2}{ab}\right)$; $y_2 = \dfrac{W l^3}{6EI}\dfrac{b}{l}\dfrac{a^2}{l^2}\dfrac{x_2}{l}\left(1 + \dfrac{l}{a} - \dfrac{x_2^2}{ab}\right)$; $\tan\varphi_A = \dfrac{y_c}{2a}\left(1+\dfrac{l}{b}\right)$; $\tan\varphi_B = \dfrac{y_c}{2b}\left(1+\dfrac{l}{a}\right)$	$W\dfrac{ab}{l}$ (C)	$R_A = W\dfrac{b}{l}$; $R_B = W\dfrac{a}{l}$	Note $a > b$
Case 3	$y_c = \dfrac{R_B l^3}{6EI}\left(3\dfrac{b}{l} - \dfrac{b^3}{l^3}\right) - \dfrac{W a^2 b}{2EI}$	$y_1 = \dfrac{R_B l^3}{6EI}\left(3\dfrac{x_1}{l} - \dfrac{x_1^3}{l^3}\right) - \dfrac{W a^2 x_1}{2EI}$; $y_2 = \dfrac{W a^3}{6EI}\left(2 - 2\dfrac{x_2}{l} + \dfrac{x_2^3}{a^3}\right) - \dfrac{R_B l^3}{6EI}\left(2 - 3\dfrac{x_2}{l} + \dfrac{x_2^3}{l^3}\right)$; $\tan\varphi_B = -W a^2 b/(4EI\,l)$	M_A (A); when $b = 0.414\,l$: $0.171\,Wl$ (C); $0.1/1\,Wl$ (A)	$R_A = W - R_B$; $R_B = W\dfrac{a^2}{l^2}\left(\dfrac{a}{l} + \dfrac{3b}{2l}\right)$; $(M_A) = W\dfrac{l+b}{2}\dfrac{a}{l}\dfrac{b}{l}$	Note $a > b$
Case 4	$y_m = \dfrac{2W l^3}{3EI}\dfrac{b^3}{l^3}\dfrac{a^2}{l^2}\left(\dfrac{l}{2b+l}\right)^2$ at point $x_1 = \dfrac{2l\,b}{2b+l}$; $y_c = \dfrac{W}{3EI}\dfrac{a^3 b^3}{l^3}$	$y_1 = \dfrac{W}{6EI}\dfrac{b^2}{l^2}\left(3ax_1^2 - 3x_1^3 + 2\dfrac{b}{a}x_1^3\right)$; $y_2 = \dfrac{W}{6EI}\dfrac{a^2}{l^2}\left(3bx_2^2 - 3x_2^3 + 2\dfrac{a}{b}x_2^3\right)$; $\tan\varphi_A = \tan\varphi_B = 0$	$-Wa\dfrac{b^2}{l^2}$ (A); $-Wb\dfrac{a^2}{l^2}$ (B); $2WL\dfrac{a^2}{l^2}\dfrac{b^2}{l^2}$ (C)	$R_A = W\dfrac{b^2}{l^2}\left(3 - 2\dfrac{b}{l}\right)$; $R_B = W\dfrac{a^2}{l^2}\left(3 - 2\dfrac{a}{l}\right)$; $M_A = W a\dfrac{b^2}{l^2}$; $M_B = W b\dfrac{a^2}{l^2}$	Note $a < b$

STRENGTH
Deflection of beams in bending

P 13

Loading (p 75)	Support reactions (p 75)	M_{max} at point (…) (p 74)	Deflection, y — Slope, $y' = \tan\varphi$ (p 73)	Deflection (p 72)	at C, y_c — Max. y_m (p 72)
(overhang beam, load W at C, span l, overhang a)	$R_A = W\dfrac{a}{l}$ $\quad R_B = W\!\left(1+\dfrac{a}{l}\right)$	$-Wa$ (B)	$y_1 = \dfrac{Wa\,l^2}{6EI}\left(\dfrac{x_1^3}{l^3} - \dfrac{x_1}{l}\right)$ $\;\;$ $y_2 = \dfrac{W}{6EI}\left(2a\,l\,x_2 + 3a\,x_2^2 - x_2^3\right) = -\dfrac{Wa\,l}{3EI}$ $\;\;$ $\tan\varphi_A = -\dfrac{Wa\,l}{6EI}$; $\tan\varphi_B = \dfrac{Wa\,l}{3EI}$ $\;\;$ $\tan\varphi_C = \dfrac{Wa}{6EI}(2l+3a)$	$y_{m1} = -\dfrac{Wa\,l^2}{9\sqrt3\,EI}$ at point $x_1 = 0.577\,l$ $\;\;$ $y_{m2} = y_c = \dfrac{Wa^2}{3EI}(l+a)$	
(cantilever, $w = $ const.)	$R_A = wl$ $\quad (M_A) = \dfrac{1}{2}wl^2$	$\dfrac{1}{2}wl^2$ (A)	$y = \dfrac{wl^4}{24EI}\left(\dfrac{x^4}{l^4} - 4\dfrac{x}{l} + 3\right)$ $\;\;$ $\tan\varphi_B = -\dfrac{wl^3}{6EI}$	$y_m = \dfrac{wl^4}{8EI}$	
(simply supported, $w = $ const.)	$R_A = \dfrac{1}{2}wl$ $\quad R_B = \dfrac{wl}{2}$	$\dfrac{wl^2}{8}$ (C)	$y = \dfrac{wl^4}{24EI}\dfrac{x}{l}\left(1 - 2\dfrac{x^2}{l^2} + \dfrac{x^3}{l^3}\right)$ $\;\;$ $\tan\varphi_A = -\tan\varphi_B = \dfrac{wl^3}{24EI}$	$y_m = \dfrac{5\,wl^4}{384\,EI}$	
(propped cantilever, $w = $ const.)	$R_B = \dfrac{3}{8}wl$ $\quad R_A = \dfrac{5}{8}wl$ $\quad (M_A) = \dfrac{1}{8}wl^2$	M_A (A)	$y = \dfrac{wl^4}{48EI}\left(\dfrac{x}{l} - 3\dfrac{x^3}{l^3} + 2\dfrac{x^4}{l^4}\right)$ $\;\;$ $\tan\varphi_B = -\dfrac{wl^3}{48EI}$	$y_m = \dfrac{wl^4}{185\,EI}$ at point $x = 0.4215\,l$	
(fixed–fixed, $w = $ const.)	$R_A = w \times l/2$ $\quad R_B = w \times l/2$ $\quad M_A = w \times l^2/12$ $\quad M_B = w \times l^2/12$	$\dfrac{wl^2}{12}$ (A,B) $\;\;$ $\dfrac{wl^2}{24}$ (C)	$y = \dfrac{wl^4}{24EI}\left(\dfrac{x^2}{l^2} - 2\dfrac{x^3}{l^3} + \dfrac{x^4}{l^4}\right)$ $\;\;$ $\tan\varphi_A = \tan\varphi_B = 0$	$y_m = \dfrac{wl^4}{384\,EI}$	

Formulae for y and y_m do not allow for shear deflection.

Mohr's analogy

Graphical method

1. Determine the bending moment curve by constructing a link polygon (see also K 4).

Fig. 1

2. Construct a link polygon as the equivalent distributed load w^* on the "equivalent beam". Another link polygon will give the tangents to the elastic curve.

Fig. 2

3. Deflection of the original beam at point x:

p 76
$$y = h^* \frac{H H^*}{E I} m_F \, m_A \, m_L^3.$$

Slope at support A and B:

p 77
$$\tan \varphi_A = R_A^* \frac{H}{E I} m_F \, m_A \, m_L^2 \quad \text{resp.} \quad \tan \varphi_B = R_B^* \frac{H}{E I} m_F \, m_A \, m_L^2$$

Mathematical method

1. Calculate the equivalent support reaction R_A^* of the "equivalent beam" carrying the equivalent distributed load $w^* = A_1 + \ldots + A_n$ (see fig. 2).

p 78

2. Calculate the equivalent bending moment M^* and the equivalent shear force V^* at the point x:

p 79
$$M^* = R_A^* z - A \, z_A \; ; \qquad V^* = R_A^* - A \qquad \text{(see fig. 1 + 2)}$$

x_A : Distance between c of g of equivalent distributed load A and the section x.

p 80

3. Deflection $\qquad y = M^*/E I \; ; \qquad$ Slope $\qquad y = V^*/E I$

continued on P 15

continued from P 14 (Mohr's analogy)

Choice of equivalent beam

The supports of the equivalent beam must be such that its maximum equivalent bending moment M^*_{max} coincides with the point of maximum deflection in the original beam.

	Original beam	Equivalent beam
Simple beam	A △ —————— △ B	A △ —————— △ B
Cantilever beam	A ————— ⌇B	A ⌇————— B

Beam of varying cross section

Fig. 1
Original beam
e.g. shaft

Plot the bending moment curve as the equivalent distributed load $w^*(z)$ on a uniform equivalent beam of cross section equal to the maximum second moment of area $I_{x\,max}$ of the original beam. (See P 14, item 1).

Plot $w^*(z)$ according to the ratio $\dfrac{I_{x\,max}}{I_x(z)}$:

Fig. 2
Equivalent beam
of the shaft
in Fig. 1

Then calculate according to P 14 (items 2 and 3) or p 78 ... p 80.

Beams of uniform strength

	maximum section dimension	typical dimension $x =$ resp. $y =$	maximum deflection f	type of beam
p 82	$h = \sqrt{\dfrac{6\,W\,l}{b\,p_{bt}}}$	$\sqrt{\dfrac{6\,W\,x}{b\,p_{bt}}}$	$\dfrac{8\,W}{b\,E}\left(\dfrac{l}{h}\right)^3$	
p 83	$b = \dfrac{6\,W\,l}{h^2\,p_{bt}}$	$\dfrac{6\,W\,x}{h^2\,p_{bt}}$	$\dfrac{6\,W}{b\,E}\left(\dfrac{l}{h}\right)^3$	
p 84	$h = \sqrt{\dfrac{3\,w\,l^2}{b\,p_{bt}}}$	$x\sqrt{\dfrac{3\,w\,l}{b\,l\,p_{bt}}}$	$\dfrac{3\,w\,l}{b\,E}\left(\dfrac{l}{h}\right)^3$	
p 85	$b = \dfrac{3\,w\,l^2}{h^2\,p_{bt}}$	$\dfrac{3\,w\,l\,x^2}{h^2\,l\,p_{bt}}$		
p 86	$h = \sqrt{\dfrac{3\,w\,l^2}{4\,b\,p_{bt}}}$	$\sqrt{\dfrac{3\,w\,l^2}{4\,b\,p_{bt}}\left(1-\dfrac{4x^2}{l^2}\right)}$	$\dfrac{w\,l^4}{64\,E\,I}$	
p 87	$d = \sqrt[3]{\dfrac{32\,W\,l}{\pi\,p_{bt}}}$	$\sqrt[3]{\dfrac{32\,W\,x}{\pi\,p_{bt}}}$	$\dfrac{192}{5}x\dfrac{W\,l^3}{E\,\pi\,d^4}$	

W	: point load	kN
w	: uniformly distributed load	kN/m
p_{bt}	: permissible bending stress	N/mm² (see Z 17)

Fig. 1

Fig. 2

1st subsystem

2nd subsystem

Convert a statically indeterminate beam (fig. 1) into a statically determinate one (fig. 2) by replacing one support by its support reaction (R_C in fig. 2).

Divide into two separate beams or subsystems. Determine the deflections at the point of the statically indeterminate support (see P 11 to P 15) from each subsystem, in terms of R_C.

Since no deflection can occur at support C:

$$|y_{c1}| = |y_{c2}|$$

Hence, calculate the support force at C, R_C and then the remaining support reactions.

Method of solution for simple statically indeterminate beams

Statically indeterminate beam	Statically determinate beam	1st subsystem	2nd subsystem
W_1 C W_2 A $\triangle$ $\triangle$ B	W_1 C W_2 A R_C B	W_1 W_2 A B y_{c1}	y_{c2} A R_C B
W_1 C W_2 A $\triangle$ B	W_1 C W_2 A R_B B	W_1 C W_2 A B y_{B1}	y_{B2} A C B R_B
W A B	W A B R_A	W A B y_{A1}	y_{A2} A B R_A
w A C B $\frac{l}{2}$ $\frac{l}{2}$	M_A w M_B A C B	w A C B y_{c1}	y_{c2} A C B M_A M_B

$\uparrow$ $\uparrow$: statically indeterminate support reactions and moments

Hooke's law for shear stress

p 89 q or $\tau = G\,\gamma$

 G : shear modulus
 γ : shear strain

Relation between shear modulus and modulus of elasticity or Young's modulus

p 90 $G = \dfrac{E}{2(1+\mu)} \cong 0.385\,E$; correspond to P 3 with $\mu = 0.3$

Mean shear stress c_f or τ_f

p 91 q_f or $\tau_f = \dfrac{F}{A} \leqslant p_q$

Permissible shear strength p_q (for values see Z 16)

type of load (see P 2)		p_q $\cong$	
	dead		$p_t/1.5$
	undulating		$p_t/2.2$
	alternating		$p_t/3.0$

Ultimate shear stress q_s

p 92 $q_s = \dfrac{Q_{max}}{A}$

 for ductile metals: $q_s = 0.8\,R_m$
 for cast iron: $q_s = R_m$

Shearing force Q

	applied by	
guillotine shears	cutting tools (punch …)	
$Q \cong 1.2\,q_s\,l\,s$	$Q \cong 1.2\,q_s\,l_p\,s$	

p 93 l : length of cut; l_p : perimeter of cut

Theorem of related shear stresses

 The shear stresses on two perpendicular faces of an element are equal in magnitude, perpendicular to their common edge and act either towards it or away from it.

p 94 $q = q'$

 q : transverse shear stress (transverse to beam axis) resulting from shear forces Q
 q' : axial shear stress (parallel to beam axis) "complementary shear"

STRENGTH
Shear

Axial shear stress due to shear forces

p 95
$$q = \frac{Q M}{b I} = q'$$

p 96
$$M = \Delta A \, y_s$$

$q = 0$ for $\sigma_b = \sigma_{b\,max}$.
q_{max} occurs when $\sigma_b = 0$.
i. e. on neutral axis.

Max. shear stress for different cross sections

$$q_{max} = q'_{max} = k \frac{Q}{A}$$

	A ▭	A ⊘	A ⊙
p 97	k	$\dfrac{3}{2}$	$\dfrac{4}{3}$	$\dfrac{4}{3} \times \dfrac{d_\alpha^2 + d_\alpha \, d_i + d_i^2}{d_\alpha^2 + d_i^2}$ for thin-wall tubes: 2 ($d_\alpha \approx d_i$)

Strain energy u due to shear

p 98
$$u = \frac{1}{2} q \, \gamma = \frac{q^2}{2 G}$$

Shear deflection of a beam

p 99
$$y = \varkappa \frac{M}{G A} + C = \varkappa \frac{2 \cdot 6 \, M}{E A} + C$$

Determine the constant C from known factors, e. g. $y = 0$ at the supports.

p100
The factor $\varkappa = A \displaystyle\int_{(A)} \left[\frac{M}{b I} \right]^2 dA$ allows for the form of cross section. For example:

	▱	◉	I 80	I 240	I 500
$\varkappa =$	1·2	1·1	2·4	2·1	2·0

Q : shear force at point x of the beam
M : bending moment at the section A
I : second moment of area of the total cross section A about the z axis
b : width of section at point y
$S_{\Delta A}$: centre of area of section ΔA

General

p 101   Shear stress due torsion $\tau_t = \dfrac{T\,a}{J} \leqslant p_{qt}$

p 102   Torque $T = \dfrac{P}{\omega} = \dfrac{P}{2\,\pi\,n} = F\,a$

P : power

a : distance from surface fibre to centre of mass

J : torsion constant; formulae see P 21 (attention: torsion constant is not the polar moment of inertia; only for circular cross section $J = I_p$, $a = D/2$).

Bars of circular cross section

Angle of twist φ (see e 5)

p 104 $\varphi = \dfrac{T\,l}{I_p\,G} = \dfrac{180°}{\pi} \times \dfrac{T\,l}{I_p\,G}$

Stepped shafts:

p 105 $\varphi = \dfrac{T}{G} \sum\limits_{i=1}^{n} \dfrac{l_i}{I_{pi}}$

p 106 $= \dfrac{180°}{\pi} \times \dfrac{T}{G} \times \sum\limits_{i=1}^{n} \dfrac{l_i}{I_{pi}}$

polar moment of inertia I_p	max. shear stress τ_t	cross section
107 $\dfrac{\pi\,D^4}{32}$	$\widehat{=}\ 5 \cdot 1\,\dfrac{T}{D^3}$	
108 $\dfrac{\pi}{32}(D^4 - d^4)$	$\widehat{=}\ 5 \cdot 1\ T\,\dfrac{D}{D^4 - d^4}$	

Bars of non-circular, solid or thin-wall hollow section

109   **Angle of twist** $\varphi = \dfrac{T\,l}{I_t\,G} = \dfrac{180°}{\pi} \times \dfrac{T\,l}{I_t\,G}$

torsion constant J	position and magnitude of τ_t	cross section
110 $c_1\,h\,b^3$	in 1: $\tau_{t1} = \tau_{t\,max}$ $= \dfrac{c_2\,T}{c_1\,h\,b^2}$ in 2: $\tau_{t2} = c_3\,\tau_{t\,max}$ in 3: $\tau_{t3} = 0$	

$h/b =$	1	1·5	2	3	4	6	8	10	∞
c_1	0·141	0·196	0·229	0·263	0·281	0·298	0·307	0·312	0·333
c_2	0·675	0·852	0·928	0·977	0·990	0·997	0·999	1·000	1·000
c_3	1·000	0·858	0·796	0·753	0·745	0·743	0·743	0·743	0·743

continued on P 21

STRENGTH
Torsion

	torsion constant J	position and magnitude of τ_t	cross section
111 112 113	$\dfrac{a^4}{46\cdot19} \simeq \dfrac{h^4}{26}$	at 1: $\tau_{t1} = \tau_{t\,max}$ $= \dfrac{20\,T}{a^3} \approx \dfrac{13\,T}{h^3}$ at 2: $\tau_{t2} = 0$	
114 115	$0\cdot1154\,s^4$ $= 0\cdot0649\,d^4$	at 1: $\tau_{t1} = \tau_{t\,max}$ $= 5\cdot297\dfrac{T}{s^3}$ $= 8\cdot157\dfrac{T}{d^3}$	
116 117	$\dfrac{\pi}{16}\times\dfrac{D^3\;d^3}{D^2+d^2}$	at 1: $\tau_{t1} = \tau_{t\,max}$ $\simeq 5\cdot1\dfrac{T}{D\,d^2}$ at 2: $\tau_{t2} = \tau_{t\,max}\dfrac{d}{D}$	
118 119 120	$\dfrac{\pi}{16}\times\dfrac{n^3(d^4-d_i^4)}{n^2+1}$ $D/d = D_i/d_i = n \geqslant 1$	at 1: $\tau_{t1} = \tau_{t\,max}$ $\simeq 5\cdot1\dfrac{T\,d}{n(d^4-d_i^4)}$ at 2: $\tau_{t2} = \tau_{t\,max}\dfrac{d}{D}$	
121 122 123	with varying wall thickness: $\dfrac{4\,A_m^{\,2}}{\displaystyle\sum_{i=1}^{n}\dfrac{s_i}{t_i}}$	at 1: $\tau_{t1} = \tau_{t\,max}$ $= \dfrac{T}{2\,A_m\,t_{min}}$ at i: $\tau_{t2} = \dfrac{T}{2\,A_m\,t_i}$	median line
124	with thin, uniform wall: $\dfrac{4\,A_m^{\,2}\,t}{s_m}$	$\tau_t = \dfrac{T}{2\,A_m\,t}$	

125	$\dfrac{\eta}{3}\displaystyle\sum_{i=1}^{n} b_i^3\,h_i$	$\tau_{t\,max} = \dfrac{T\,b_{max}}{I_t}$ midway along the long side h of the rectangular section of max. thickness b_{max} (e.g. position 1 in the sketch).	profiles built up of rectangular cross sections

Föppl's factor:

	I $n=3$	L $n=2$	$\perp$ $n=2$
η	$\simeq 1\cdot3$	$\simeq 1\cdot0$	$1\cdot12$
	C $n=3$	$+$ $n=2$	
η	$1 < \eta < 1\cdot3$	$1\cdot17$	

A_m : area enclosed by the median line
s : length of the median line
t (t_{min}) : wall thickness, (min. wall thickness)
s_i : part length of median line when wall thickness $t_i = $ const.

Euler's formula

Applies for elastic instability of struts. Minimum load P_e at which buckling occurs:

p 126

$$P_e = \pi^2 \frac{E \, I_{min}}{l_k^2}$$

p 127	$l_k = 2\,l$	$l_k = l$	$l_k = 0.707\,l$	$l_k = 0.5\,l$
p 128	Permissible working load		$F = P_e / \nu_k$	
p 129	Slenderness ratio		$\lambda = \dfrac{l}{k} = l\sqrt{\dfrac{A}{I_{min}}}$	

Limit 1 based on $R_{p0.01}$	Limit 2 based on $R_{p0.2}$
p 130 $\lambda_{\lim 0.01} = \pi\sqrt{\dfrac{E}{R_{p\,0.01}}}$	$\lambda_{\lim 0.2} = \pi\sqrt{\dfrac{E}{R_{p\,0.2}}}$

Tetmajer formula

Valid in the range $\qquad R_{p\,0.01} \leqslant \dfrac{P_e}{A} \leqslant R_{p\,0.2}$

Material of strut fails due to bending and compression

p 131

$$p_t = \frac{F}{A} = a - b\lambda + c\lambda^2 = p_c\,\nu_k$$

Material			a	b	c	valid
	GB-Standard	US. ASTM	N/mm^2			for $\lambda =$
mild steel	BS 970, 050 A20	A 283 Gr. C	289	0.818	0	80...100
mild steel	BS 970, 080 M30	A 440	589	3.918	0	60...100
cast iron	BS 1452–220	A 43 A 258	776	12.000	0.053	5... 80
timber			30	0.20	0	2...100
beach or oak			38	0.25	0	0...100

Calculation method

First determine the minimum second moment of area using the Euler formula:

p 132

$$I_{min} = \frac{P_e\,l_k^2}{\pi^2 E} \; ; \quad P_e = \nu_k \times F.$$

Then select a suitable cross section, e.g. circular tube, solid rectangle, etc., and find I and A.

continued on P 23

Continued from P 22

ν_k = 3 ... 5 in the Tetmajer range
$\dfrac{\nu_k}{\nu_k}$ $\begin{array}{l} = 4 ... 6 \\ = 6 ... 8 \end{array}$ in the Euler range $\left|\begin{array}{l} \text{for large} \\ \text{for small} \end{array}\right|$ structures

$\left.\begin{array}{l} \text{Present} \\ \text{Limiting} \end{array}\right|$ slenderness ratio $\left|\dfrac{\lambda}{\lambda_{\lim 0\cdot 01} \text{ and } \lambda_{\lim 0\cdot 2}}\right|$ calculate from $\left|\begin{array}{l} \text{p 129} \\ \text{p 130} \end{array}\right.$

Determine buckling and compressive stress as follows:

$$\text{If} \quad \lambda \quad \geqslant \lambda_{\lim 0\cdot 01} \qquad \text{use p 127}$$
$$\lambda_{\lim 0\cdot 01} > \quad \lambda \quad \geqslant \lambda_{\lim 0\cdot 2} \qquad \text{use p 131}$$
$$\lambda \quad < \quad \lambda_{\lim 0\cdot 2} \qquad \text{use p 8.}$$

If $P_e < F \, \nu_k$. redesign with larger cross section.

Method of buckling coefficient ω (DIN 4114)
Specified for building and bridge construction, steelwork and cranes.

⊃ 133

⊃ 134

$\left.\begin{array}{l} \text{Buckling} \\ \text{coefficient} \end{array}\right\} \omega = \dfrac{p_c}{p_k} = \dfrac{\text{permissible compressive stress}}{\text{buckling stress}}$

$$\sigma_w = \omega \dfrac{F}{A} \leqslant p_c \qquad \text{where} \quad \omega = f(\lambda)$$

λ	BS	Standard	\multicolumn{4}{c}{Buckling coefficient ω for}
			mild steel 050 A 20	BS 970 080 M 30	alum. alloy BS L 102	cast iron BS 1452-220
	USA		mild steel A 283 Grade C	ASTM-A 440	alum. alloy AA 2017	cast iron ASTM-A 48 A 25 B
20			1·04	1·06	1·03	1·05
40			1·14	1·19	1·39	1·22
60			1·30	1·41	1·39	1·67
80			1·55	1·79	3·36	3·50
100			1·90	2·53	5·25	5·45
120			2·43	3·65	7·57	////////
140			3·31	4·96	10·30	not valid
160			4·32	6·48	13·45	in this
180			5·47	8·21	17·03	range
200			6·75	10·31	21·02	////////

Calculation method:
Estimate ω and choose cross section calculate A, I_{min} and λ from p 134. Then from table read off ω. Repeat the calculation with the appropriate new value of ω, until the initial and final values are identical.

Combination of direct stresses

Bending in two planes with end loads

The stresses σ arising from bending and end loads must be added together.

> 135

$$F_x = F \cos \alpha$$

> 136

$$F_y = F \cos \beta$$

> 137

$$F_z = F \cos \gamma$$

> 138

where $\quad \cos^2 \alpha + \cos^2 \beta + \cos^2 \gamma = 1.$

For any point $P(x, y)$ on the cross section $B_1 B_2 B_3 B_4$ the resultant normal stress is in the z-direction:

> 139

$$\sigma = \frac{F_z}{A} - \frac{F_y}{I_x} \, l \, y - \frac{F_x}{I_y} \, l \, x$$

Note the sign of x and y. If F_z is a compressive force, α, β and γ will be in different quadrants. For the sign of cosine functions see E 3.

Long beams in compression should be examined for buckling.

Neutral axis of $\sigma = 0$ is the straight line:

140

$$y = - \frac{F_x}{F_y} \times \frac{I_x}{I_y} \, x + \frac{F_z}{F_y} \times \frac{I_x}{A \, l}$$

which intercepts the axes at:

141

$$x_0 = \frac{F_z}{F_x} \times \frac{I_y}{A \, l} \; ; \qquad y_0 = \frac{F_z}{F_y} \times \frac{I_x}{A \, l}$$

With asymmetrical cross section F resolve in the directions of the principal axes (see P 9).

Bending in one axis with end load

Either F_x or F_y in formulae p 139 ... p 141 is zero

Bending with	tension	displaces the neutral axis towards the	compression	zone
	compression		tension	

Stress in curved beams $(R < 5\,h)$

The direct force F_n and bending moment M_x (see P 8) act at the most highly stressed cross section A.

For the stress distribution over the cross section:

p 142
$$\sigma_t = \frac{F_n}{A} + \frac{M_x}{A\,R} + \frac{M_x\,R}{C} \times \frac{y}{R+y}$$

The stresses at the inner and outer surfaces are:

p 143
$$\sigma_{ra} = \frac{F_n}{A} + \frac{M_x}{A\,R} + \frac{M_x\,R}{C} \times \frac{|e_1|}{R+|e_1|} \leqslant p_t$$

p 144
$$\sigma_{ri} = \frac{F_n}{A} + \frac{M_x}{A\,R} - \frac{M_x\,R}{C} \times \frac{|e_2|}{R-|e_2|} \leqslant p_t$$

Formulae for coefficient C:

p 145
$$C = b\,R^3\left(\ln\frac{1+\dfrac{d}{2R}}{1-\dfrac{d}{2R}} - \frac{d}{R}\right)$$

p 146
$$C = e^2\,\pi\,R^2\,\frac{1-\sqrt{1-\left(\dfrac{e}{R}\right)^2}}{1+\sqrt{1-\left(\dfrac{e}{R}\right)^2}}$$

p 147
$$C = R^4\left[\frac{a-b}{h}\left(1+\frac{a\,e_1+b\,e_2}{R(a-b)}\right)\times\right.$$
$$\left.\times\ln\frac{1+\dfrac{e_1}{R}}{1-\dfrac{e_2}{R}} - \frac{a-b}{R} - \frac{(a+b)h}{2R^2}\right]$$

Position of the center of mass, see K 7

p 148
$$C = R^4\left[\frac{b}{3h}\left(3+2\frac{h}{R}\right)\ln\frac{3+\dfrac{2h}{R}}{3-\dfrac{h}{3}} -\right.$$
$$\left.- \frac{b}{R} - \frac{b\,h}{2R^2}\right]$$

Combination of shear stresses

The stresses arising from shear and torsion at any cross section must be added vectorially.

The maximum shear stress τ_{res} occurs at point 1 and acts in the cross sectional plane. A complementary shear acts perpendicular to it.

	Maximum torsional stress τ_{res} in point 1	cross section
p 149	$\dfrac{5 \cdot 1\ T}{d^3} + \dfrac{1 \cdot 7\ F}{d^2} \leqslant p_{qt}$ where $T = F\dfrac{d}{2}$:	
p 150	$4 \cdot 244 \times \dfrac{F}{d^2} \leqslant p_{qt}$	
p 151	$\dfrac{5 \cdot 1\ T\ D}{D^4 - d^4} + 1 \cdot 7\ F \times \dfrac{D^2 + Dd + d^2}{D^4 - d^4} \leqslant p_{qt}$ where $T = F\dfrac{D}{2}$:	
p 152	$F\ \dfrac{4 \cdot 244\ D^2 + 1 \cdot 7\ d(D+d)}{D^4 - d^4} \leqslant p_{qt}$	
	For thin wall tubes:	
p 153	$\dfrac{5 \cdot 1\ T\ D}{D^4 - d^4} + \dfrac{2 \cdot 55\ F}{D^2 - d^2} \leqslant p_{qt}$	
p 154	$2 \cdot 55\ F \times \dfrac{2D^2 + d^2}{D^4 - d^4} \leqslant p_{qt}$	
p 155	$\dfrac{c_2}{c_1} \times \dfrac{T}{b^2 h} + \dfrac{1 \cdot 5\ F}{b\ h} \leqslant p_{qt}$ where $T = F\dfrac{b}{2}$:	
p 156	$\dfrac{F}{2\ b\ h}\left(\dfrac{c_2}{c_1} + 3\right) \leqslant p_{qt}$	

p_{qt} : permissible shear stress (see Z 16)
τ : shear stress
τ_q : calculated maximum torsional shear stress
F : force producing torsion
T : torque produced by F
for c_1 and c_2 see P 20

Combination of direct and shear stresses

Material strength values can only be determined for single-axis stress conditions. Therefore, multi-axis stresses are converted to single-axis equivalent stresses σ_v (see P 29). The following then applies, according to the type of load:

$$\sigma_v \lessgtr p_t \quad \text{or} \quad p_c \quad \text{or} \quad p_{bt}$$

Stresses in two dimensions

An element is subject to

direct stress	shear stress
σ_z in z direction	$\tau_{zy} = \tau$
σ_y in y direction	$\tau_{yz} = \tau$ } in y–z plane

By rotating the element through the angle φ_σ the mixed stresses can be converted to tensile and compressure stresses only, which are called
Principal stresses

p 157
$$\sigma_1, \sigma_2 = 0.5(\sigma_z + \sigma_y) \pm 0.5\sqrt{(\sigma_z - \sigma_y)^2 + 4\tau^2}$$

Direction of the highest principal stress σ_1 at angle of rotation φ_σ from the original position is:

p 158
$$\tan 2\varphi_\sigma = \frac{2\tau}{\sigma_z - \sigma_y} \quad ^{*)} \qquad \text{(where the shear stress is zero).}$$

Rotating the element through the angle φ_τ gives the
Maximum shear stresses

p 159
$$\tau_{max}, \tau_{min} = \pm 0.5\sqrt{(\sigma_z - \sigma_y)^2 + 4\tau^2} = \pm 0.5(\sigma_1 - \sigma_2)$$

The direct stresses act simultaneously:

p 160
$$\sigma_M = 0.5(\sigma_z + \sigma_y) = 0.5(\sigma_1 + \sigma_2)$$

Direction of the maximum shear stress τ_{max} is:

p 161
$$\tan 2\varphi_\tau = -\frac{\sigma_z - \sigma_y}{2\tau} \quad ^{*)}$$

The Principal stresses and Maximum shear stresses lie at 45° to each other.

$^{*)}$ The solution gives 2 angles. It means that both the Principal stresses and the Maximum shear stresses occur in 2 directions at right angles.

Stress in three dimensions

The stress pattern can be replaced
by the

Principal stresses σ_1, σ_2, σ_3
They are the 3 solutions of the
equation:

p 162 $$\sigma^3 - R\,\sigma^2 + S\,\sigma - T = 0$$

p 163   where $$R = \sigma_x + \sigma_y + \sigma_z$$

p 164 $$S = \sigma_x\,\sigma_y - \sigma_y\,\sigma_z + \sigma_z\,\sigma_x - \tau_{xy}^2 - \tau_{yz}^2 - \tau_{zx}^2$$

p 165 $$T = \sigma_x\sigma_y\sigma_z + 2\,\tau_{xy}\,\tau_{yz}\,\tau_{zx} - \sigma_x\,\tau_{yz}^2 - \sigma_y\,\tau_{zx}^2 - \sigma_z\,\tau_{xy}^2$$

Solve the cubic equation p 162 for σ_1, σ_2 and σ_3 as follows:

Put equation p 162 = y (or substitute y for 0 on the right
hand side), then plot $y = f(\sigma)$. The points of intersection
with the zero axis give the solution. Substitute these values
in p 162 and obtain more accurate values by trial and interpola-
tion.

The case where $\sigma_1 > \sigma_2 > \sigma_3$ gives the Maximum shear stress
$\tau_{max} = 0.5\,(\sigma_1 - \sigma_3)$.

Bending and torsion in shafts of circular cross section

According to the theory of maximum strain energy:

p 166   Equivalent stress $$\sigma_E = \sqrt{f_{bt}^2 + 3(a_o\,f_{qt})^2} \leqslant p_{bt}$$

p 167   Equivalent moment $$M_E = \sqrt{M_b^2 + 0.75(a_o\,T)^2}$$

To find the diameter of the shaft, determine the necessary section
modulus Z from:

p 168 $$Z = \frac{M_E}{p_{bt}}$$

f_{bt}	: tensile stress due to bending
f_{qt}	: shear stress due to torsion
M	: bending moment
T	: torque
a_o	: according to P 29

STRENGTH
Combination of stresses

	Based on theory of maximum strain energy		
	direct stress	shear stress	equivalent stress
three-dimensional stress	tension: $\sigma_1 > 0$: $\sigma_{vN} = \sigma_1 = \sigma_{max}$ compr.: $\sigma_3 < 0$: $\sigma_{vN} = \sigma_3 = \sigma_{min}$	$\sigma_{vS} = 2\,\tau_{max} = \sigma_1 - \sigma_3$	$\sigma_{vGe} = \sqrt{0\cdot5\left[(\sigma_1-\sigma_2)^2 + (\sigma_2-\sigma_3)^2 + (\sigma_3-\sigma_1)^2\right]}$
two-dimensional stress	tension: $\sigma_1 > 0$: $\sigma_{vN} = \sigma_1 = \sigma_{max}$ $= 0\cdot5\left[(\sigma_z+\sigma_y) + \sqrt{(\sigma_z-\sigma_y)^2 + 4(a_0\,\tau)^2}\right]$ compr.: $\sigma_2 < 0$: $\sigma_{vN} = \sigma_2 = \sigma_{min}$ $= 0\cdot5\left[(\sigma_z+\sigma_y) - \sqrt{(\sigma_z-\sigma_y)^2 + 4(a_0\,\tau)^2}\right]$	$\sigma_{vS} = 2\,\tau_{max} = \sigma_1 - \sigma_2$ $= \sqrt{(\sigma_z-\sigma_y)^2 + 4(a_0\,\tau)^2}$	$\sigma_{vGe} = \sqrt{\sigma_1^2 + \sigma_2^2 - \sigma_1\,\sigma_2}$, σ_1, σ_2 $= \sqrt{\sigma_z^2 + \sigma_y^2 - \sigma_z\,\sigma_y + 3(a_0\,\tau)^2}$
loads I, II, III for σ and τ — equal	$a_0 = 1$	$a_0 = 1$	$a_0 = 1$
loads I, II, III for σ and τ — unequal	$a_0 = \dfrac{p_t\,\text{I, II, III}}{p_q\,\text{I, II, III}}$ $= \dfrac{\sigma_{lim}\,\text{I, II, III}}{\tau_{lim}\,\text{I, II, III}}$	$a_0 = \dfrac{p_t\,\text{I, II, III}}{2\,p_q\,\text{I, II, III}}$ $= \dfrac{\sigma_{lim}\,\text{I, II, III}}{2\,\tau_{lim}\,\text{I, II, III}}$	$a_0 = \dfrac{p_t\,\text{I, II, III}}{1\cdot73\,p_q\,\text{I, II, III}}$ $= \dfrac{\sigma_{lim}\,\text{I, II, III}}{1\cdot73\,\tau_{lim}\,\text{I, II, III}}$
type of stress and material	tension, bending, torsion of brittle materials: cast iron, glass, stone	compression of brittle and ductile materials. Tension, bending, torsion of steel having pronounced yield point	all stressing of ductile materials: rolled, forged and cast steel; aluminium, bronze
expected failure	cut off fracture	sliding fracture, flowing, deformation	permanent-, sliding-, cut off fraction; flowing, deformation

*) Give the best agreement with test results.

σ_{lim}; τ_{lim} are the typical values for the materials, e.g. R_m; q_s

σ_1; σ_2; σ_3 see P 27 + P 28

Lead screws see K 11

Fixing bolts

Bolted joints (approximate calculation)
Prestressed

	axial working load F_A	shear load F_S

q 1 — axial working load F_A:
$$A_3 \triangleq A_s = \frac{F_{max}}{p_t}$$

shear load F_S: calculation for friction effect:
$$A_3 \triangleq A_s = \frac{F_{C\,req}}{(0 \cdot 25 \ldots 0 \cdot 5)\sigma_{0 \cdot 2}}$$

q 2
$$F_{max} = (1 \cdot 3 \ldots 1 \cdot 6)\, F_A$$
(using load-extension diagram, see P 1)

$$F_{K\,erf} = \frac{\nu\, F_S}{\mu\; m\; n}$$

q 3
$$p_t = (0 \cdot 25 \ldots 0 \cdot 5)\, \sigma_{0 \cdot 2}$$
(allowing for torsion and safety factor)

(for values of μ see Z 7)

High-stress bolted joints see VDI 2230

Bracket attachment (precise calculation not possible)

Practical assumption: that the centre of pressure is the point of rotation,

q 4 e.g. $a \triangleq h/4$.

For a rigid attachment:

q 5
$$F\, l = F_{A1}\; b_1 + F_{A2}\; b_2 + \ldots F_{An}\; b_n$$

q 6
$$F_{A1} : F_{A2} : \ldots F_{An} = b_1 : b_2 \ldots b_n$$

Allow for the extra shear load $F_S = F$. There must be compressive stress over the whole attachment plane, when under load.

A_3 : core cross section
A_s : stress cross section $\left(A_s = \frac{\pi}{4} \left(\frac{d_2 + d_3}{2} \right)^2 \right)$
$F_{C\,req}$: required clamping force
m : no. of bolts

n : no. of joint faces   e.g. $m = 3; n = 1$ $m = 3; n = 2$

ν : safety factor against slipping $[\nu = 1 \cdot 5 \ldots (2)]$
$\sigma_{0 \cdot 2}$: proof stress d_2 : outside diameter of bolt
p_t : permissible stress d_3 : core diameter of bolt

Axles and shafts (approximate calculation)[1]

Axles

Axle	required section modulus for bending	solid axle of circular cross section ($Z \stackrel{\sim}{=} d^3/10$)	permissible bending stress[3]
q 7 / q 8 — fixed[2]	$Z = \dfrac{M}{p_{bt}}$	$d = \sqrt[3]{\dfrac{10\,M}{p_{bt}}}$	$p_{bt} = \dfrac{\sigma_{btU}}{(3\ldots5)}$
q 9 — rotating			$p_{bt} = \dfrac{\sigma_{btA}}{(3\ldots5)}$

Shafts

Stress	diameter for solid shaft	permissible torsional stress[3]
q 10 / q 11 — pure torsion	$d = \sqrt[3]{\dfrac{5\,T}{p_{qt}}}$	$p_{qt} = \dfrac{\tau_{tU}}{(3\ldots5)}$
q 12 — torsion and bending		$p_{qt} = \dfrac{\tau_{tU}}{(10\ldots15)}$

Bearing stress

q 13

$$\left.\begin{array}{l}\text{on shaft}\\ \text{extension}\end{array}\right\} f_{bm} = \frac{F}{d\,b} \leqslant p_b$$

(p_b see Z 18)

simplified   actual

Shear due to lateral load: Calculation unnecessary when

$l > d/4$ for all shafts	with	circular	cross
$l > 0 \cdot 325\,h$ for fixed axles		rectangular	sections

Deflection due to bending see P 12
           due to torsion see P 20

Vibrations   see M 6.

[1] For precise calculation see DIN 15017
[2] Formulae are restricted to load classes I + II (P 2)
[3] p_{bt} and p_{qt} allow for stress concentration-, roughness-, size-, (see DIN 15017), safety-factor and combined stresses

---

l : arm of force F
M, T : bending moment torque
f_{bm} (p_b) : mean (permissible) bearing stress (see Z 18)
$f_{b\,max}$ see q 47 for hydrodynamically lubricated plain bearings, other
$\sigma_{btU}, \sigma_{btA}, \tau_{tU}$: values see Z 16.   [cases see Z 18

Friction-locked joints

Proprietary devices (e.g. annular spring, Doko clamping device, Spieth sleeve, etc.): see manufacturer's literature.

For interference fits see DIN 7190 (graphical method).

Clamped joint

imaginary joint, not too stiff

q 14 $$F_n = \frac{T\,v}{\mu\,d}$$

Taper joint

q 15   Taper from $\tan a = \dfrac{D-d}{l}$

For tapered shaft extensions see DIN 1448, 1449, (254).

Approximate formula for axial force F_A on the nut:

q 16 $$F_A = \frac{2\,T\,v}{\mu\,d_m}\,\tan\!\left(\frac{a}{2} + \varrho\right)$$

q 17 $$d_m = \frac{D+d}{2}$$

Specially machined joints

Proprietary splined fittings, hub to shaft e.g. polygon: see manufacturer's literature.

Plain key (approximate calculation)

Calculation is based on the bearing pressure on the side of the keyway in the weaker material. Allowing for the curvature of the shaft and the chamfer r_1, the bearing height of the key can be taken approximately as t_2.

The bearing length l is to transmit a torque T:

q 18 $$l = \frac{2\,T}{d\,t_2\,p_b}$$

Dimensions to DIN 6885, preferably Sheet 1. Allowance for fillets with form A.

For precise calculations refer to Mielitzer, Forschungsvereinigung Antriebstechnik e.V. Frankfurt/M., Forschungsheft 26, 1975.

continued on Q 4

continued from Q 3

Splined shaft

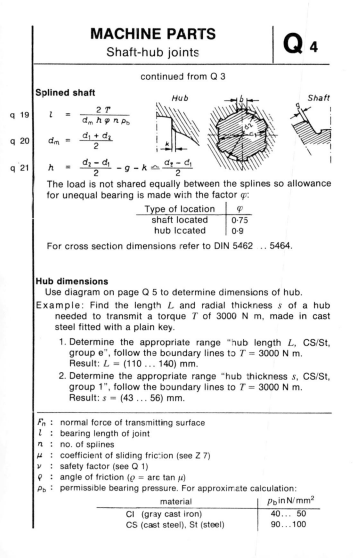

Hub   *Shaft*

q 19

$$l = \frac{2\,T}{d_m\,h\,\varphi\,n\,p_b}$$

q 20

$$d_m = \frac{d_1 + d_2}{2}$$

q 21

$$h = \frac{d_2 - d_1}{2} - g - k \triangleq \frac{d_2 - d_1}{2}$$

The load is not shared equally between the splines so allowance for unequal bearing is made with the factor φ:

Type of location	φ
shaft located	0·75
hub located	0·9

For cross section dimensions refer to DIN 5462 .. 5464.

Hub dimensions

Use diagram on page Q 5 to determine dimensions of hub.

Example: Find the length L and radial thickness s of a hub needed to transmit a torque T of 3000 N m, made in cast steel fitted with a plain key.

1. Determine the appropriate range "hub length L, CS/St, group e", follow the boundary lines to $T = 3000$ N m.
   Result: $L = (110 \ldots 140)$ mm.

2. Determine the appropriate range "hub thickness s, CS/St, group 1", follow the boundary lines to $T = 3000$ N m.
   Result: $s = (43 \ldots 56)$ mm.

F_n : normal force of transmitting surface
l : bearing length of joint
n : no. of splines
μ : coefficient of sliding friction (see Z 7)
ν : safety factor (see Q 1)
ϱ : angle of friction ($\varrho = $ arc tan μ)
p_b : permissible bearing pressure. For approximate calculation:

material	p_b in N/mm²
CI (gray cast iron)	40... 50
CS (cast steel), St (steel)	90...100

Diagram to obtain hub geometry for Q 4

These empirical values are for steel shafts made of steel to ASTM A 572 Grade 42 – resp. to BS 4360 43 B – but not for special cases (such as high centrifugal force, etc.). Increase L when there are other forces or moments being carried.

Example on page Q 4

Ranges for hub

Type of joint	length L			thickness s		
	CI	CS, St		CI	CS, St	
shrink-fit, interference fit, taper	a	d		g	k	
keyed, clamped	b	e		h	l	
splined shaft to DIN 5463 (medium)	c	f		i	m	

T in N m

L, s in mm

MACHINE PARTS
Springs

Spring rate R and spring work W (Strain energy)

		Characteristic general	const.
q 22	R	$\dfrac{dF}{ds}$	$\dfrac{F}{s}$
q 23	W_1	$\displaystyle\int_0^{s_1} F \, ds$	$F \dfrac{s_1}{2}$

Springs in

		parallel	series
q 24	$s_{tot} =$	$s_1 = s_2 = s_3 \ldots = s_i$	$s_1 + s_2 + s_3 \ldots + s_i$
q 25	$F_{tot} =$	$F_1 + F_2 + F_3 \ldots + F_i$	$F_1 = F_2 = F_3 \ldots = F_i$
q 26	R	$R_{tot} = R_1 + R_2 + R_3 \ldots + R_i$	$\dfrac{1}{R_{tot}} = \dfrac{1}{R_1} + \dfrac{1}{R_2} + \ldots \dfrac{1}{R_i}$

Springs in tension and compression
e. g. ring spring (Belleville spring)

Springs in bending

Rectangular, trapezoidal, triangular springs

q 27	bending stress	$f_{bt} = \dfrac{6 F l}{b_0 h^2}$
q 28	permissible load	$F = \dfrac{b_0 h^2 \rho_{bt}}{6 l}$
q 29	deflection	$s = 4 \psi \dfrac{l^3}{b_0 h^3} \times \dfrac{F}{E}$

b_l/b_0	1 [1]	0·8	0·6	0·4	0·2	0 [2]
ψ	1·000	1·054	1·121	1·202	1·315	1·5

[1] Rectangular spring
[2] Triangular spring

continued on Q 7

continued from Q 6

Laminated leaf springs

Laminated leaf springs can be imagined as trapezoidal springs cut into strips and rearranged (spring in sketch can be replaced by two trapezoidal springs in parallel) of total spring width:

q 30
$$b_o = z\, b$$

z : no. of leaves.

Then (as q 28):

q 31
$$F_n \simeq \frac{b\, h^2\, p_{bt}}{6\, l}$$

If leaves 1 and 2 are the same length (as in the sketch):

q 32
$$b_l = 2\, b$$

The calculation does not allow for friction. In practice, friction increases the carrying capacity by between 2 ... 12%.

Precise calculation according to Sheet 394, 1st edition 1974 Beratungsstelle für Stahlverwendung, Düsseldorf.

Disc springs (Ring springs)

Different characteristics can be obtained by combining n springs the same way and i springs the opposite way:

q 33
$$F_{tot} = n\, F_{single}$$

q 34
$$s_{tot} = i\, s_{single}$$

DIN 2092: Precise calculation of single disc springs.
DIN 2093: Dimensions and charact. of standard disc springs.

Material properties: Hot-worked steels for springs to ASTM A 322 e.g. for leaf springs 9255; 6150 – resp. to BS 970/5 e.g. 250 A 53; 735 A 50 – (Modulus of elasticity: $E = 200\,000$ N/mm^2).

p_{bt} : static 910 N/mm^2
oscilating (500 ± 225) N/mm^2 scale removed and tempered

continued on Q 8

continued from Q 7

Coiled torsion spring The type shown in the sketch has both ends free and must be mounted on a guide post. Positively located arms are better.

q 35	Spring force[1]	$F_p \simeq \dfrac{Z\,F\,b\,t}{r}$
q 36	Angle of deflection	$\alpha \simeq \dfrac{F \cdot l}{I\,E}$
q 37	Spring coil length	$l \simeq D_m\,\pi\,i_f$

i_f : no. of coils.

(Additional correction is needed for deflection of long arms).

For precise calculation see DIN 2088.

Springs in torsion

Torsion bar spring

	Shear stress	Torque	Angle of twist
q 38	$\tau = \dfrac{5\,T}{d^3}$	$T = \dfrac{d^3}{5}p_{qt}$	$\vartheta = \dfrac{T\,l_s}{G\,I_p} \simeq \dfrac{10\,T\,l_s}{G\,d^4}$

l_s : spring length as shown in sketch.

Stress p_{qt} and fatigue strength τ_f in N/mm²

		static		oscillating[2]
q 39	p_{qt}	not preloaded	700	$\tau_f = \tau_m \pm \tau_A$
		preloaded	1020	

$d = 20$ mm	500 ± 350
$d = 30$ mm	500 ± 240

τ_m : mean stress
τ_A : alternating stress amplitude of fatigue strength

Precise calculation see DIN 2091, especially for the spring length.

[1] Not allowing for the stress factor arising from the curvature of the wire.
[2] Surface ground and shot-blasted, preloaded.

continued on Q 9

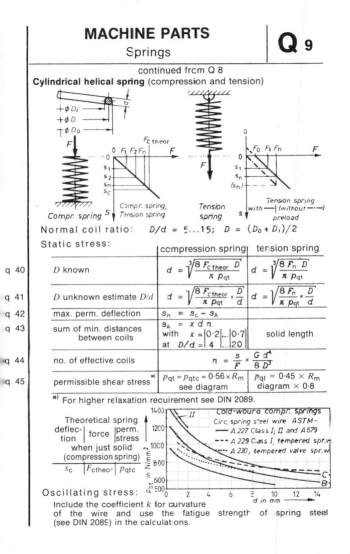

continued frcm Q 8

Cylindrical helical spring (compression and tension)

Compr. spring / Tension spring

Compr. spring, Tension spring

Tension spring

Tension spring with — (without ---) preload

Normal coil ratio: $D/d = 5...15; \quad D = (D_0 + D_i)/2$

Static stress:

		compression spring	tension spring
q 40	D known	$d = \sqrt[3]{\dfrac{8\,F_{c\,theor}}{\pi\,p_{qt}}\cdot D}$	$d = \sqrt[3]{\dfrac{8\,F_n}{\pi\,p_{qt}}\cdot D}$
q 41	D unknown estimate D/d	$d = \sqrt{\dfrac{8\,F_{c\,theor}}{\pi\,p_{qt}}\times\dfrac{D}{d}}$	$d = \sqrt{\dfrac{8\,F_n}{\pi\,p_{qt}}\times\dfrac{D}{d}}$
q 42	max. perm. deflection	$s_n = s_c - s_A$	
q 43	sum of min. distances between coils	$s_A = x \times d \times n$ with $x = \begin{vmatrix}0\cdot2\\4\end{vmatrix}...\begin{vmatrix}0\cdot7\\20\end{vmatrix}$ at $D/d = $	solid length
q 44	no. of effective coils	$n = \dfrac{s}{F}\times\dfrac{G\,d^4}{8\,D^3}$	
q 45	permissible shear stress[*]	$p_{qt} = p_{qtc}\times0\cdot56\times R_m$ see diagram	$p_{qt} = 0\cdot45\times R_m$ diagram $\times\,0\cdot8$

[*] For higher relaxation recuirement see DIN 2089.

Theoretical spring			Cold-wourd compr. springs
deflec-tion	force	perm. stress	Circ. spring steel wire ASTM-
s_c	F_{ctheor}	p_{qtc}	

— A 227 Class I; II and A 679
--- A 229 Class I, tempered spr.v
···· A 230, tempered valve spr.w

when just solid (compression spring)

p in N/mm^2

Oscillating stress:

Include the coefficient k for curvature of the wire and use the fatigue strength of spring steel (see DIN 2089) in the calculations.

Rolling bearings

Use the formulae from the manufacturer's literature which gives load capacities and dimensions, e. g. S.K.F., Timken.

Journal bearings

Hydrodynamically-lubricated plain journal bearing

Bearing must be running at proper temperatures and without excessive wear, i.e. separation of the journal and bearing by a film of lubricant.

Pressure distribution in transverse and longitudinal sections

Length/diameter ratio l/d

Auto-mobile engines Aero engines	Pumps Machine tools Gearing	Marine bearings Steam turbines	Grease lubrication

General properties

Short bearings	Long bearings
Large pressure drop at each end, therefore good cooling with adequate oil flow.	Small pressure drop at each end, therefore high load capacity.
Excellent for high rotational speeds.	Good at low rotational speeds.
	Poor cooling facilities.
Low load capacity at low rotational speeds.	Danger of edge loading.

continued on Q 11

continued from Q 10 (journal bearings)

Bearing pressure $f_{b.m}$, $f_{b\,max}$

q 46	mean	bearing	$f_{b.m} = \dfrac{F}{d\ b}$
q 47	max.	pressure	$f_{b\,max} \leqslant \dfrac{2}{3}\ \sigma_{dF}$

$f_{b\,max}$ depends mainly on the relative thickness δ of the lubricating film (see Sommerfeld number q 56).

The adjacent diagram shows the ratio of maximum pressure to mean bearing pressure in relation to the relative thickness of the lubrication film. (According to Bauer, VDI 2204).

Bearing clearance s relative bearing clearance ψ

q 48 $s = D - d$; $\psi = s/d$

ψ is basically the relative bearing clearance established during operation (including thermal expansion and elastic deformation).

q 49   Typical values $\psi = (0\cdot3 \ldots 1 \ldots 3)\ 10^{-3}$ [1]

Criteria for the choice of ψ:

	Lower value	Upper value
bearing material	soft (e. g. white metal)	hard (e. g. phosphor)
viscosity	relatively low	relatively high
peripheral speed	relatively low	relatively high
bearing pressure	relatively high	relatively low
length/diameter ratio	$l/d \leq 0\cdot8$	$l/d \geq 0\cdot8$
support	self-aligning	rigid

50	Minimum values for plastics	$\psi \geq (\ 3 \ldots 4)\ 10^{-3}$
51	sintered metals	$\psi \geq (1 \ 5 \ldots 2)\ 10^{-3}$
52	[1] Grease-lubricated plain bearings	$\psi = (\ 2 \ldots 3)\ 10^{-3}$

continued on Q 12

continued from Q 11 (journal bearings)

Minimum thickness of lubricating film h_{min} in μm

q 54

Theoretical	Actual
$h_0 \geq h_{min}$ shaft deflection + bearing distortion + sum of peak-to-valley heights $(R_{t1} + R_{t2})$	$h_{min} = [(1)\ldots 3,5 \ldots 10 \ldots (15)]\ \mu m$

special cases, e.g. some automobile crankshaft bearings

small- | large shaft diameters

Relative thickness of lubricating film δ

q 55

$$\delta = \frac{h_0}{s/2} = \frac{2\,h_0}{\psi\,d}$$

Upper limit for bearings under steady conditions (rotational) speed, load, constant load direction): $\delta \leq 0.35$ to prevent instability and rough running.

Sommerfeld number So
(Dimensionless)

q 56

$$S_0 = \frac{p_m\,\psi^2}{\eta_m\,\omega}$$

Inserting So in the adjacent diagram gives δ and therefore also h_0 from q 55.

η_m viscosity based on mean temperature, t_m.

continued on Q 13

continued from Q 12 (journal bearings)

Lubricant flow rate Q

The theoretical flow rate required to maintain hydrodynamic lubrication is:

q 57
$$\dot{Q} = 0 \cdot 5 \; b \; v \; (s - 2 \; h_0)$$

Rules: Oil inlet to the expanding part of the bearing.

q 58   In supply lines: $v \triangleq 2$ m/s ; $p_r = 0 \ldots 1 \ldots (5)$ bar

q 59   In return lines: $v \triangleq 0 \cdot 5$ m/s ; $p_r = 0$.

Oil grooves (depth $\triangleq 2s$) must not be cut into the surfaces of the high pressure area (Q 10) and must not extend to the edges of the bearing. Only short oil grooves are needed with high pressures, but in some cases larger oil grooves are needed to remove heat

No oil grooves in the load zone!

Heat removal

Requirement: Friction power $(P_F = \mu \, F \, v) =$ rate of heat removal.

q 60
$$\mu = \frac{3\,\psi}{So} \qquad \text{for } So < 1 \text{ (high-speed range)}$$

q 61
$$\mu = \frac{3\,\psi}{\sqrt{So}} \qquad \text{for } So > 1 \text{ (heavy-load range)}$$

Natural cooling (determining oil type): Heat removal mainly from the housing surface A, therefore

q 62
$$P_F = h \, A \, (t_m - t_0) \qquad \text{by empirical formula}$$

for h:

q 63
$$h\left(\frac{W}{m^2 \, K}\right) = 7 + \sqrt{w} \;, \qquad \text{where } w \text{ is in m/s.}$$

If effect of heat-transmitting surface A is unknown, guide values for pedestal bearings are:

q 64 $A \triangleq (20 \ldots 30) \; d \, b \qquad$ for $d \leq 100$ mm.

q 65 $A \triangleq (15 \ldots 25) \; d \, b \qquad$ for $d < 100$ mm.

For a given design, load and required operating temperature, the necessary viscosity is:

q 66
$$\eta_m = \frac{p_m}{\omega} \times \frac{\psi \, h \, A \, (t_m - t_0)}{3 \, F \, v} \qquad \text{(high-speed range)}$$

q 67
$$\eta_m = \frac{p_m}{\omega} \times \left[\frac{h \, A \, (t_m - t_0)}{3 \, F \, v}\right]^2 \qquad \text{(heavy-load range)}$$

The required type of oil can be determined knowing t_m and η_m (see q 56).

continued on Q 14

continued from Q 13 (journal bearings)

Natural cooling (given oil type)

Since η is temperature-sensitive and the running oil temperature is initially unknown, use iteration method with q66 or q67 for preliminary and successively improved estimates of t_m.

Graphical method according to VDI 2204.

Forced cooling

Heat removal through oil circuit, with oil cooler if necessary (convection, radiation and conduction from bearing are neglected).

q 68
$$P_F = \dot{Q} c \varrho (t_2 - t_1)$$

Guide values for simple calculations for mineral oils:

q 69
$$c \triangleq 1 \cdot 86 \quad kJ/(kg\ K)$$

q 70
$$\varrho \triangleq 900 \quad kg/m^3$$

For more detailed calculations see VDI 2204.

---

c : specific heat (values see Z 5)
μ : coefficient of friction
F : radial bearing force
h : heat transfer coefficient
h_0 : min. thickness of lubricating film at running speed (r.p.m.)
h_{min} : min. thickness of lubricating film at lowest running r.p.m. (min thickness of oil lubricating film)
p_r : pressure (relative to atmospheric) of oil flow
p_m, p_{max} : mean, max. bearing pressure
s : radial clearance
υ : peripheral speed of bearing journal or velocity of oil flow
$\dot{Q}$: flow rate of lubricant
w : velocity of cooling air (m/s)
t : operating temperature of housing surface
t_0 : ambient temperature
t_1, t_2 : inlet, outlet temperature of oil
η : dynamic or absolute viscosity, see N 1
η_m : dynamic viscosity based on mean temperature of bearing t_m
ϱ : density of lubricant (values see Z 5)
ψ : relative bearing clearance (values see Q 11)
ω : angular velocity

Crosshead guide

Crosshead guide will operate smoothly only when

q 71
$$\tan \alpha < \frac{l}{(2h + l)\mu} \quad \text{or}$$

the length ratio is

q 72
$$\frac{l}{h} = \lambda > \frac{2\mu \tan \alpha}{1 - \mu \tan \alpha}$$

If the above conditions for $\tan \alpha$ are not satisfied there is a danger of tilting and jamming.

Friction clutches

Slip time and energy loss per operation

Drive side   *Clutch* T_C *Driven side*

$$\boxed{I_1, \ T_M, \ \omega_1} \quad \dashv\vdash \quad \boxed{I_2, \ T_L, \ \omega_2}$$

A simplified model with the following conditions is sufficent for approximate calculation:

Acceleration of driven side from $\omega_2 = 0$ to $\omega_2 = \omega_1$, $\omega_1 = \text{const.}$; $T_L = \text{const.}$; $T_C = \text{const.} > T_L$. Then, per operation:

q 73
    energy loss
$$W_l = I_2 \times \frac{\omega_1^2}{2} \times \left(1 + \frac{T_L}{T_C - T_L}\right)$$

q 74
    slip time
$$t_f = \frac{I_2 \omega_1}{T_C - T_L}$$

Calculating the area of the friction surface

		flat		cone	cylin-drical
single-plate	twin-plate	multi-plate			
	clutches			clutches	

Number and size of friction surfaces depend on the permissible contact pressure p_b and the permissible thermal capacity per unit area q_p.

continued on Q 16

continued from Q 15 (friction clutches)

Calculation of contact pressure p_b
(for values see Z 19)

For all types of friction surfaces:

q 75
$$i\,A \geqslant \frac{T_C}{p_b\,\mu\,r_m}$$

q 76 where
$$r_m = \frac{2}{3} \times \frac{r_a^3 - r_i^3}{r_a^2 - r_i^2} \cong \frac{r_a + r_i}{2}$$

		flat	conical friction surfaces	cylindrical
q 77	operating force (axial)	$F_a = A\,p_b$	$F_a = A\,p_b\,\sin a$	$r_a = r_i = r_m$
q 78		for multiplate clutches usually:	to prevent locking:	
q 79		$\dfrac{r_i}{r_a} = 0.6 \dots 0.8$	$\tan a > \mu$	

Calculation permissible temperature rise
In HEAVY-LOAD STARTING the maximum temperature is reached in one operation. It depends on the energy loss, slip time, heat conduction, specific heat and cooling. These relationships cannot be incorporated in a general formula.

With CONTINUOUS OPERATION constant temperature is only established after several operations. There are empirical values for permissible thermal capacity per unit area q_p with continuous operation (see Z 19).

q 80 Friction power
$$P_F = W_l\,z$$

q 81 Condition
$$i\,A \geqslant \frac{W_l\,z}{q_p}$$

Symbols see Q 17

Friction brakes

A l friction clutches can also be used as brakes. But there are also:

Disc brakes

with caliper and pads.

Braking torque T_B:

q 82

$$T_B = 2 \mu F_s j r_m$$

Expanding-shoe drum brakes

(Drawing of simplex brake showing, simpified, the forces acting on the shoes).

Leading	Trailing
shoes	

$$F_{n1} = \frac{F_s l}{a - \mu r} \qquad F_{n2} = \frac{F_s l}{a + \mu r}$$

(Servoaction)

Braking torque T_B:

q 85

$$T_B = (F_{n1} + F_{n2}) \mu r$$

83/84

Band brakes see K 13

Notation for friction clutches and brakes (Q 15 ... Q 17)

A : area of friction surface
T_C : operating torque of clutch
T_L : load torque
T_M : motor torque
W_l : energy loss per operation
μ : coefficient of friction
i : no. of friction surfaces
j : no. of calipers on a disc brake
r : radius of friction surface
r_m , r_o , r_i : mean, outside, inside radius of friction surface
z : operating frequency (EU: s^{-1}, h^{-1})
ω : angular velocity

(For properties of friction materials see Z 19)

Involute-tooth gears

Spur gears, geometry

q 86 Gear ratio
$$u = \frac{z_2}{z_1}$$

q 87 Transmission ratio
$$i = \frac{\omega_a}{\omega_b} = \frac{n_a}{n_b} = -\frac{z_b}{z_a}^{1)}$$

Transmission ratio of multi-stage gearing:

q 88
$$i_{tot} = i_I \times i_{II} \times i_{III} \times \ldots \times i_r$$

q 89 Involute function
$$\text{inv}\, \alpha = \tan \alpha + \alpha$$

Showing the transverse path of contact (see ISO/R 1122)

If A and E do not fall between T_1 and T_2, interference will occur and "modified" gears as in Q 20 should be used.

[1)] Negative for external gears because rotation is opposite. Positive for internal gears. The sign can normally be disregarded.

	Standard gears	
	spur	helical
q 90 q 91 q 92 normal pitch circular pitch	$p = \dfrac{\pi\, d}{z} = m\, \pi$	$p_n = m_n\, \pi$ $p_t = \dfrac{m_n\, \pi}{\cos \beta}$
q 93 q 94 q 95 normal module circular module	$m = \dfrac{p}{\pi} = \dfrac{d}{z}$	$m_n = \dfrac{p_n}{\pi} = \dfrac{d}{z}\cos \beta$ $m_t = \dfrac{m_n}{\cos \beta} = \dfrac{d}{z}$
q 96 addendum	$h_a = h_{aP} = m$	
q 97 dedendum	$h_f = h_{fP} = m + c$	
q 98 bottom clearance	$c = (0.1 \ldots 0.3)\, m \doteq 0.2\, m$	

continued on Q 19

For symbols see Q 29, suffixes see Q 23

continued from Q 18 (spur gears)

		Standard gears	
		spur	helical
99/100	reference diameter	$d = m\,z$	$d = \dfrac{m_n\,z}{\cos\beta} = m_t\,z$
q 101	tip diameter	$d_a = d + 2\,h_a$	
q 102	root diameter	$d_f = d - 2\,h_f$	
q 103	pressure angle	$a = a_n = a_t = a_p$	$a_n = a_p$
q 104			$\tan a = \dfrac{\tan a_n}{\cos\beta}$
05/106	base diameter	$d_b = d\,\cos a$	$d_b = d\,\cos a_t$
q 107	equivalent no of teeth		$z_{nx} = z\,\dfrac{1}{\cos^2\beta \times \cos\beta}$
			table see DIN 3960
q 108			$\simeq \dfrac{z}{\cos^3\beta}$
q 109	min. no. of teeth — theory	to avoid interference	$z_{lim} = \dfrac{2}{\sin^2 a} \simeq 17$ for $a_p = 20°$
10/111	practice	$z'_{lim} \simeq 14$	$z'_{lim\,h} \simeq 14\cos^3\beta$
q 112	spread		$U = b\,\tan|\beta|$

		Standard gearing	
		spur	helical
3/114	centre distance	$a = \dfrac{d_1+d_2}{2} = m\dfrac{z_1+z_2}{2}$	$a = \dfrac{d_1+d_2}{2} = m_n\dfrac{z_1+z_2}{2\cos\beta}$
q 115	length of path of contact (total length)	$g_\alpha = \dfrac{1}{2}\left[\sqrt{d_{a1}^2 - d_{b1}^2} + \sqrt{d_{a2}^2 - d_{b2}^2} - (d_{b1}+d_{b2})\tan a_t\right]$	
6/117	transverse contact ratio	$\varepsilon_\alpha = \dfrac{g_\alpha}{p\,\cos a}$	$\varepsilon_\alpha = \dfrac{g_\alpha}{p\,\cos a}$
q 118	overlap ratio		$\varepsilon_\beta = \dfrac{b\,\sin|\beta|}{m_n\,\pi}$
q 119	contact ratio		$\varepsilon_\gamma = \varepsilon_\alpha + \varepsilon_\beta$

continued on Q 20

For symbols see Q 29, suffixes see Q 23

continued from Q 19 (gearing)

			modified gears	
			spur	nelical
	p, p_n, p_t, z, z_{nx} m, m_n, m_t, d, d_b		see standard gears	
20/121 22/123	profile offset		$x\,m$	$x\,m_n$
		to avoid interference	$x_{min} = -\dfrac{z\,\sin^2\alpha}{2} +$ $+\dfrac{h_{a0}-\varrho_{a0}\,(1-\sin a)}{m}$	$x_{min} = -\dfrac{z\,\sin^2\alpha}{2\cos\beta} +$ $+\dfrac{h_{a0}-\varrho_{a0}\,(1-\sin a_n)}{m_n}$ can be up to 0·17 mm
24/125	profile offset factor	ditto[1]	$x \simeq \dfrac{14-z}{17}$	$x \simeq \dfrac{14-(z/\cos^3\beta)}{17}$
q 126		to give a specific centre distance (total)	$x_1 + x_2 = \dfrac{(z_1+z_2)\times(inv\,a_{wt}-inv\,a_t)}{2\,\tan a_n}$	
q 127	a_{wt} calculated from		$\cos a_{wt} = \dfrac{(z_1+z_2)\,m_t}{2\,a}\cos a_t$	
q 128	or		$inv\,a_{wt} = inv\,a_t + 2\,\dfrac{x_1+x_2}{z_1+z_2}\tan a_n$	
q 129	centre distance		$a = a_d\,\dfrac{\cos a_t}{\cos a_{wt}}$	
q 130	addendum modification coefficient		$k\,m_r = a - a_d - m_n\times(x_1+x_2)$ [2]	
q 131	addendum		$h_a = h_{aP} + x\,m_n + k\,m_n$	
q 132	dedendum		$h_f = h_{fP} - x\,m_r$	
q 133	outside diameter		$d_a = d + 2\,h_a$	
q 134	root diameter		$d_f = d - 2\,h_f$	
q 135	length of path of contact		$g_\alpha = \dfrac{1}{2}\left[\sqrt{d_{a1}^2-d_{b1}^2} + \sqrt{d_{a2}^2-d_{b2}^2} - (d_{b1}+d_{b2})\,\tan a_{wt}\right]$	
36/137	transverse contact ratio		$\varepsilon_c = g_\alpha/(p\,\cos a)$	$\varepsilon_\alpha = g_\alpha/(p_t\,\cos a_t)$
q 138	overlap ratio			$\varepsilon_\beta = b\,\sin|\beta|/(m_n\,\pi)$
q 139	contact ratio			$\varepsilon_\gamma = \varepsilon_\alpha + \varepsilon_\beta$

[1] If tool data unknown take $a_P = 20°$.

[2] Note the sign. With external gears $k \times m_n < 0$! When $k < 0·1$ addendum modification can often be avoided

For symbols see Q 29, suffixes see Q 23

Spur gears, design

The dimensions are derived from

> load-carrying capacity of the tooth root
> load-carrying capacity of the tooth flank,

which must be maintained independently.

Gearing design is checked in accordance with DIN 3990. By conversion and rough grouping of various factors it is possible to derive some approximate formulae from DIN 3990.

Load capacity of tooth (approximate calculation)
Safety factor S_F against fatigue failure of tooth root:

q 140
$$S_F = \frac{\sigma_{F\,lim}}{\dfrac{F_t}{b\,m_n} \times Y_F \times Y_\varepsilon \times Y_\beta} \times \frac{Y_S \times K_{FX}}{K_1 \times K_V \times K_{F\alpha} \times K_{F\beta}} \geqslant S_{F\,min}$$

Giving the approximate formulae:

q 141
$$m_n \geqslant \frac{F_t}{b} \; Y_F \times \underbrace{K_1 \times K_V \times Y_\varepsilon \times Y_\beta \times K_{F\alpha}}_{\cong 1} \times \underbrace{\frac{K_{F\beta}}{Y_S \times K_{FX}}}_{\cong 1} \times \frac{S_{F\,min}}{\sigma_{F\,lim}}$$

Y_F : tooth from factor for external gearing (see diagram)

q 142
$K_1 \times K_V = 1 \dots 3$, rarely more, (allowing for external shock and irregularities exceeding the rated torque, additional internal dynamic forces arising from tooth errors and circumferential velocity).

q 143
$S_{F\,min} = 1 \cdot 7$ (guide value)

q 144
$\sigma_{F\,lim}$: guide values see table on Q 22

continued on Q 22

For symbols see Q 29, suffixes see Q 23

continued from Q 21 (spur gears, design)

Load capacity of tooth flank (approximate calculation)

Safety factor S_H against pitting:

q 145
$$S_H = \frac{\sigma_{Hlim}}{\sqrt{\frac{u+1}{u} \times \frac{F_t}{b \, d_1}} \times Z_H \times Z_M \times Z_\epsilon} \times \frac{Z_V \times K_{HX} \times Z_R \times Z_L}{\sqrt{K_1 \times K_V \times K_{H\alpha} \times K_{H\beta}}} \geq S_{H \, min}$$

For metals the material factor Z_M is simplified to:

q 146
$$Z_M = \sqrt{0 \cdot 35 \, E} \quad \text{where} \quad E = \frac{2 \, E_1 \, E_2}{E_1 + E_2}$$

Therefore, the approximate formula becomes: $\cong 1$

q 147
$$d_1 \geq \sqrt{\frac{2 \, T_1}{b} \times \frac{u+1}{u} 0 \cdot 35 \, E} \times Z_H \times Z_\epsilon \sqrt{K_{H\alpha}} \frac{\sqrt{K_1 \times K_V} \times \sqrt{K_{H\beta}}}{Z_V \times K_{HX} \times Z_R \times Z_L} \times \frac{S_{Hmin}}{\sigma_{Hlim}}$$

$\cong 1$

| Mat. | Specification to | | $\sigma_{F\,lim}$ | $\sigma_{H\,lim}$ |
	Norm	Grade	N/mm²	
CI		A 48-50 B	80	360
	ASTM	A 536-20-90-02	230	560
CS		A 572 Gr. 65	200	400
		1064	220	620
AS	SAE	4140	290	670
ASCH		9240	500	1630

CI: cast iron
CS: carbon steel
AS: alloy steel
ASCH: case hardened alloy steel

only valid for $\alpha_n = 20°$

continued on Q 23

148   Z_H : flank form factor (see diagram)
149   $K_1 \times K_V$: see load capacity of tooth root (q 142)
150   $S_{Hmin} \cong 1 \cdot 2$ (guide value)
  $\sigma_{H\,lim}$: guide values see table
151   $Z_V \times K_{HX} \times Z_R \times Z_L = 0 \cdot 5 \ldots 1$. Higher value for higher circumferential velocity, higher lubricating oil viscosity and lower roughness

For symbols see Q 29, for suffixes see Q 23

continued from Q 22, (spur gears, design)

In q 141, q 145 and q 147 b or b and d must be known. The following ratios are for estimating purposes and should be used for the initial calculation:

Pinion dimensions

		$\dfrac{d_1}{d_{\text{shaft 1}}}$	Or:
q 152	pinion integral with shaft	1·2 ... 1·5	from gear ratio i and a specified centre distance a (see q 113–114–129)
q 153	pinion free to turn on shaft	2	

Tooth width ratios

	Tooth- and bearing-quality	$\dfrac{b}{m}$	$\dfrac{b}{d_1}$
q 154	teeth smoothly cast or flame cut	6 ... 10	
q 155	teeth machined; bearings supported each side on steel construction or pinion overhung	(6) ... 10 ... 15	
q 156	teeth well machined; bearings supported each side in gear casing	15 ... 25	
q 157	teeth precision machined; good bearings each side and lubrication in gear casing: $n_1 \leq 50\ \text{s}^{-1}$.	20 ... 40	
q 158	overhung gearwheel		$\leq 0\cdot7$
q 159	fully supported		$\leq 1\cdot2$

Suffixes for Q 18 ... 25

- $_a$: driving wheel
- $_b$: driven wheel
- $_1$: small wheel or pinion
- $_2$: large wheel or wheel
- $_t$: tangential
- $_n$: normal
- $_m$: tooth middle for bevel gears
- $_v$: on back cone (or virtual cylindrical gear)

For symbols see Q 29

Bevel gears

Bevel gears, geometry
Equations q 86...q 88
are applicable and also:

cone angle δ:

q 160
$$\tan \delta_1 = \frac{\sin \Sigma}{\cos \Sigma + u} \;;$$

q 161
$$\left(\Sigma = 90° \Rightarrow \tan \delta_1 = \frac{1}{u} \right)$$

q 162
$$\tan \delta_2 = \frac{\sin \Sigma}{\cos \Sigma + 1/u} \;;$$

q 163
$$(\Sigma = 90° \Rightarrow \tan \delta_2 = u)$$

q 164
$$\left. \begin{array}{c} \text{angle between} \\ \text{shafts} \end{array} \right\} \quad \Sigma = \delta_1 + \delta_2$$

q 165
$$\left. \begin{array}{c} \text{external pitch} \\ \text{cone distance} \end{array} \right\} \quad R_e = \frac{d_e}{2 \sin \delta}$$

Only the axial and radial forces acting one mesh wheel 2 are shown

Development of the back cone to examine the meshing conditions gives the virtual cylindrical gear (suffix "v" = virtual) with the values:

q 166	straight		$z_v = \dfrac{z}{\cos \delta}$	$u_v = \dfrac{z_{v2}}{z_{v1}}$
q 167		bevel gears		
q 168	spiral		$z_v \approx \dfrac{z}{\cos \delta \times \cos^3 \beta}$	

Formulae q 92, q 95 ... q 100 are also applicable to the surface of the back cone (suffix "e").

Bevel gears, design

The design is referred to the MID-POINT OF THE WIDTH b (suffix "m") with the values:

69/170
$$R_m = R_e - \frac{b}{2} \qquad\qquad m_m = \frac{d_m}{z}$$

71/172
$$d_m = 2 R_m \sin \delta \qquad\qquad F_{tm} = \frac{2\, T}{d_m}$$

continued on Q 25

For symbols see Q 29, for suffixes see Q 23

continued from Q 24

Axial and radial forces in mesh

q 173   axial force $F_a = F_{tm} \, \tan a_n \times \sin \delta$

q 174   radial force $F_r = F_{tm} \, \tan a_n \times \cos \delta$

Load capacity of tooth root (approx. calculation)

Safety factor S_F against fatigue failure of tooth root:

q 175
$$S_F = \frac{\sigma_{Flim}}{\frac{F_{tm}}{b \, m_{nm}} \times Y_\varepsilon \times Y_{\varepsilon V} \times Y_\beta} \times \frac{Y_S \times K_{FX}}{K_I \times K_V \times K_{F\alpha} \times K_{F\beta}} \geqslant S_{Fmin}$$

Giving the approximate formula:

q 176
$$m_{nm} \geqslant \frac{F_{tm}}{b} \times Y_F \times K_I \times K_V \times \underbrace{Y_{\varepsilon V} \times f_\beta \times K_{F\alpha}}_{\simeq 1} \times \underbrace{\frac{K_{F\beta}}{Y_S \times K_{FX}}}_{\simeq 1} \times \frac{S_{Fmin}}{\sigma_{Flim}}$$

q 177 Y_F : substitute the number of teeth of the complementary spur gear z_v
or, with spiral gears $z_{vn} \simeq z_v/\cos^3 \beta$. The graph for spur gears
on page Q 21 is then also applicable to bevel gears.

For all other data see q 142, q 143 and q 144.

Load capacity of tooth flank (approximate calculation)

Safety factor S_H against pitting of tooth surface.

q 178
$$S_H = \frac{\sigma_{Hlim}}{\sqrt{\frac{u+1}{u} \times \frac{F_{tm}}{b \, d_1} \times Z_H \times Z_M \times Z_{\varepsilon V}}} \times \frac{Z_V \times K_{HX} \times Z_R \times K_L}{\sqrt{K_I \times K_V \times K_{H\alpha} \times K_{H\beta}}} \geqslant S_{Hmin}$$

For metals the material factor Z_M is simplified to:

q 179
$$Z_M = \sqrt{0 \cdot 35 \; E} \quad \text{with} \quad E = \frac{2 \, E_1 \, E_2}{E_1 + E_2}$$

Giving the approximate formula:

q 180
$$d_{vm1} \geqslant \sqrt{\frac{2 \, T_1}{b} \times \frac{u_v + 1}{u_v}} \; 0 \cdot 35 \; E \times Z_{HV} \times \underbrace{Z_{\varepsilon V} \times \sqrt{K_{H\alpha}}}_{\simeq 1} \times \frac{\sqrt{K_I \times K_V} \times \overbrace{\sqrt{K_{H\beta}}}^{\simeq 1}}{Z_V \times K_{HX} \times Z_R \times K_L} \times \frac{S_{Hmin}}{\sigma_{Hlim}}$$

q 181 Z_{HV} : see diagram for Z_H (page Q 22), but only valid for
$(x_1 + x_2)/(z_1 + z_2) = 0$ with $\beta = \beta_m$.
For all other data see q 148 ... q 151.

Velocity diagram and angular velocities
(referred to fixed space)

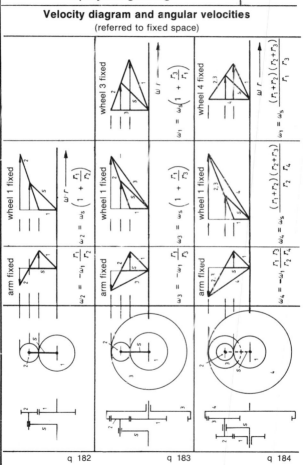

wheel 3 fixed

$$\omega_3 = \omega_s \left(1 + \frac{r_3}{r_1}\right)$$

wheel 4 fixed

$$\omega_1 = \omega_s \frac{(r_1 + r_2)(r_2 + r_3)}{r_1 r_3}$$

wheel 1 fixed

$$\omega_2 = \omega_s \left(1 + \frac{r_1}{r_2}\right)$$

wheel 1 fixed

$$\omega_3 = \omega_s \left(1 + \frac{r_1}{r_3}\right)$$

wheel 1 fixed

$$\omega_4 = \omega_s \frac{(r_1 + r_2)(r_2 + r_3)}{r_2 r_4}$$

arm fixed

$$\omega_2 = -\omega_1 \frac{r_1}{r_2}$$

arm fixed

$$\omega_3 = -\omega_1 \frac{r_1}{r_3}$$

arm fixed

$$\omega_4 = -\omega_1 \frac{r_1 r_3}{r_2 r_4}$$

q 182   q 183   q 184

Worm gearing, geometry
(Cylindrical worm gearing, normal module in axial section, BS 2519, angle between shafts $\Sigma = 90°$).

Drive worm
All the forces acting on the teeth in mesh are shown by the three arrows F_a, F_t and F_r.

In the example:
$z_1 = 2$, right-hand helix.

Gear tooth ratio and transmission ratio as q 86 .., 88

		Worm, suffix 1	Worm wheel, suffix 2
q 185	module	$m_x = m = m_t$	
q 186	pitch	$p_x = m\,\pi = p_2 = d_2\,\pi/z_2$	
q 187	mean diameter	$d_{m1} = 2\,r_{m1}$	
	(free to choose, for normal values see DIN 3976)		
q 188	form factor	$q = d_{m1}/m$	
q 189	centre helix angle	$\tan\gamma_m = \dfrac{m\,z_1}{d_{m1}} = \dfrac{z_1}{q}$	
q 190	pitch diameter		$d_2 = m\,z_2$
q 191	addendum	$h_{a1} = m$	$h_{a2} = m(1+x)$ [1]
q 192	dedendum	$h_{f1} = m(1+c_1{}^*)$	$h_{z2} = m(1-x+c_2{}^*)$
q 193	tip clearance factor	$c_1{}^* = (0\cdot167\ldots0\cdot2\ldots0\cdot3) = c_2{}^*$	
q 194	outside diameter	$d_{a1} = d_{m1} + 2\,h_{a1}$	$d_{a2} = d_2 + 2\,h_{a2}$
q 195	tip groove radius		$r_k = a - d_{a2}/2$
q 196	tooth width	$b_1 \geqslant \sqrt{d_{a2}{}^2 - d_2{}^2}$	$b_2 \doteqdot 0\cdot9\,d_{m1} - 2\,m$
q 197	root diameter	$d_{f1} = d_{m1} - 2\,h_{f1}$	$d_{f2} = d_2 - h_{f2}$
q 198	centre distance	$a = (d_{m1} + d_2)/2 + x\,m$ [1]	

[1] Profile offset factor x for check of a pre-set centre distance, otherwise $x = 0$.

continued on Q 28

For symbols see Q 29, for suffixes see Q 23

continued from Q 27

Worm gearing, design (worm driving)

		Worm	Worm wheel
q 199	peripheral force	$F_{t1} = \dfrac{2\,T_1}{d_{m1}}\,K_1 \times K_v$	$F_{t2} = F_{a1}$
q 200	axial force	$F_{a1} = F_{t1} \times \dfrac{1}{\tan(\gamma + \varrho)}$	$F_{a2} = F_{t1}$
q 201	radial force	$F_{r1} = F_{t1} \times \dfrac{\cos\varrho \times \tan a_n}{\sin(\gamma + \varrho)}$	$= F_r = F_{r2}$
q 202	rubbing speed	$v_g = \dfrac{d_{m1}}{2} \times \dfrac{u_1}{\cos\gamma_m}$	

Efficiency

	Worm driving	Worm wheel driving
q 203	$\eta = \tan\gamma_m / \tan(\gamma_m + \varrho)$	$\eta' = \tan(\gamma_m - \varrho)/\tan\gamma_m$
		$(\gamma_m < \varrho) \implies$ self-locking!

Coefficient of friction (typical values) $\mu = \tan\varrho$

	$v_g \approx 1$ m/s	$v_g \approx 10$ m/s
worm teeth hardened and ground	0·04	0·02
worm teeth tempered and machine cut	0·08	0·05

For calculation of worm shaft deflection see P 12

Calculation of module m

Load capacity of teeth root and flanks and temperature rise are combined in the approximate formula:

q 204
q 205
q 206

$$F_{t2} = C\, b_2\, p_2\,;$$

where $b_2 \approx 0.8\, c_{m1}$; $p_2 = m\,\pi$.

$$m \approx \sqrt[3]{\dfrac{0.3\,T_2}{C_{perm}\,q\,z_2}}$$

$F_{t2} = 2\,T_2/d_2 = 2\,T_2/(m\,z_2)$

$q \approx 10$ for $i = 10, 20, 40$

$q \approx 17$ for $i = 80$, self-locking

Assumed values for normal, naturally-cooled worm gears (worm hardened and ground steel, worm wheel of bronze):

v_g	m s^{-1}	1	2	5	10	15	20
C_{perm}	N mm^{-2}	8	8	5	3·5	2·4	2·2

When cooling is adequate this value can be used for all speeds:

$$C_{perm} \geq 8 \text{ N mm}^{-2}$$

q 207

For all symbols see Q 29, for suffixes see Q 23

Notation for Q 18 … Q 28 (suffixes see Q 23)

a : standard centre distance
b : tooth width
h_{a0} : addendum of cutting tool
h_{aP} : addendum of reference profile (e.g. DIN 867)
h_{fP} : dedendum of reference profile
k : change of addendum factor
p_e : normal pitch ($p_e = p \cos a$, $p_{et} = p_t \cos a_t$)
z : no. of teeth
z_{nx} : equivalent no. of teeth
(C_{perm}), C : (permissible) load coefficient
F_t : peripheral force on pitch cylinder (plane section)
K_I : operating factor (external shock)
K_v : dynamic factor (internal shock)
$K_{F\alpha}$: end load distribution factor ⎫
$K_{F\beta}$: face load distribution factor ⎬ for root stress
K_{FX} : size factor ⎭
$K_{H\alpha}$: end load distribution factor ⎫ for flank stress
$K_{H\beta}$: face load distribution ⎭
R_e : total pitch cone length (bevel gears)
R_m : mean pitch cone length (bevel gears)
T : torque
Y_F (Y_S) : form factor, (stress concentration factor)
Y_β : skew factor
Y_ε : load proportion factor
Z_H : flank form factor
Z_ε : engagement factor
Z_R : roughness factor
Z_v : velocity factor
a_P : reference profile angle (DIN 867 : $a_P = 20°$)
a_W : operating angle
$\dfrac{\beta}{\beta_b}$ skew angle for helical gears $\begin{array}{l}\text{pitch cylinder}\\\text{base cylinder}\end{array}$
ϱ : sliding friction angle (tan $\varrho = \mu$)
ϱ_{a0} : tip edge radius of tool
$\sigma_{F\,lim}$: fatigue strength
$\sigma_{H\,lim}$: Hertz pressure (contact pressure)

Precise calculations for spur and bevel gears: DIN 3990.
Terms and definitions for
$\left.\begin{array}{l}\text{spur gears and gearing} \quad : \quad \text{DIN 3960}\\\text{bevel gears and gearing} \quad : \quad \text{DIN 3971}\\\text{straight worm gearing} \quad : \quad \text{DIN 3975}\end{array}\right\}$ or BS 2519

Machine tool design: general considerations

Components of machine tools which are subjected to working stresses (frames with mating and guide surfaces, slides and tables, work spindles with bearings) are designed to give high accuracy over long periods of time. They are made with generous bearing areas and the means to readjust or replace worn surfaces should is become necessary.

The maximum permissible deflection at the cutting edge (point of chip formation) is approximately 0·03 mm. For spindle deflection refer to formula P 13 and for cutting forces see r 4.

Cutting drives (main drives) with v = const. over the entire working range (max. and min. workpiece or tool-diameter are obtainable with output speeds in geometric progression:

r 1
$$n_k = n_1 \, \varphi^{k-1}$$

The progressive ratio φ for the speeds $n_1 \ldots n_k$ with k number output speeds

r 2
are calculated by:
$$\varphi = \sqrt[k-1]{\frac{n_k}{n_1}}$$

and the preferred series is selected.

Standardized progressive ratio φ: 1·12–1·25–1·4–1·6–2·0

Speed basic series R_{20} where $\varphi = \sqrt[20]{10} = 1·12$:

... 100–112–125–140–160–180–200–224–250–280–315–355–400– –450–500–560–630–710–800–900–1000–... rpm.

Cutting gears are designated by the number of shafts and steps.

Example: A III/6 gear drive incorporates 3 shafts and provides 6 output speeds. Representation of gear unit as shown (for $k = 6$; $\varphi = 1·4$; $n_1 = 180$; $n_k = 1000$):

--- Network of scales (symmetrical)
—— Speed diagram

Gear arrangement

For explanation of symbols refer to R 4

Cutting power P_s

r 3	Cutting power	$P_s = \dfrac{F_s \cdot v}{\eta_{mech} \cdot \eta_{electr}}$
r 4	Cutting force	$F_s = K \cdot k_{s1.1} \cdot b \cdot h^{1-z} \cdot z_e$

where h and b are in mm,

$k_{s1.1}$ is in N/mm² and F_s is in N.

Table of values for K, b, h, z_e $k_{s1.1}$; $1-z$ see Z 17)

No	Method	Sketch	K	b	h	z_e	Notes
r5	Turning external longitud.		1 HM + HSS	$\dfrac{a}{\sin \varkappa}$	$s \cdot \sin \varkappa$	1	
r6	internal	analogous to r 5	1·1 HM				
r7	Planing and shaping		1·2 HSS				
r8	Drilling and boring		0·85 HM, 1 HSS	$\dfrac{D-d}{2\sin\frac{\delta}{2}}$	$s_z \times \sin\frac{\delta}{2}$, $s_z = 0{,}5\,s$	2 for twist drill	$d = 0$ when drilling, $\sigma = 118°$ for steel
r9	Plane milling down-cut and up-cut		1 HSS	$\dfrac{B}{\sin\delta}$	$\dfrac{2a}{D}\,s_z \times \sin\varkappa$	$\dfrac{\varphi_s z_s}{360°}$	$\varkappa = 90°-\delta$, $\cos\varphi_s = 1 - 2a/D$
r10	End milling		1·1 HM, 1·2 HSS	$\dfrac{a}{\sin\varkappa}$	$(\cos\varphi_1 - \cos\varphi_2)\times\dfrac{1}{\varphi_s}\,s_z \times \sin\varkappa$		$\varphi_s = \varphi_2-\varphi_1$, $\cos\varphi_1 = \dfrac{D-2B_1}{D}$, $\cos\varphi_2 = \dfrac{D-2B_2}{D}$ calculate φ_1 and φ_2 in direction of rotation

For explanation of symbols refer to R 4

Feed drives

Feeds in geometrical progression with progressive ratio
$$\varphi = 1 \cdot 12 - 1 \cdot 25 - 1 \cdot 4 - 1 \cdot 6 - 2 \cdot 0.$$

Feed rate

	Method	Feed rate	Notes
r 11	Turning, longitudinal (external and internal)	$u = n \times s$	
r 12	Drilling	$u = n \times s_z \times z_s$	for twist drills $z_e = z_s = 2$ $s_z = 0 \cdot 5\, s$
r 13	Planing, shaping	$u = v$	
r 14	Milling, plane milling and end milling	$u = s_z \times n \times z_s$	

Cutting times t_s

r 15
$$t_s = \frac{l_1}{u} ; \quad \text{where} \quad l_1 = l + l'.$$

When calculating the cycle and machining times for each workpiece, the feed and infeed travels and also the lengths covered during non-cutting motions, divided by the corresponding speeds, must be taken into account.

Feed power P_V

r 16	Feed power	$P_V = \dfrac{u(F_R + F_V)}{\eta_{mech} \times \eta_{electr}}$
r 17	Feed force	$F_V \approx 0 \cdot 2\, F_S$; (F_s from r 4)
r 18	Friction force	$F_R = m_b \times g \times \mu$

where m_b is the mass moved, e.g. in the case of milling machines the sum of the table and workpiece masses.

It must be determined whether the feed power as calculated under r 16 is sufficient to accelerate the moving components to rapid motion speed u_E within a given time t_b (in production machines $u_E \approx 0 \cdot 2$ m/s).
Otherwise the following applies:

r 19
$$P_V = u_E\, m_b \left(\mu\, g + \frac{u_E}{t_b} \right) \frac{1}{\eta_{mech} \times \eta_{electr}}$$

For explanation or symbols refer to R 4

PRODUCTION ENGINEERING
Machining

R 4

Explanation of symbols
used on pages R 1 ... R 3

a : infeed
b : width of chip
B : milling width
B_1, B_2 : milling width measured from tool centre
d : diameter of pre-drilled hole
D : tool diameter
F_R : friction force
F_S : cutting force
F_V : feed force
g : gravitational acceleration
h : chip thickness
k : number of output speeds
k_{S1} : basic cutting force related to area
K : method factor
l : cutting travel
l_1 : work travel
l' : overrun travel at both ends with feed rate u
n : speed
n_1 : minimum output speed
n_k : maximum output speed
s : feed
s_z : feed per cutting edge
t_b : acceleration time
t_s : cutting time
u : feed rate
u_E : rapid traverse speed
v : cutting speed
z_e : number of cutting edges in action
z_s : number of cutting edges per tool
δ : cutter helix angle
ε_S : slenderness ratio ($\varepsilon_S = a/s$)
η_{electr} : electrical efficiency
η_{mech} : mechanical efficiency
$\varkappa$: setting angle
μ : friction coefficient, see Z 7
δ : drill tip angle
φ : progressive ratio
φ_S : entrance angle of milling cutter

HM : carbide tip
HSS : high-speed tip

Cold working of sheet
Deep drawing

Initial blank diameter D

r 20
$$D = \sqrt{\frac{4}{\pi} \times \Sigma A_{mi}}$$

A_{mi} are the surface areas of the finished item which can be calculated from the following formulae b 30, c 12, c 16, c 21, c 25, c 27 or c 30. The surface areas at the transition radii for both drawing and stamping dies are calculated as follows:

r 21
$$A_m = \frac{\pi}{4}\left[2\pi d_1 r_z + 4(\pi - 2)r_z^2\right] \qquad A_m = \frac{\pi}{4}(2\pi d_4 + 8r_s)r_s + \frac{\pi}{4}d_4^2$$

Example: (assume $r_s = r_z = r$)

r 22
$$D = \sqrt{d_4^2 + d_6^2 - d_5^2 + 4d_1 h + 2\pi r(d_1 + d_4) + 4\pi r^2}$$

1st and 2nd stages

1st stage	2nd stage

r 23 | $\beta_1 = \dfrac{D}{d_1}$ | $\beta_2 = \dfrac{d_1}{d_2}$

r 24 | $\beta_{1max} = \beta_{100} + 0\cdot1 - \left(\dfrac{d_1}{s} C\cdot001\right)$ | $\beta_{2max} = \beta_{100} + 0\cdot1 - \left(\dfrac{d_2}{s} 0\cdot001\right)$

r 25 | $F_{D1} = \pi d_1 s k_{fm1} \varphi_1 \dfrac{1}{r_{E1}}$ | $F_{D2} = \dfrac{F_{D1}}{2} + \pi d_2 s k_{fm2} \varphi_2 \dfrac{1}{\eta_{E2}}$

r 26 | $\varphi_1 = \left|\ln\sqrt{0\cdot6\,\beta_1^2 - 0\cdot4}\right|$ | $\varphi_2 = \left|\ln\sqrt{0\cdot6\,\beta_2^2 - 0\cdot4}\right|$

| | | | without | inter-mediate | $k_{fm2} = \dfrac{k_{f1} + k_{f2}}{2}$ |

r 27
r 28
r 29 | $k_{fm1} = \dfrac{w}{\varphi_1}$ | | with | anneal-ing | $k_{fm2} = \dfrac{w}{\varphi_2}$

continued on R 6

continued from R 5

The work w, related to the volume and the yield strength k_f is obtained from the deformation curves for the appropriate value of logarithmic deformation ratio φ (see Z 20).

Blank holding forces F_{B1} and F_{B2}

1st stage	2nd stage
r 30	$F_{B1}=(D^2-d_1^2)\dfrac{\pi}{4}\dfrac{R_m}{400}\left[(\beta_1^2-1)+\dfrac{d_1}{s}\right]$	$F_{B2}=(d_1^2-d_2^2)\dfrac{\pi}{4}\dfrac{R_m}{400}\left[(\beta_2^2-1)+\dfrac{d_2}{s}\right]$

Bottom tearing occurs if

r 31 $R_m\leqslant\dfrac{F_{D1}+0.1\,F_{B1}}{\pi\,d_1\,s}$ $\qquad$ $R_m\leqslant\dfrac{F_{D2}+0.1\,F_{B2}}{\pi\,d_2\,s}$

r 32 **Maximum drawing conditions β and R_m**

Material – Sheet metal Specification to				β_{100}	intermediate		R_m N/mm²
	U.S.A.	BS	Grade		without annealing	with β_{2max}	
	366-79		15	1·7	1·2	1·5	390
	619-75		4	1·8	1·2	1·6	360
Carbon steel	ASTM- —	1449 P. 1	3	1·9	1·25	1·65	350
	620-75		2	2·0	1·3	1·7	340
	283 Gr. C		1	1·7	–	–	410
Stainless steel (18% Cr; 9% Ni)	SAE 3310	970	321 S 20	2·0	1·2	1·8	600
Al Mg Si soft	AA 6004 soft	1490	LM 5	2·05	1·4	1·9	150

Notation for R 5 and R 6

A_{mi} : surface area

F_{D1}, F_{D2} : drawing force in 1st and 2nd stage

k_{fm1} or k_{fm2} : mean yield strength, 1st or 2nd stage

k_{f1}, k_{f2} : yield strength for φ_1 and φ_2

r : radius

r_s : radius of stamping die

r_d : radius of drawing die

w : work per unit volume $=\dfrac{\text{work of deformation}}{\text{forminged volume}}$

β_1, β_2 : drawing ratio, 1st and 2nd stage

β_{100} : max. drawing ratio for $s=1$ mm and $d=100$ mm

β_{1max}, β_{2max} : max. drawing ratio, 1st and 2nd stage

η_{E1}, η_{E2} : process efficiency, 1st and 2nd stage

φ_1, φ_2 : logarithmic deformation ratio, 1st and 2nd stage

The most important electrical quantities and their units. – Basic rules

s 1 **Note regarding capital and small letters used as symbols**

Electrical engineering quantities that are independent of time are mainly denoted by capital letters. Quantities that vary with time are denoted by small letters or by capital letters provided with the subscript t

Examples: formulae s 8, s 9, s 13

Exceptions: f, ω, $\hat{\imath}$, $\hat{u}$, $p_{Fe1,0}$

Electrical work W

Electrical work W is equivalent to mechanical work W as explained on M 1. Energy conversion, however, is subject to losses.

Units: J; W s (wattsecond); kW h; MW h

$$1 \, W \, s = 1 \, \text{Joule} = 1 \, J = 1 \, N \, m$$

Further the following relation applies, using quantities explained on S1 and S2:

s 2
$$W = I \, V \, t = \frac{V^2}{R} t = I^2 R \, t$$

Electrical power P

Electrical power P is equivalent to mechanical power P, as explained on M 1. Energy conversion, however, is subject to losses.

Units: W (Watt); kW; MW

$$1 \, W = 1 \, \frac{J}{s} = 1 \, \frac{N \, m}{s}$$

Further the following relation applies, using quantities explained on S1 and S2:

s 3
$$P = \frac{V^2}{R} = I^2 R$$

Frequency f   see L 1

Period T   see L 1

Angular frequency ω, angular velocity ω see L 1

Current I

Is a base quantity (see preface and instructions)

Units: A (ampere); mA; kA

The current of 1 A has been defined by means of the attracting force which two parallel current-carrying conductors exert on each other.

continued on S 2

continued from S 1

Current density J

s 4

$$J = \frac{I}{A}$$

Applicable only where distribution of current I is uniform over cross section A.
Units: A/m^2; A/mm^2

Potential difference V

s 5

$$V = \frac{P}{I}$$

Units: V (volt); mV; kV

Where a direct current of 1 A through a conductor converts energy at a rate of 1 W, the voltage across this conductor is 1 V.

$$1 V = \frac{W}{A} = 1\frac{J}{s\,A} = 1\,A\,\Omega = 1\frac{N\,m}{s\,A}$$

Resistance R

s 6

$$R = \frac{V}{I}$$ (Ohm's law)

Units: Ω (ohm); kΩ; MΩ

Where a voltage of 1 V across a conductor causes a current of 1 A to the flow through it, resistance is 1 Ω.

$$1\,\Omega = \frac{1\,V}{1\,A} = 1\frac{W}{A^2} = 1\frac{W}{s\,A^2} = 1\frac{N\,m}{s\,A^2}$$

Conductance G

Conductance G is the reciprocal of resistance R.

s 7

$$G = 1/R$$

Unit: $1/\Omega$

$$1/\Omega = [1\,\text{Mho}]$$

Quantity of electricity, charge Q

s 8

$$q = \int i\ dt$$ (see s 1)

For direct current:

s 9

$$Q = I\,t$$

Unit: C (coulomb);

$$1\,C = 1\,A\,s$$

continued on S 3

continued from S 2

Capacitance C

The capacitance C of a capacitor is the ratio of quantity of electricity Q stored in it and voltage V across it:

s 10

$$C = \frac{Q}{V}$$

Units: F (farad); µF; nF; pF

Where a capacitor requires a charge of 1 C to be charged to a voltage of 1 V, its capacitance is 1 F.

$$1\,F = 1\frac{C}{V} = 1\frac{A\,s}{V} = 1\frac{A^2\,s}{W} = 1\frac{A^2\,s^2}{J} = 1\frac{A^2\,s^2}{N\,m}$$

Magnetic flux $\bar{\phi}$

s 11

$$\phi = \frac{1}{N}\int v\ dt \qquad \text{(see s 1)}$$

Here N is the number of turns of a coil and v the voltage induced, when the magnetic flux $\bar{\phi}$ linked with the coil varies with time.

Units: Wb (weber) = V s = 10^8 M (maxwell)

1 Wb is the magnetic flux which, linking a circuit of 1 turn, induces in it a voltage of 1 V as it is reduced to zero at a uniform rate in 1 s.

Magnetic induction (flux density) B

The magnetic induction in a cross section A is:

s 12

$$B = \frac{\phi}{A}$$

Here A is the cross-sectional area traversed perpendicularly by the homogeneous magnetic flux $\bar{\phi}$.

Units: T (tesla); µT; nT; V s/m²; G (gauss)

$$1\,T = 1\frac{V\,s}{m^2} = 10^{-4}\frac{V\,s}{cm^2} = \left[10^4 G = 10^4\frac{M}{cm^2}\right]$$

Where a homogeneous magnetic flux of 1 Wb perpendicularly traverses an area of 1 m², its magnetic induction is 1 T.

continued on S 4

continued from S 3

Inductance L

s 13

$$L = N\frac{\phi}{I} = N\frac{\phi_t}{i}$$ (see s 1)

Here I is the current flowing through a coil of N turns and ϕ the magnetic flux linked with this coil.

Units: H (henry); mH

1 H is the inductance of a closed loop of one turn which, positioned in vacuum and passed through by a current of 1 A, enclosed a magnetic flux of 1 Wb.

$$1\,H = 1\frac{Wb}{A} = 1\frac{V\,s}{A}$$

Magnetic field strength H

s 14

$$H = \frac{B}{\mu_0\,\mu_r}$$

Units: A/m; A/cm; A/mm; (Ampere Turn/m)

Magnetomotive force F

s 15

$$F = N I$$

Units: A; kA; mA; (Ampere Turn)

Magnetomotive force F_i in the i-th section of a magnetic circuit:

s 16

$$F_i = H_i\,l_i$$

here l_i is the length of this section.

s 17

$$\sum_{i=1}^{n} F_i = F$$

Reluctance S of a homogeneous section of a magnetic circuit:

s 18

$$S = \frac{F}{\phi} \quad \left(\begin{array}{c}\text{equivalent to}\\ \text{Ohm's law for}\\ \text{magnetic circuits}\end{array}\right)$$

Units: 1/H; = A/V s; (Ampere Turn/Wb)

for symbols see S 16

Basic properties of electric circuits

Directions of currents, voltages, arrows representing them

s 20	Direction of the current and of arrows	generator $-\!\!\rightarrow\!+$
s 21	representing positive currents in	load $+\!\!\rightarrow\!-$
s 22	Direction of the potential difference and of arrows representing positive voltages always	$+\!\!\rightarrow\!-$

Directions of arrows representing currents or voltages

	where function of element (generator or load) as well as polarity is	determine directions of arrows	where calculation results in a positive value, direction with respect to arrow of current or voltage is	negative
s 23	known	as stated above	—	—
s 24	unknown	at random	equal	opposite

Special rule

Arrows representing voltage drop across a resistor and current causing it, should always be determined in same direction (as $R > 0$).

Ohm's Law

Current through a resistor:

s 25
$$I = \frac{V}{R} \qquad \text{(see also s 6)}$$

Resistance R of conductor

s 26
$$R = \frac{\varrho \, l}{A} = \frac{l}{\gamma \, A}$$

Resistance R of conductor at temperature ϑ
(in degrees centigrade)

s 27
$$R = R_{20} \left[1 + a \left(\vartheta - 20^\circ C \right) \right]$$

Electric heating of a mass m

s 28
$$V \, I \, t \, \eta = c \, m \, \Delta \vartheta$$

a :	temperature coefficient	(see Z 21)	$\Delta \vartheta$:	temperature change
γ :	conductivity	(see Z 21)	t :	time
ϱ :	resistivity	(see Z 21)	R_{20} :	resistance at $\vartheta = 20^\circ C$
c :	specific heat	(see Z 1 … 4 and O 2)		
η :	efficiency			

continued on S 6

continued from S 5

1st Kirchhoff Law

The algebraic sum of all currents entering a branch point (node) is zero.

s 29
$$\Sigma I \;=\; 0$$

$$I - I_1 - I_2 - I_3 = 0$$

Here currents	into	the node	positive
	out of	are considered	negative

Ratio of currents

Where several resistors are connected in parallel, total current and partial currents are inversely proportional to their respective resistances.

s 30
$$I : I_1 : I_2 : I_3 \;=\; \frac{1}{R} : \frac{1}{R_1} : \frac{1}{R_2} : \frac{1}{R_3}$$

Current division

Partial currents of 2 resistors connected in parallel:

s 31
$$I_1 \;=\; I \, \frac{G_1}{G_1 + G_2} \;=\; I \, \frac{R_2}{R_1 + R_2}$$

2nd Kirchhoff Law

The algebraic sum of all voltages around a closed mesh (loop) is zero.

s 32
$$\Sigma V \;=\; 0$$

Here voltages traversed in <u>accordance with</u> (opposite to) direction of arrow are considered <u>positive</u> (negative).

$$V_1 + V_{01} - V_2 + V_3 + V_4 - V_{02} = 0$$

Ratio of voltages

Where several resistors are connected in series, the ratio of partial voltages is equal to the ratio of the respective resistances.

s 33
$$V_1 : V_2 : V_3 \;=\; R_1 : R_2 : R_3$$

Voltage divider

Partial voltages across 2 resistors connected in series:

s 34
$$V_1 \;=\; V \, \frac{G_2}{G_1 + G_2} \;=\; V \, \frac{R_1}{R_1 + R_2}$$

Series connection

Total resistance R (according to s 26)

generally:

s 35
$$R_S = R_1 + R_2 + R_3 + \ldots$$

for n equal resistances R:

s 36
$$R_S = n R$$

Parallel connection

Total resistance R (according to s 30)

generally:

s 37
$$\frac{1}{R_p} = \frac{1}{R_1} + \frac{1}{R_2} + \frac{1}{R_3} + \ldots$$

s 38
$$G_p = G_1 + G_2 + G_3 + \ldots$$

for 2	for 3	for n equal
several resistances		resistances

s 39
$$R_p = \frac{R_1 R_2}{R_1 + R_2} \quad \Big| \quad R_p = \frac{R_1 R_2 R_3}{R_1 R_2 + R_2 R_3 + R_1 R_3} \quad \Big| \quad R_p = \frac{R}{n}$$

s 40
$$= \frac{1}{G_1 + G_2} \quad \Big| \quad = \frac{1}{G_1 - G_2 + G_3} \quad \Big| \quad = \frac{1}{n G}$$

Multiple connection

A multiple connection of several known resistances is subdivided into parallel and series connections, proceeding outwards. These are separately converted as to be conveniently combined again, e.g.:

s 41
$$I = \frac{R_2 + R_3}{R_1 R_2 + R_1 R_3 + R_2 R_3} \, V = \frac{G_1 (G_2 + G_3)}{G_1 + G_2 + G_3} \, V$$

s 42
$$I_3 = \frac{R_2}{R_1 R_2 + R_1 R_3 + R_2 R_3} \, V = \frac{G_1 G_3}{G_1 + G_2 + G_3} \, V$$

s 43
$$V_2 = \frac{R_2 R_3}{R_1 R_2 + R_1 R_3 + R_2 R_3} \, V = \frac{G_1}{G_1 + G_2 + G_3} \, V$$

Transformation of a delta to a star-circuit and vice versa

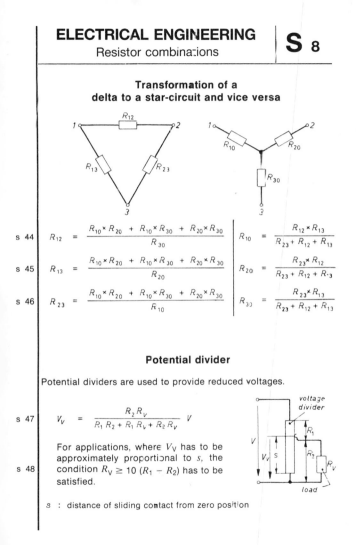

s 44 $\quad R_{12} = \dfrac{R_{10} \times R_{20} + R_{10} \times R_{30} + R_{20} \times R_{30}}{R_{30}}$ $\qquad R_{10} = \dfrac{R_{12} \times R_{13}}{R_{23} + R_{12} + R_{13}}$

s 45 $\quad R_{13} = \dfrac{R_{10} \times R_{20} + R_{10} \times R_{30} + R_{20} \times R_{30}}{R_{20}}$ $\qquad R_{20} = \dfrac{R_{23} \times R_{12}}{R_{23} + R_{12} + R_3}$

s 46 $\quad R_{23} = \dfrac{R_{10} \times R_{20} + R_{10} \times R_{30} + R_{20} \times R_{30}}{R_{10}}$ $\qquad R_{30} = \dfrac{R_{23} \times R_{13}}{R_{23} + R_{12} + R_{13}}$

Potential divider

Potential dividers are used to provide reduced voltages.

s 47 $\quad V_V = \dfrac{R_2 R_V}{R_1 R_2 + R_1 R_V + R_2 R_V}\; V$

For applications, where V_V has to be approximately proportional to s, the condition $R_V \geq 10\,(R_1 - R_2)$ has to be satisfied.

s 48

s : distance of sliding contact from zero position

Applications in electrical measurements

Extending the range of a voltmeter

s 49
$$R_V = R_M\left(\frac{V_{max}}{V_{Mmax}} - 1\right)$$

Extending the range of an ammeter

s 50
$$R_N = R_M \frac{I_{Mmax}}{I_{max} - I_{Mmax}}$$

Wheatstone bridge for measuring an unknown resistance R_X

A slide-wire Wheatstone bridge may be used for measuring resistances of between 0·1 and 10^6 ohms. The calibrated slide wire is provided with a scale reading $a/(l-a)$. The sliding contact is adjusted, until the detector current I_B is zero. Then

s 51
$$\frac{R_X}{R} = \frac{a}{l - a}$$

s 52   and hence $R_X = R\dfrac{a}{l - a}$

Wheatstone bridge used as a primary element

In many types of measuring equipment Wheatstone bridges serve as comperators for evaluating voltage differences.

R_1 : sensor resistor, the variation of which is proportional to the quantity x to be measured (e.g. temperature, distance, angle etc.)

R_2 : zero value of R_1

Approx. the relation applies

s 53
$$V_M \sim \Delta R \sim x$$

R_M : internal resistance of the measurement

Capacitance C of a capacitor

s 54
$$C = \frac{\varepsilon_0\, \varepsilon_r\, A}{a}$$

Quantity of electricity Q (see s 8)

Electrical work W_C stored in an electric field

s 55
$$W_C = \frac{1}{2}\, C\, V^2$$

Capacitors connected in parallel
Where capacitors are added in parallel,
the total capacitance C increases.

s 56
$$C = C_1 + C_2 + C_3$$

Capacitors connected in series
Where capacitors are added in series,
the total capacitance C decreases.

s 57
$$\frac{1}{C} = \frac{1}{C_1} + \frac{1}{C_2} + \frac{1}{C_3}$$

Capacitance of two coaxial cylinders

s 58
$$C = 2\, \pi\, \varepsilon_0\, \varepsilon_r \frac{l}{\ln\frac{r_2}{r_1}}$$

s 59

ε_r :	relative permittivity
ε_0 :	absolute permittivity
A :	plate area (one side)
a :	thickness of dielectric
r_1 :	radius of inner cylinder
r_2 :	radius of outer cylinder
l :	length of cylinders

(see Z 22)
$\varepsilon_0 = 3.85 \times 10^{-12}\,\text{A s/(V m)}$

s 60
Deflection of a magnetic needle

The N-pole of a magnetic needle is attracted by a magnetic S-pole and repelled by a magnetic N-pole.

Fixed conductors and coils

s 61
Magnetic flux about a current-carrying conductor
Assuming a corkscrew were screwed in the direction of the current, its direction of rotation would indicate the direction of the lines of magnetic flux.

s 62
Magnetic flux within a current-carrying coil
Assuming a corkscrew were rotated in the direction of the current through the coil, the direction of its axial motion would indicate the direction of the lines of magnetic flux through the coil.

Movable conductors and coils

s 63
Parallel conductors
Two parallel conductors carrying currents of the same direction attract. Two carrying currents of opposite direction repel each other.

s 64
Two coils facing each other
Where two coils positioned face to face carry currents of the same direction, they attract, where they carry currents of opposite directions, they repel each other.

Machines

s 65
Right Hand Rule (generator)
Where the thumb points in the direction of the magnetic flux and the middle finger in the direction of motion, the index finger indicates the direction of current flow.

s 66
Left Hand Rule (motor)
Where the thumb points in the direction of the magnetic flux and the index finger in the direction of current flow, the middle finger indicates the direction of motion.

Quantities of magnetic circuits

Magnetic flux ϕ

s 67
$$\phi = \frac{F}{S} = \frac{N\,I}{R_m}$$
(see also s 11)

Magnetic induction (flux density) B

s 68
$$B = \frac{\phi}{A} = \mu_r\,\mu_0\,H$$
(see also s 12)

Inductance L

s 69
$$L = N\frac{\phi}{I} = N^2\Lambda = \frac{N^2}{R_m}$$
(see also s 13)

For calculation of L see also s 140 through s 146

Magnetic field strength H (Magnetising force)

s 70
$$H = \frac{B}{\mu_r\,\mu_0} = \frac{F_i}{l_i}$$
(see also s 14)

Magnetomotive force F

s 71
$$F = N\,I = \sum_{i=1}^{n}F_i$$
(see also s 15)

Magnetomotive force F_i

s 72
$$F_i = H_i\,l_i$$
(see also s 16)

Reluctance S

s 73
$$S = \frac{F}{\phi} = \frac{l}{\mu_r\,\mu_0\,A}$$
(see also s 18)

Energy W_m stored in a magnetic field

s 74
$$W_m = \frac{1}{2}\,N\,I\,\phi = \frac{1}{2}\,L\,I^2$$

Leakage flux ϕ_L

Part of the total magnetic flux ϕ leaks through the air and is thus lost for the desired effect. ϕ_L is related to the useful flux ϕ_u. Hence the leakage

s 75
coefficient is:
$$\sigma = \frac{\phi}{\phi_u} = \frac{\text{total flux}}{\text{useful flux}}$$
(1·15 ... 1·25)

For symbols see S 16

The magnetic field and its forces

Force F_m acting between magnetic poles

In the direction of the magnetic flux a tensile force F_m occurs:

s 78
$$F_m = \frac{1}{2} \times \frac{B^2 A}{\mu_o}$$

Forces F_l acting on a current-carrying conductor

A conductor carrying a current I encounters a transverse force F_l over its length l perpendicular to the lines of magnetic flux:

s 79
$$F_l = B \, l \, I$$

When applied to the armature of a DC-machine, the moment is:

s 80
$$M_i = \frac{1}{2\pi} \, \phi \, I \, \frac{p}{a} \, z$$

s 81 ϕ : flux per pole

Induced voltage V_i (induction law)

Where a coil of N turns and resistance R_i is threaded by a magnetic flux ϕ that varies with time, an open-circuit voltage

s 82
$$V_i = N \frac{d\phi}{dt} \quad \text{(see also s 11)}$$

is induced across its terminals. This voltage causes a current through an external load resistor R_v.

motion of conduction perpendicular to flux	voltage induced by rotation of conductor loop in magnetic field	rotation of generator armature
s 83 $V_i = B \, l \, \upsilon$	$V_i = \omega \, \phi_{max} \times \sin(\omega t)$	$V_i = \phi \, n \, z \, \dfrac{p}{a}$
s 84	$\phi_{max} = l \, d \, B$	$= l \, d \, B \, \dfrac{z \, p}{2\pi a} \, \omega$

s 85 **Voltage V_i due to self-induction:** $\qquad\qquad V_i = L \times di/dt$

Continued on page S 16

For symbols see S 16

General terms relating to alternating-current circuit

Sense of phase angles

In vector diagrams arrows are sometimes used to represent phase angles. Here counter-clockwise arrows are taken positive, clockwise arrows negative.

Example:

sense of phase angles

$$\varphi_1 - \varphi_2 = 360° = 0$$
$$\varphi_1 = \varphi_2$$

Peak values (see also s 1)

Current i and voltage v of an alternating current vary periodically with time t, usually sinusoidally. The maximum values $\hat{i}$ and $\hat{v}$ are called peak values. At an angular frequency $\omega = 2\pi f$ the angle covered in time t is:

period $T = 1/f$

$$a = \omega t = 2\pi f t$$

Hence at this time

the current is $\qquad i = \hat{i}\,\sin(\omega t) = \hat{i}\,\sin a$

the voltage is $\qquad v = \hat{v}\,\sin(\omega t) = \hat{v}\,\sin a$

Root-mean-square (rms) values

These are used for practical calculations and are usually indicated by meters

generally	for sine waves
$I = I_{eff} = \sqrt{\dfrac{1}{T}\displaystyle\int_0^T i^2\,dt}$	$I = I_{eff} = \dfrac{\hat{i}}{\sqrt{2}}$
$V = V_{eff} = \sqrt{\dfrac{1}{T}\displaystyle\int_0^T v^2\,dt}$	$V = V_{eff} = \dfrac{\hat{v}}{\sqrt{2}}$

With these values the relation $P = V\,I$ also applies for alternating current, if $\cos\varphi = 1$ (see s 105).

continued on S 15

continued from S 14

Phase shift, phase angle φ

Where different kinds of load (resistance, inductance and/or capacitance) are present in an alternating-current circuit, a phase shift between current and voltage occurs.

s 94 $\qquad v = \hat{v}\, \sin(\omega t)$ $\qquad\qquad i = \hat{\imath}\, \sin(\omega t - \varphi)$

Q factor, damping factor tan δ, loss angle δ

The Q factor of a circuit has been defined by:

$$ s\ 95 \qquad Q = \frac{2\,\pi\,\hat{w}}{W_{VP}} $$

Here $\hat{w}$ is the peak value of the energy stored in the circuit and W_{VP} the loss energy dissipated in one period.

The reciprocal of Q factor is called damping factor

s 96 $\qquad \tan \delta = 1/Q$ $\qquad\qquad$ (δ is the loss angle)

For a choke (s 115 and s 118) and for a capacitor-resistor combination (s 116 and s 119) this definition results in the simple relations:

s 97 $\quad Q = \tan \varphi$	$\tan \delta = 1/Q = 1/\tan \varphi$
s 98 $\quad \delta = 90^{\circ} - \varphi$	$= V_w/V_b$ (for series connection)
s 99	$= I_w/I_b$ (for parallel connection)

For formulae regarding tan φ see S 17 and S 18.
Formulae s 128 and s 129 applicable for resonant circuits are not so simple.

Basic equations for single phase alternating current

	Impedance		Z	see S 17 and S 18		
s 100	Admittance		Y	$= 1/Z$		
s 101	Voltage across impedance		V	$= I\,Z$		
s 102	Current through impedance		I	$= \dfrac{V}{Z}$		
s 103	Reactance		X	$= Z \sin \varphi$		
s 104	Active power		P	$= V\,I \cos \varphi$	$= I^2 R$	
s 105	Reactive power		P_q	$= V\,I \sin \varphi$	$= I^2 X$	
s 106	Apparent power		P_s	$= V\,I = \sqrt{P^2 + P_q{}^2}$		$= I^2 Z$
s 107	Power factor	$\cos \varphi$	$= \dfrac{P}{V\,I}$	$= \dfrac{P}{P_s}$		
s 108	Alternating magnetic flux in a coil		$\hat{\phi}$	$= \dfrac{V_L}{4 \cdot 44\ N\,f}$		

s 85 continued (V_i due to self-induction)

Where the current i flowing through a coil changes with time, the magnetic field caused by this current also changes. Thereby a voltage V_i is induced in the coil. Its direction is such that it counteracts the instantaneous change of current (Lenz's law).

Symbols used on page S 15:

s 109		
μ_o :	absolute permeability	($\mu_o = 4\,\pi \times 10^{-7}$ V s/A m)

μ_r : relative permeability

for vacuum, gases, fluids, and most solids: $\mu_r = 1$,
for magnetic materials take μ_r from Z 23

a : number of parallel paths through winding
l : length of magnetic circuit
N : number of turns of coil
p : number of pole pairs
z : number of conductors

$\dfrac{R_R}{R_P}$	resistance in	series	equivalent circuit
		parallel	of choke
$\dfrac{L_R}{L_P}$	inductance in	series	
		parallel	

Components, series- and parallel connections carrying alternating current

No.	component	symbol	vector diagram	phase relation	phase angle	impedance	$\tan\varphi =$
s 110	resistive lamp, coil with bifilar winding	R, V_R, I	V_R, I	I and V in phase	$\varphi = 0°$	$Z = R$	0
s 111	inductive Ideal inductance	X_L, V_L, I		I lags V by $90°$	$\varphi = 90°$	$Z = X_L = \omega L$	∞
s 112	capacitive capacitor	X_C, V_C, I		I leads V by $90°$	$\varphi = -90°$	$Z = X_C = \dfrac{1}{\omega C}$	∞
s 113	resistive inductive capacitive connected in series $\omega L_R < \dfrac{1}{\omega C}$	X_{LR}, R_R, V_R, V		I leads V	$-90° < \varphi < 0°$	$Z = \sqrt{R_R^2 + \left(\omega L_R - \dfrac{1}{\omega C}\right)^2}$	$\dfrac{\omega L_R - \dfrac{1}{\omega C}}{R_R}$
s 114	choke in series with capacitor $\omega L_R > \dfrac{1}{\omega C}$	X_{LR}, V_L, V_C, R_R, V_R, V_D, V		I lags V	$0° < \varphi < 90°$		
s 115	resistive and inductive in series choke	X_{LR}, R_R, V_R, V_L, V		I lags V by less than $90°$	$0° < \varphi < 90°$	$Z = \sqrt{R_R^2 + (\omega L_R)^2}$	$\dfrac{\omega L_R}{R_R}$

continued on S 18

continued from S 17

kind of load	symbol	vector diagram	phase relation	phase angle	impedance	$\tan \varphi =$
resistive + capacitive in series; resistor in series with capacitor			I leads V by less than 90°	$-90° < \varphi < 0°$	$Z = \sqrt{R_R^2 + \left(\frac{1}{\omega C}\right)^2}$	$-\dfrac{1}{R_R\,\omega C}$
resist. + induct. + capacitive in parallel; choke + capacitor in parallel			I leads or lags V depending on values	$-90° < \varphi < 90°$	$Z = \cfrac{1}{\sqrt{\left(\frac{1}{R_P}\right)^2 + \left(\frac{1}{\omega L_P} - \omega C\right)^2}}$	$R_P\left(\dfrac{1}{\omega L_P} - \omega C\right)$
resistive + inductive in parallel; choke			I lags V	$0° < \varphi < 90°$	$Z = \cfrac{1}{\sqrt{\left(\frac{1}{R_P}\right)^2 + \left(\frac{1}{\omega L_P}\right)^2}}$	$\dfrac{R_P}{\omega\,L_P}$
resist. + capac. in parallel; resistor + capac. in parallel			I leads V	$-90° < \varphi < 0°$	$Z = \cfrac{1}{\sqrt{\left(\frac{1}{R_P}\right)^2 + (\omega C)^2}}$	$-R_P\,\omega C$
					s 116 · s 117 · s 118 · s 119	s 120/121

The given values R and L of a choke always are the values R_R and L_R of the series equivalent circuit (see s 115). However, where a choke is connected in parallel with a capacitor, it is desirable to use the parallel equivalent circuit of a choke (see s 118). The values R_P and L_P contained therein may be calculated by:

$$R_P = R_R + \frac{(\omega L_R)^2}{R_R}$$

$$L_P = L_R + \frac{R_R^2}{\omega^2 L_R}$$

Resonant circuits

		series- resonant circuit	parallel- resonant circuit
	symbol and general vector diagram	see s 113	see s 117
	vector diagram at resonance		
s 122 s 123 s 124	resonance condition	$V_L = V_C$ $\omega_r L_R - \dfrac{1}{\omega_r C} = 0$ $\omega_r^2 L_R C = 1$	$I_L = I_C$ $\dfrac{1}{\omega_r L_P} - \omega_r C = 0$ $\omega_r^2 L_P C = 1$
s 125	resonant frequency	$f_r = \dfrac{1}{2\pi\sqrt{L_R C}}$	$f_r = \dfrac{1}{2\pi\sqrt{L_P C}}$
		where line frequency $f = f_r$, resonance occurs	
s 126 s 127	current at resonance	$I_r = \dfrac{V}{R_R}$ at $V_b = V_L - V_C = 0$ $\varphi = 0$	$I_r = \dfrac{V}{R_P} = \dfrac{R_R C\, V}{L_R}$ at $I_b = I_L - I_C = 0$ $\varphi = 0$
s 128	Q factor	$Q_R = \dfrac{\omega_r L_R}{R_R} = \dfrac{1}{\omega_r C R_R}$	$Q_P = \omega_r C R_P = \dfrac{R_P}{\omega_r L_P}$
s 129	loss angle δ from	$\tan\delta_R = \dfrac{1}{Q_R} = \dfrac{R_R}{\omega_r L_R}$	$\tan\delta_P = \dfrac{1}{Q_P} = \dfrac{1}{\omega_r C R_P}$
s 130	wavelength	$\lambda = \dfrac{c}{f_r} = \dfrac{300 \cdot 10^6\ m}{f_r s}$	
s 131	resonant period	$T_r = 2\pi\sqrt{L_R C}$	$T_r = 2\pi\sqrt{L_P C}$

Wave trap

A parallel resonant circuit has its maximum impedance Z_{max} at its resonant frequency. Therefore it acts as a rejector for currents of this frequency.

s 132

$$Z_{max} = R_P = \frac{L_R}{R_R C} \qquad \text{and current} \qquad I = \frac{V}{Z_{max}}$$

for symbols see S 16

Alternating-current bridge

AC bridges are used to determine capacitances and inductances.
For balancing the bridge variable capacitor C_2 and resistor R_2
are adjusted until the sound in the low resistance headphone K
reaches its minimum or vanishes. The following circuits are independent of frequency.

measurement of

capacitance	inductance

s 133 $$C_x = \frac{R_4}{R_3} C_2 \qquad\qquad L_x = C_2 R_3 R_4$$

s 134 $$R_x = \frac{R_3}{R_4} R_2 \qquad\qquad R_x = \frac{R_3 R_4}{R_2}$$

s 135 $$\tan \delta_x = \frac{1}{R_x \omega C_x} \qquad\qquad \tan \delta_x = \frac{R_x}{\omega L_x}$$

Determination of an unknown impedance by measuring the voltages
across this impedance and an auxiliary resistor:

136 $$P_{wz} = \frac{V^2 - V_R{}^2 - V_Z{}^2}{2 R}$$

137 $$\cos \varphi_z = \frac{P_{wz}}{V_z I}$$

138 $$Z = \frac{V_z}{I}$$

139 select auxiliary resistor R such that $\quad V_R \approx |V_Z|$

C_x : unknown capacitance	δ_x : loss angle, see S 15
L_x : unknown inductance	$R_{2\ldots 4}$: known resistances
R_x : unknown resistance of coil or capacitor	
C_2, : C_4 : calibrated adjustable capacitances	
Z : unknown impedance (inductive or capacitive)	

Inductance L from impedance and resistance

Calculating L from impedance and resistance

s 140   Pass an alternating current ($J = I/A \approx 3 \text{ A/mm}^2$) through a coil and measure the terminal voltage V, current I, active power P:

s 141   impedance $\qquad Z = \dfrac{V}{I}$; $\qquad$ resistance $\qquad R = \dfrac{P}{I^2}$

s 142 $$L = \frac{1}{\omega} \sqrt{Z^2 - R^2}$$

Calculating L for a toroidal coil

s 143 $$L = \frac{\mu_0 \, h \, N^2}{2 \pi} \ln \frac{r_2}{r_1}$$

Calculating L for a square coil

armatures must be circular

$\dfrac{D}{u}$	inductance
s 144 < 1	$L = 1{\cdot}05 \, \dfrac{D}{m} \, N^2 \sqrt{\left(\dfrac{D}{u}\right)^3}$ μH
s 145 > 1	$L = 1{\cdot}05 \, \dfrac{D}{m} \, N^2 \sqrt{\dfrac{D}{u}}$ μH
s 146 $\geqq 3$	values become unreliable

$$1 \text{ μH} = 10^{-6} \frac{\text{V s}}{\text{A}}$$

a : thickness of winding
A : cross section of wire
b : width of coil
d_a : external diameter of wire and insulation
D : mean diameter of coil
l_o : internal length of armature winding
147 l_m : mean length of armature winding ($l_m = l_o + \pi a$)
N : number of turns
u : circumference of coil cross section
α : ratio $a : b$
148 β : degree of loosening of turns $\left(\beta = \dfrac{a\,b}{N\,d_a^2} \right)$

Non-magnetic coils with specified inductance L

High frequency coils

$\dfrac{D}{u}$	formula	
s 149	< 1	$\left(\dfrac{D}{m}\right)^{3\cdot5} N^{3\cdot25} \approx \dfrac{1}{39}\left(\dfrac{d_0}{m}\right)^{1\cdot5}\left(\dfrac{L}{H}\right)^2 \times 10^{-22}$
s 150	> 1	$\left(\dfrac{D}{m}\right)^{3} N^{3\cdot5} \approx \dfrac{1}{55}\left(\dfrac{d_0}{m}\right)\left(\dfrac{L}{H}\right)^2 \times 10^{-22}$

here:
$$d_0 = \dfrac{u}{2\sqrt{N}}$$
$$= d_\alpha(1+a)\sqrt{\dfrac{\beta}{\alpha}}$$

Low frequency coils
Assuming that

s 151
$$\beta = 1 \quad \text{and} \quad D = u, \qquad \text{then}$$

s 152
$$N \approx 975 \times 10^3 \sqrt{\dfrac{L}{H}\dfrac{m}{D}}$$

s 153
$$a = \dfrac{1}{4}\left(u \pm \sqrt{u^2 - 16 N d_\alpha^2}\right); \qquad b = \dfrac{u}{2} - a$$

Calculation of number of turns N of a coil

From cross section

s 154
$$N \approx \dfrac{a\,b}{d_\alpha^{\,2}}$$

From resistance

s 155
$$N \approx \dfrac{R\,A}{\varrho\,l_m}$$

Using reference coil
Position unknown coil of N_x turns and reference coil of N_0 turns at short distance on closed iron core. Magnetize core by alternating voltage V_e applied to magnetizing coil N_e. Measure voltages V_x and V_0 using high impedance voltmeter. Then

156
$$N_x = N_0 \dfrac{V_x}{V_0}$$

For explanation of symbols see S 21

Hysteresis

Remanent-flux density B_r

A residual magnetism of flux density B_r remains in the iron core, after the external magnetic field strength H has been removed.

Coercive force H_C

The coercive force H_C has to be applied to reduce the flux density B to zero.

Hysteresis work W_H

The energy W_w dissipated during a single cycle of the hysteresis loop is equal to the product of area of the hysteresis loop w_H and core volume V_{Fe}:

s 157

$$W_H = w_H V_{Fe}$$

Hysteresis power P_{VH}

s 158

$$P_{VH} = W_H f = w_H V_{Fe} f$$

Eddy currents

According to the induction law alternating voltages are also induced inside an iron core. Depending on the resistivity of the core iron these voltages cause induction currents called eddy currents. They are kept small by lamination (making up the core of thin metal sheets, which are insulated from each other).

Core losses (iron losses)

Core losses per unit mass p_{Fe}

They are the combined hysteresis and eddy-current losses per unit mass. They are measured at a peak induction $\hat{B} = 1\,T = 10\,kG$ or $1 \cdot 5\,T = 15\,kG$ and at a frequency $f = 50\,Hz$ and are then denoted p_{Fe10} or p_{Fe15} respectively. For values see Z 24.

Total core losses P_{Fe}

s 159

$$P_{Fe} = p_{Fe10} \left(\frac{\hat{B}}{T} \times \frac{f}{50\,Hz} \right)^2 m_{Fe}(1 + \varkappa)$$

m_{Fe}: mass of core | $\varkappa$: addition for punching ridges etc. ($0 \cdot 1 \ldots 1 \cdot 0$)

Choke coil

Choke coil used as a dropping impedance

It is used in an ac circuit to reduce the line voltage V down to a value V_V for a restitive load with minimum losses.

s 160

s 161

| impedance of | choke | $Z_D = \sqrt{R_R^2 + (\omega L_R)^2}$ |
| | total circuit | $Z = \sqrt{(R_R + R_V)^2 + (\omega L_R)^2}$ |

s 162

inductance $\qquad L_R = \dfrac{1}{\omega}\sqrt{\left(\dfrac{V\,R_V}{V_V}\right)^2 - (R_V + R_R)^2}$

In a rough calculation of L_R neglect the unknown resistance R_R of the choke. After dimensioning the choke R_R is known, and Z may be determined exactly. Check V_V by

s 163

$$V_V = \frac{V\,R_R}{Z}$$

and repeat procedure, if necessary.

Choke of constant inductance without core

Dimension according to S 21. Make preliminary assumptions regarding values r_2/r_1 (toroid coil) or D/u (straight coil). In case of unfavourable results repeat procedure. Determine resistance of choke according to s 26.

Choke coil of constant inductance with iron core

The iron core essentially serves for guiding the magnetic flux and should incorporate as many as possible single air gaps δ_1. These should be filled with insulating layers and should not exceed 1 cm in length. The m.m.f. required to magnetize the core is neglected. Peak values of H and B are used for calculations. The variation of inductance L_R may be expressed

air gaps

winding to be
distributed on both legs

continued on S 25

continued from S 24

in terms of the maximum relative current-depending variation of inductance

s 164

$$g_L = \frac{|L_{R\,tot} - L_R|}{L_R} \;;\quad \frac{1}{g_L} = \frac{A_{Fe}\,\hat{B}_{Fe}\,\delta}{\hat{H}_{Fe}\,l_{Fe}\,\mu_0\,A_L} + 1$$

If $g_L > g_{L\,requ}$, repeat dimensioning with greater A_{Fe} and smaller $\hat{B}_{Fe}$ at unchanged product $A_{Fe} \times \hat{B}_{Fe}$.

Dimensioning. Given: $L_R, f\ g_{L\,requ}, V_{L\,eff}$ or I_{eff}, then the

		preliminary	final
		dimensions are	
s 165	effective cross section of core	$A_{Fe}' = \sqrt{K_{eff}\,V_{L\,eff}}$	take A_{Fe} from standards or determine a and b by
s 166		with $I_{eff} = \dfrac{V_{L\,eff}}{2\,\pi\,f\,L_R}$	$A_{Fe} = 0.9\,a\,b \approx A_{Fe}'$
s 167	number of turns	$N = \dfrac{V_{L\,eff}}{4\cdot44\,f\,\hat{B}_{Fe}\,A_{Fe}}$	
s 168	cross section of air gap	$A_L' = ab + 5cm(a+b)$	$A_L = ab + 5(a+b)\delta_1$
s 170	total | length of air	$\delta' = \dfrac{N^2\,\mu_0\,A_L'}{L_R}$	$\delta = \dfrac{a\,b\,n\,N^2\,\mu_0}{n\,L_R - 5\,N^2\,\mu_0(a+b)}$
s 171	single | gap	$\delta_1' = \delta'/n < 1$ cm	$\delta_1 = \delta/n < 1$ cm
s 172	diameter of wire	$d' = 2\sqrt{\dfrac{I}{J'\,\pi}}$	Use next standard values for d, d_a including insulation
	cross section of winding	$A_w = 1\cdot12\,d_a^2\,N$	
	length of limb	l_s to be determined from dimensions of core section and A_w	

Choke coil of current-depending inductance

This type of choke employs an iron core without an air gap. It is used only for special purposes, e. g. as a magnetic amplifier.

K : power coefficient of choke
$\approx 0\cdot24$ cm^4/VA for air-cooled chokes $\Big\}$ core section see S 24
$\approx 0\cdot15$ cm^4/VA for oil chokes
for $\boxed{\square\square}$ core section increase values by 75%

J' : preliminary current density for air-cooled choke $J' = 2$ A/mm^2, for oil choke $J' \approx 3 \dots 4$ A/mm^2

$\hat{B}_{Fe}$: core induction (take approx. 1 ... 1·2 T)

$\hat{H}_{Fe}$: field strength in core corr. to $\hat{B}_{Fe}$ to be taken from Z 23 according to material employed

n : number of single air gaps, increase reduces stray flux

R_{Cu} : resistance of winding according to s 26

R_R : resistance of choke includ. core losses ($R_R \approx 1\cdot3\,R_{Cu}$)

l_{Fe} : mean length of magnetic path through iron

Transformer

Designation of windings

distinction by			
nominal voltages		function in circuit (direction of power transfer)	
winding with		input	output
higher | lower nominal voltage		winding	
high-end | low-end winding		primary (index 1) | secondary (index 2) winding	

Nominal values (index N)

s 173   rated power $\qquad P_{SN} = V_{1N} \times I_{1N} = V_{2N} \times I_{2N}$

s 174   nominal trans-formation ratio$\Big\}$ $\qquad i = V_{1N} / V_{20} = I_{2N} / I_{1N}$

By the rated secondary voltage V_{2N} we mean the open-circuit secondary voltage ($V_{2N} = V_{20}$), not the one at nominal load.

Core losses P_{Fe} and open-circuit measurements

The core losses P_{Fe} only depend on primary voltage V_1 and frequency f, not on the kind of load.

s 175 $\qquad\qquad\qquad P_{10} = P_{Fe}$

Core losses P_{Fe} and nominal transformation ratio $\ddot{u}$ are determined by open-circuit measurements (see circuit diagram: secondary open, values provided with index o). The primary current's resistive component I_{RFe} covers the core losses, its reactive component is the magnetizing current I_m. The copper losses are negligibly small. The core losses P_{Fe} are required for calculating operational power dissipation and efficiency.

continued on S 27

continued from S 26

Copper losses P_{Cu} and short-circuit measurements

P_{Cu} depends only on the primary current I_1
and is determined by short-circuit measure-
ments (see circuit diagram, values provided with index κ). With
the secondary shorted, the primary voltage is adjusted to a
value V_{1K}, which causes the rated currents to flow. V_{1K} is so
small that I_{RFe} and I_m are negligible. Then the short-circuit
primary power P_{1K} is equal to the rated copper losses P_{CuN} of the
total transformer at rated currents. P_{1K} is required for calculating operational power dissipation and efficiency.

s 176
$$P_{1K} = P_{CuN}$$

The values measured are used for calculating the relative short-
circuit voltage v_k, which for bigger transformers, is always
s 177 indicated on the name plate: $v_K = 100(V_{1K}/V_{1N})\%$

The following quantities may be determined using the vector
diagram:
s 178 $\quad R_{Cu} = V_R/I_N$; $\quad L = V_L/\omega I_{1N}$; $\quad \cos\varphi_{1K} = V_R/V_{1K} = \dfrac{P_{CuN}}{v_K P_{SN}}$

Operating conditions

For calculating the operational secondary voltage
V_2 for a given load all
secondary quantities are
first computed into those
of an equivalent trans-
former having a transfor-
mer ratio of $i = 1$ (index '):

simplified equivalent circuit

simplified vector diagram

s 179 $\quad V_2' = i\,V_2$; $\quad I_2' = I_2/i$; $\quad R_2' = i^2 R_2$

Load-dependent variation ΔV of V_2'
(approximation for $v_K \leqq 4\%$)
s 180 $\quad \Delta V \approx v_{1K}(\cos\varphi_{1K}\cos\varphi_2 + \sin\varphi_{1K}\sin\varphi_2)\,I_2/I_{2N}$
$\quad\quad \approx v_{1K}\cos(\varphi_{1K} - \varphi_2)\,I_2/I_{2N}$

Secondary voltage V_2
s 181 $\quad V_2' \approx V_1 - \Delta V$; $\quad\quad V_2 = V_2'/i$

Basic connections

Star

s 182 $\quad V = V_{ph}\sqrt{3}$

s 133 $\quad I = I_{ph}$

Delta

s 184 $\quad V = V_{ph}$

s 185 $\quad I = I_{ph}\sqrt{3}$

Measuring threephase power

Load balanced

connection

with neutral point (star connected)	without neutral point (delta connected)

s 186   total power $P = 3\,P_{w\,ph} = \sqrt{3}\,V\,I\,\cos\varphi$

Load unbalanced (Two wattmeter method)

For delta connected without neutral point. (Also for balanced load without neutral point).

s 187   total power $P = P_1 + P_2$

I_{ph} : phase current	V_{ph} : phase voltage
I : line current	V : line voltage
L_1, L_2, L_3 : outer conductor	
N : neutral conductor	
$P_{w\,ph}$: active power of one phase	

Reactive and active power, power factor
(for symmetrical load)

s 188	reactive power	$P_q = \sqrt{3}\, V I \sin\varphi$
s 189	active power	$P = \sqrt{3}\, V I \cos\varphi$
s 190	power factor	$\cos\varphi = \dfrac{P}{\sqrt{3}\, V I}$

Power factor correction
(for inductive consumers)

General
Adjust to power factor according to current rate, usually $\cos\varphi = 0.8 \ldots 0.9$. Adjust large consumers separately and directly and small consumers centrally to main or subdistributors.

Calculating the required capacitor power
Calculate power factor $\cos\varphi$ as above, use wattmeter (see connection in S 28) or a current meter to determine P.

| s 191 | capacitor power | $P_q = (\tan\varphi_1 - \tan\varphi_2) P_w$ |
| s 192 | inherent consumption of condenser | $P_c \approx 0.003\, P_q$ |

Table (numerical)

cos φ	tan φ	cos φ	tan φ	cos φ	tan φ	cos φ	tan φ
0.42	2.161	0.62	1.265	0.81	0.724	0.91	0.456
0.44	2.041	0.64	1.201	0.82	0.698	0.92	0.426
0.46	1.930	0.66	1.138	0.83	0.672	0.93	0.395
0.48	1.828	0.68	1.078	0.84	0.646	0.94	0.363
0.50	1.732	0.70	1.020	0.85	0.620	0.95	0.329
0.52	1.643	0.72	0.964	0.86	0.593	0.96	0.292
0.54	1.559	0.74	0.909	0.87	0.567	0.97	0.251
0.56	1.479	0.76	0.855	0.88	0.540	0.98	0.203
0.58	1.405	0.78	0.802	0.89	0.512	0.99	0.142
0.60	1.333	0.80	0.750	0.90	0.484	1	0.000

$\tan\varphi_1$ or $\tan\varphi_2$ can be calculated from the above table, $\cos\varphi_1$ representing the required power factor and $\cos\varphi_2$ the consumer power factor.

Direct-current machine
(motor and generator)

General

s 193	moment constant	$C_M = \dfrac{p\,z}{2\,\pi\,a}$
s 194	rotational source voltage	$V_q = C_M \phi\, \omega = 2\,\pi\,C_M\,\phi\,n$
s 195	torque	$M = C_M\,\phi\,I_a$
s 196	armature current	$I_a = \dfrac{\pm(V - V_q)}{R_a}$ *)
s 197	terminal voltage	$V = V_q \pm I_a\,R_a$ *)
s 198	speed	$n = \dfrac{V \mp I_a\,R_a}{2\,\pi\,C_M\,\phi}$ **)
s 199	internal power	$P_i = M_i\,\omega = V_q\,I_a$

	mechanical power supplied	to generator	$P_G = \dfrac{1}{\eta}\,V\,I_{tot}$
s 200			
s 201		by motor	$P_M = \eta\,V\,I_{tot}$

Shunt motor (for circuit diagram see S 31)
Easy starting, speed is fairly independent of load and, within certain limits, easy to regulate.

Series motor (for circuit diagram see S 31)
Easy starting with powerful starting torque. Speed depends greatly on load. When running free may run away.

Compound wound motor (for circuit diagram see S 31)
Operates almost like a shunt motor. Main circuit winding ensures a powerful starting torque.

a : number of armature pairs	z : number of conductors
p : number of pole pairs	R_a : armature resistance
ϕ : magnetic flux	

*)₊ motor	**)₋ motor
₋ generator	₊ generator

		motors		generators	
	rotation	clockwise	counter-clockwise	clockwise	counter-clockwise
s 202	with shunt winding				
s 203	with series winding				
s 204	with compound winding				

Three-phase motor

Speed

At a given frequency f the speed is determined by the number of pole pairs p.

s 205

$$\text{speed} \quad n = \frac{f}{p} = \frac{60\,f\,s}{p} \times \frac{1}{\min}$$

Switching

Where both terminals of each winding are accessible on the switchboard, the three-phase motor can be connected either in star or in delta.

s 206

	phase voltage	
	in star	in delta
	$V_{ph} = \dfrac{V}{\sqrt{3}}$	$V_{ph} = V$

A 400/230 volt motor operates with its nominal values of current, torque and power, when connected to

s 207 $V = 230$ V in delta, meaning $V_{ph} = V = 230$ V

s 208 $V = 400$ V in star, meaning $V_{ph} = \dfrac{V}{\sqrt{3}} = \dfrac{400\text{ V}}{\sqrt{3}} = 230$ V

Star-delta connection

Higher powered motors usually operate in delta. To avoid excessive inrush currents, particularly in relatively low current networks, the motor is started in star and then switched over into delta. If, for instance, a 400/230 volt motor is connected in star to a 230/135 volt network, it is supplied with only $1/\sqrt{3}$ times its nominal voltage.

Induction motor

The rotating field of the stator causes voltage and current to be induced in the armature winding. Due to slip the rotational speed of the armature is about 3 to 5% lower than that of the rotating field; it remains almost constant under load.

Synchronous motor

Requires direct current for excitation and is synchronized with the speed of the rotating field by means of an auxiliary squirrel-cage armature. Can be used directly as a generator.

Switch groups generally used for transformers

	type		sign		switch diagram		ratio
	key-numb.	switch group	PV	SV	PV	SV	$V_1 : V_2$
Threephase-output transformers							
s 209	0	D d 0					$\dfrac{N_1}{N_2}$
s 210		Y y 0					$\dfrac{N_1}{N_2}$
s 211		D z 0					$\dfrac{2 N_1}{3 N_2}$
s 212	5	D y 5					$\dfrac{N_1}{\sqrt{3} N_2}$
s 213		Y d 5					$\dfrac{\sqrt{3} N_1}{N_2}$
s 214		Y z 5					$\dfrac{2 N_1}{\sqrt{3} N_2}$
s 215	6	D d 6					$\dfrac{N_1}{N_2}$
s 216		Y y 6					$\dfrac{N_1}{N_2}$
s 217		D z 6					$\dfrac{2 N_1}{3 N_2}$
s 218	11	D y 11					$\dfrac{N_1}{\sqrt{3} N_2}$
s 219		Y d 11					$\dfrac{\sqrt{3} N_1}{N_2}$
s 220		Y z 11					$\dfrac{2 N_1}{\sqrt{3} N_2}$
Single phase-output transformers							
s 221	0	I i 0					$\dfrac{N_1}{N_2}$

PV: primary voltage
SV: secondary voltage

$\begin{vmatrix} D \\ d \end{vmatrix}$ delta $\qquad \begin{vmatrix} Y \\ y \end{vmatrix}$ star $\qquad \begin{vmatrix} - \\ z \end{vmatrix}$ zig-zag

Key numbers are used to calculate the phase angle
(= key number × 30°) between the primary and secondary voltage,
e. g. for Dy5 the phase angle is 5 × 30 = 150°.

Note: Use the framed switch groups for preference.

The most important measuring instruments

Symbol	Type of instrument	Construction	Basically measured quantity	Scale	Used for measuring
	moving coil	moving coil in uniform radial field of a permanent magnet. 2 spiral springs or tension bands serve for counter moment and application of current	dc value (arithmetical mean)	linear	I and V, —
	moving coil with rectifier		arithmetical mean of rectified value	~ linear	I and V, 1)
	cross coil	2 coils fixed to each other moving In non uniform field of a permanent magnet 2 current leads without counter moment	$\dfrac{I_1}{I_2}$	almost square-law	$\dfrac{I_1}{I_2}$, 2)
	moving coil with thermo-couple	Thermocouple in close thermal contact with heater. Thermocouple feeds moving coil instruments	root-mean-square value	almost square-law	I and V, 2) 3)
	soft iron	1 moving and 1 fixed piece of soft iron, fixed coil, spiral spring as counter moment	root-mean-square value	non-linear	I and V, 2) 4)
	electro-dynamic	moving coil in uniform field of fixed coil, 2 spiral springs or tension bands as counter moment and current leads, magnetic screen	$I_1 \times I_2 \times \cos \varphi$	square-law for I and V, linear for P	$I, V, P,$ and $\cos \varphi$
	electro-static	1 fixed and 1 moving capacitor plate	root-mean-square value	non-linear	V 100 V, 2)

1) for sinusoidal waveforms only   2) also for non-sinusoidal waveform
3) also for rf currents and voltages   4) $f < 500$ Hz

RADIATION PHYSICS
Photometry and Optics

General

For every photometric quantity there is a corresponding radiation-physical quantity and the same relationships apply to both. They are differentiated by different suffixes, v for visual and e for energy.

	Photometry			Radiation physics		
	Quantity	Symbol	Units	Quantity	Symbol	Units
t 1	luminous intensity	I_v	candela cd	radiant intensity	I_e	W sr
t 2	luminous flux	$\Phi_v = \Omega\, I_v$	lumen lm = cd sr	radiant power	$\Phi_e = \Omega\, I_e$	W = J/s
t 3	quantity of light, luminous energy	$Q_v = \Phi_v\, t$	lumen-second lm s, also lm h	radiant energy, quantity of radiation	$Q_e = \Phi_e\, t$	J = W s
t 4	luminance	$L_v = \dfrac{I_v}{A_1\,\cos\varepsilon_1}$	$\dfrac{cd}{m^2}$	radiance	$L_e = \dfrac{I_e}{A_1\,\cos\varepsilon_1}$	$\dfrac{W}{sr\, m^2}$
t 5	illuminance	$E_v = \dfrac{\Phi_v}{A_2}$	lux lx = $\dfrac{lm}{m^2}$	irradiance	$E_e = \dfrac{\Phi_e}{A_2}$	$\dfrac{W}{m^2}$
t 6	light exposure	$H_v = E_v\, t$	x s	radiant exposure	$H_e = E_e\, t$	$\dfrac{W\,s}{m^2}$

Definition of the base unit 'candela" (cd)
  The luminous intensity of a surface of 1/600 000 m^2 (= 1⅔ mm^2) of a black body at a temperature of 2042 K.

Photometric radiation equivalent
t 7
  1 watt = 680 lm for wavelength 555 nm.

Luminous flux consumption for lighting (values see Z 25)
  A surface A lit to an illumination E_v will require a luminous flux of
t 8
$$\Phi_v = \frac{A\, E_v}{\eta}$$

For symbols see T 2

Optical distance law

The illumination of a surface is inversely proportional to the square of its distance from the light source:

t 9
$$\frac{E_{v1}}{E_{v2}} = \frac{r_2^2}{r_1^2} = \frac{A_2}{A_1}$$

Where two light sources produce equal illumination of a surface, the ratio of the squares of their distances from the surface is equal to the ratio of their luminous intensities:

t10
$$\frac{I_{v1}}{I_{v2}} = \frac{r_1^2}{r_2^2}$$

Light refraction

t11
$$\frac{n_b}{n_a} = \frac{\sin \alpha}{\sin \beta}$$
= const. for all angles.

t12 Where $\sin \beta \geqslant \dfrac{n_a}{n_b}$ total reflection occurs

t13 **Refractive index** for yellow sodium lightning $\lambda = 589\cdot3$ nm

solid matter in relation to atmosphere		fluid matter in relation to atmosphere		gaseous matter in relation to vacuum	
plexiglas	1·49	water	1·33	hydrogen	1·000292
quartz	1·54	alcohol	1·36	oxygen	1·000271
crown glass	1·56	glycerine	1·47	atmosphere	1·000292
diamond	2·41	benzol	1·50	nitrogen	1·000297

A_1 : area of radiating surface

A_2 : area of illuminated or irradiated surface

$A_1 \cos \varepsilon_1$: projection of the radiating surface A_1 perpendicular to the direction of radiation

n_a, (n_b) : refractive index of thin (dense) medium

ε_1 : angle between emergent beam and normal to radiating surface A_1

Ω : solid angle Ω is the ratio of the area A_k intercepted on a sphere of radius r_k to the square of the radius: $\Omega = A_k/r_k^2$; unit sr = m²/m².

t14   The solid angle of a point is $\Omega = 4\pi$ sr = 12·56 sr

t15 η : luminous efficacy (see table Z 25)

Wavelengths (in atmosphere)

Type of radiation		Wavelength $\lambda = c/f$
X-rays	hard	0·0057 nm ... 0·08 nm
	soft	0·08 nm ... 2·0 nm
	ultra-soft	2·0 nm ... 37·5 nm
optical radiation	UV-C ... IR-C	100 nm ... 1 mm
ultra-violet radiation	UV-C	100 nm ... 280 nm
	UV-B	280 nm ... 315 nm
	UV-A	315 nm ... 380 nm
visible radiation, light	violet	380 nm ... 420 nm
	blue	420 nm ... 490 nm
	green	490 nm ... 530 nm
	yellow	530 nm ... 650 nm
	red	650 nm ... 780 nm
infra-red radiation	IR-A	780 nm ... 1·4 μm
	IR-B	1·4 μm ... 3·0 μm
	IR-C	3·0 μm ... 1 mm

t 16

Mirrors

Plane mirrors

The image is at the same distance behind the mirror as the object is in front of it:

$$u = -v$$

t 17

Concave mirrors

$$\frac{1}{f} = \frac{1}{u} + \frac{1}{v}$$

Depending upon the position of object, the image will be real or virtual:

t 18

u	v	image
∞	f	at focal point
$> 2f$	$f < v < 2f$	real, inverted, smaller
$2f$	$2f$	real, inverted, of equal size
$2f > u > f$	$> 2f$	real, inverted, larger
f	∞	no image
$< f$	negative	virtual, larger

Convex mirrors

Produce only virtual and smaller images. Similar to concave mirror where:

$$f = -r/2$$

t 19 $c \simeq 0\cdot3 \times 10^9$ m/s (velocity of light)

Lenses

Refraction D of a lens

t 20 $\qquad D = \dfrac{1}{f}$; $\qquad\qquad$ Unit: 1 dpt = 1 dioptrics = $\dfrac{1}{m}$

Lens equation (thin lenses only)

t 21 $\qquad \dfrac{1}{f} = \dfrac{1}{v} + \dfrac{1}{u}$

t 22 $\qquad\quad = (n-1)\left(\dfrac{1}{r_1} + \dfrac{1}{r_2}\right)$

t 23 $\qquad m = \dfrac{B}{G} = \dfrac{v}{u}$

Where two lenses with focal depths f_1 and f_2 are placed immediately one behind the other, the equivalent focal length f, is given by

t 24 $\qquad\qquad\qquad \dfrac{1}{f} = \dfrac{1}{f_1} + \dfrac{1}{f_2}$

Magnifying lens

general	where object is in focus
t 25 | $m = \dfrac{s}{f} + 1$ | $m = \dfrac{s}{f}$ |

Microscope

total magnification

t 26 $\qquad m = \dfrac{t}{f_1} \dfrac{s}{f_2}$

t 27 $\qquad\quad = m_1 \times m_2$

Macro photograpy

t 28 $\quad$ camera extension $\qquad a = f(m + 1)$

t 29 $\quad$ distance of object $\qquad c = \dfrac{a}{m} = f\left(1 + \dfrac{1}{m}\right)$

B : size of image	n : refractive index (see T2)
F : focus	r : radius of curvature
f : focal length	t : optical length of tube
G : size of object	m : magnification factor
s : range of vision (= 25 cm for normal vision)	

Ionizing radiation

Ionizing radiation is any radiation of charged particles which causes direct or indirect ionization or excitation of a permanent gas.

	Accumulated values	Units	time rate values	Units
	amount of absorbed energy (measured value)	$1\dfrac{A\,s}{kg} = 1\dfrac{C}{kg}$	rate of absorbing energy	$1\dfrac{A}{kg}$
t 30		$\left[\begin{array}{l} 1 \text{ Röntgen} = \\ 1\text{ R} = 258\dfrac{\mu C}{kg} \end{array}\right.$		$\left[\begin{array}{l} 1\dfrac{R}{s} = 258\dfrac{\mu A}{kg} \\ 1\dfrac{R}{a} = 8.2\dfrac{pA}{kg} \end{array}\right.$
t 31	$J = \dfrac{Q}{m}$		$j = \dfrac{J}{t} = \dfrac{I}{m}$	
	absorbed dose	$\begin{array}{l}1 \text{ gray} = 1\text{ gy} \\ 1\dfrac{V\,A\,s}{kg} = 1\dfrac{W\,s}{kg} \\ = 1\dfrac{J}{kg}\end{array}$	absorbed dose, -rate	$1\dfrac{gy}{s} = 1\dfrac{W}{kg}$
t 32	$D = f\,J$		$\dot{D} = \dfrac{D}{t} = \dfrac{P}{m}$	$= 31.56 \times 10^6\dfrac{J}{kg\,a}$
t 33	$= \dfrac{W}{m}$	$\left[\begin{array}{l} 1 \text{ rad} = 1\text{ rd} = \\ = \dfrac{cJ}{kg} = 0.01\text{ gy} \\ = 6.242 \times 10^{16}\dfrac{eV}{kg} \end{array}\right.$		$\left[\begin{array}{l} 1\dfrac{rd}{s} = 10\dfrac{mW}{kg} \\ = 0.01\dfrac{gy}{s} \end{array}\right.$
	dose equivalent (theoretical value)	$\begin{array}{l}1\dfrac{V\,A\,s}{kg} = 1\dfrac{W\,s}{kg} \\ = 1\dfrac{J}{kg}\end{array}$	dose equivalent, -rate	$1\dfrac{W}{kg} = 1\dfrac{gy}{s}$
t 34	$H = D_q = q\,D$	$\left[\begin{array}{l} 1 \text{ REM} = 1\text{ rem} \\ = 1\dfrac{cJ}{kg} \end{array}\right.$	$\dot{H} = \dot{D}_q = \dfrac{D_q}{t}$	$\left[\begin{array}{l} 1\dfrac{rem}{s} = 10\dfrac{mW}{kg} \\ 1\dfrac{rem}{a} = 317\dfrac{pW}{kg} \end{array}\right.$
t 35	$= q\,f\,J$		$= q\,\dot{D}$	

t 36	**Activity** $A = -dN/dt = \lambda N$	$\begin{array}{l}1 \text{ Becquerel} = 1\text{ Bq} = 1/s \\ [1 \text{ Curie} = 1\text{ Ci} = 37 \times 10^9\text{ Bq}]\end{array}$
t 37	**Decay** $\lambda = \ln 2/T_{1/2}$	$(s, min, h, d, a)^{-1}$

Units in [ ] are valid until 31. 12. 85

Explanation of terms, symbols and units see T 6

Ionization current I: When air molecules are ionized by radiation and a voltage is applied, an ionization current I flows. (Instrument: the ionization chamber).

Charge Q: When an ionization current I flows for a time t it produces a charge

t 38
$$Q = I t$$

Radiation energy W: W is the radiation energy necessary for ionization. Each pair of ions in the air molecule requires the energy

t 39
$$W_L = 33 \cdot 7 \text{ eV}.$$

t 40 (Charge of one electron: $1 \text{ e} = 1 \cdot 602 \times 10^{-19}$ As)
t 41 (1 electron volt: $1 \text{ eV} = 1 \cdot 602 \times 10^{-19}$ As $\times 1 \text{ V} = 1 \cdot 602 \times 10^{-19}$ J)

t 42 **Dose:** Dose is a value related to mass m, e. g. $J = Q/m$.

Activity A: The activity A is the number of atoms of a radioactive substance that disintegrates per unit time.

Notation of symbols used

N :	number of radioactive atoms	
$T_{1/2}$:	half-life	
t 43 f_L :	ionization constant for air	$\left(f_L = \dfrac{W_L}{e} = 33 \cdot 7 \text{ V}\right)$
f :	ionization constant for	
t 44	tissue	$f = f_L$
t 45	bone	$f = (1 \dots 4) f_-$
m :	mass (base unit)	
q :	quality factor for	
t 46	β, γ and X-rays	$q = 1$
t 47	other radiation	$q = 1 \dots 20$

Notation of units used

A : ampere	C : coulomb	J : joule
t 48 a : annum (1 annum = 1 a = $31 \cdot 56 \times 10^{6}$ s or approx. 1 year)		

Exposure to radiation (dose equivalent): In 1975 the average person in the Federal Republic of Germany would have been exposed to the follwing radiation:

Type	H in	
	mJ/kg	[m rem]
from natural sources	1·1	110
for medical reasons	0·5	50
other artificial radiation[*]	<0·1	<10
[*] permitted by law	$\leqq 0 \cdot 3$	$\leqq 30$

CHEMISTRY
Elements

U 1

element	symbol	atomic mass in u	element	symbol	atomic mass in u
aluminum	Al	26·9815	neodymium	Nd	144·240
antimony	Sb	121·75	neon	Ne	20·183
argon	Ar	39·948	nickel	Ni	58·71
arsenic	As	74·92·6	niobium	Nb	92·906
barium	Ba	137·34	nitrogen	N	14·0067
beryllium	Be	9·0122	osmium	Os	190·2
bismuth	Bi	2C8·980	oxygen	O	15·9994
boron	B	10·811	palladium	Pd	106·4
bromine	Br	79·909	phosphorus	P	30·9738
cadmium	Cd	112·40	platinum	Pt	195·09
caesium	Cs	132·905	potassium	K	39·102
calcium	Ca	40·C8	praseodymium	Pr	140·907
carbon	C	12·0112	radium	Ra	226·04
cerium	Ce	140·12	rhodium	Rh	102·905
chlorine	Cl	35·453	rubidium	Rb	85·47
chromium	Cr	51·996	ruthenium	Ru	101·07
cobalt	Co	58·9332	samarium	Sm	150·35
copper	Cu	63·54	scandium	Sc	44·956
erbium	Er	167·26	selenium	Se	78·96
fluorine	F	18·9984	silicon	Si	28·086
gadolinium	Gd	157·25	silver	Ag	107·870
gallium	Ga	69·72	sodium	Na	22·9898
germanium	Ge	72·59	strontium	Sr	87·62
gold	Au	196·967	sulfur	S	32·064
helium	He	4·0026	tantalum	Ta	180·948
hydrogen	H	1·008	tellurium	Te	127·6
indium	In	114·82	thallium	Tl	204·37
iodine	I	126·9044	thorium	Th	232·038
iridium	Ir	192·2	thulium	Tm	168·934
iron	Fe	55·847	tin	Sn	118·69
krypton	Kr	83·80	titanium	Ti	47·90
lanthanum	La	138·91	tungsten	W	183·85
lead	Pb	207·19	uranium	U	238·03
lithium	Li	6·939	vanadium	V	50·942
magnesium	Mg	24·312	xenon	Xe	131·30
manganese	Mn	54·9381	yttrium	Y	88·905
mercury	Hg	200·59	zinc	Zn	65·37
molybdenum	Mo	95·94	zirconium	Zr	91·22

u : atomic mass unit (1 u = 1·66 × 10^{-27} kg)

Chemical terms

trade	chemical	chemical formula
	name	
acetone	acetone	$(CH_3)_2 \cdot CO$
acetylene	acetylene	C_2H_2
ammonia	ammonia	NH_3
ammonium (hydroxide of)	ammonium hydroxide	NH_4OH
aniline	aniline	$C_6H_5 \cdot NH_2$
bauxite	hydrated aluminium oxides	$Al_2O_3 \cdot 2\ H_2O$
bleaching powder	calcium hypochlorite	$CaCl\ (OCl)$
blue vitriol	copper sulfate	$CuSO_4 \cdot 5\ H_2O$
borax	sodium tetraborate	$Na_2B_4O_7 \cdot 10\ H_2O$
butter of zinc	zinc chloride	$ZnCl_2 \cdot 3\ H_2O$
cadmium sulfate	cadmium sulfate	$CdSO_4$
calcium chloride	calcium chloride	$CaCl_2$
carbide	calcium carbide	CaC_2
carbolic acid	phenol	C_6H_5OH
carbon dioxide	carbon dioxide	CO_2
carborundum	silicon carbide	SiC
caustic potash	potassium hydroxide	KOH
caustic soda	sodium hydroxide	$NaOH$
chalk	calcium carbonate	$CaCO_3$
cinnabar	mercuric sulfide	HgS
ether	di-ethyl ether	$(C_2H_5)_2O$
fixing salt or hypo	sodium thiosulfate	$Na_2S_2O_3 \cdot 5\ H_2O$
glauber's salt	sodium sulfate	$Na_2SO_4 \cdot 10\ H_2O$
glycerine or glycerol	glycerine	$C_3H_5\ (OH)_3$
graphite	crystaline carbon	C
green vitriol	ferrous sulfate	$FeSO_4 \cdot 7\ H_2O$
gypsum	calcium sulfate	$CaSO_4 \cdot 2\ H_2O$
heating gas	propane	C_3H_8
hydrochloric acid	hydrochlorid acid	HCl
hydrofluoric acid	hydrofluoric acid	HF
hydrogen sulfide	hydrogen sulfide	H_2S
iron chloride	ferrous chloride	$FeCl_2 \cdot 4\ H_2O$
iron sulfide	ferrous sulfide	FeS
laughing gas	nitrous oxide	N_2O
lead sulfide	lead sulfide	PbS

continued on U 3

continued from U 2

trade	chemical name	chemical formula
limestone	calcium carbonate	$CaCO_3$
magnesia	magnesium oxide	MgO
marsh gas	methane	CH_4
minimum or red lead	plumbate	$2\ PbO \cdot PbO_2$
nitric acid	nitric acid	HNO_3
phosphoric acid	ortho phosphoric acid	H_3PO_4
potash	potassium carbonate	K_2CO_3
potassium bromide	potassium bromide	KBr
potassium chlorate	potassium chlorate	$KClO_3$
potassium chloride	potassium chloride	KCl
potassium chromate	potassium chromate	K_2CrO_4
potassium cyanide	potassium cyanide	KCN
potassium dichromate	potassium dichromate	$K_2Cr_2O_7$
potassium iodide	potassium iodide	KI
prussic acid	hydrogen cyanide	HCN
pyrolusite	manganese dioxide	MnO_2
quicklime	calcium monoxide	CaO
red prussiate of potassium	potassium ferrocyan.	$K_3Fe(CN)_6$
salammoniac	ammonium chloride	NH_4Cl
silver bromide	silver bromide	$AgBr$
silver nitrate	silver nitrate	$AgNO_3$
slaked lime	calcium hydroxide	$Ca(OH)_2$
soda ash	hydrated sodium carb.	$Na_2CO_3 \cdot 10\ H_2O$
sodium monoxide	sodium oxide	Na_2O
soot	amorphous carbon	C
stannous chloride	stannous chloride	$SnCl_2 \cdot 2\ H_2O$
sulphuric acid	sulphuric acid	H_2SO_4
table salt	sodium chloride	$NaCl$
tinstone, tin putty	stannic oxide	SnO_2
trilene	trichlorethylene	C_2HCl_3
urea	urea	$CO(NH_2)_2$
white lead	basic lead carbonate	$2\ PbCO_3 \cdot Pb\ (OH)_2$
white vitriol	zinc sulphate	$ZnSO_4 \cdot 7\ H_2O$
yellow prussiate of potass.	potass. ferrocyanide	$K_4Fe(CN)_6 \cdot 3\ H_2O$
zinc blende	zinc sulphide	ZnS
zinc or chinese white	zink oxide	ZnO

pH values

The negative log of the hydrogen-ion-concentration c_{H^+} indicates its pH value:

$$pH = -\log c_{H^+}$$

u 1

c_{H^+}	1	10^{-1}	10^{-2}	...	10^{-7}	...	10^{-12}	10^{-13}	10^{-14}
pH–value	0	1	2		7		12	13	14

| acid | neutral | alkaline |

Establishing pH values by using suitable indicators.

Acid-base-indicators

Indicator	pH-Range	Colour change from	to
thymol blue [benz.	1·2...2·8	red	yellow
p-dimethylamino-azo-	2·9...4·0	red	orange-yellow
bromophenolblue	3·0...4·6	yellow	red-violet
congo red	3·0...4·2	blue-violet	red-orange
methyl orange	3·1...4·4	red	yellow-(orange)
brom cresol green	3·8...5·4	yellow	blue
methyl red	4·4...6·2	red	(orange)-yellow
litmus	5·0...8·0	red	blue
bromocresol purple	5·2...6·8	yellow	purple
brom phenol red	5·2...6·8	orange yell.	purple
bromothymol blue	6·0...7·6	yellow	blue
phenol red	6·4...8·2	yellow	red
neutral red	6·4...8·0	(blue)-red	orange-yellow
cresol red	7·0...8·8	yellow	purple
meta cresol purple	7·4...9·0	yellow	purple
thymol blue	8·0...9·6	yellow	blue
phenolphtalein	8·2...9·8	colourless	red-violet
alizarin yellow 66	10·0...12·1	light-yellow	light brown-yellow

Reagents

		reagent	indicator	colouration
u	2		blue litmus paper	red
u	3	acids	red phenolphthalein	colourless
u	4		yellow methylorange	red
u	5		red litmus paper	blue
u	6	bases	colourless phenolphthalein	red
u	7		red methylorange	yellow
u	8	ozone	potassium-iodide starch paper	blue-black
u	9	H_2S	lead iodide paper	brown-black
u	10			
u	11	ammonia solution	hydrochloric acid	white fumes
		carbonic acid	calcium hydroxide	sediment

Preparation of chemicals

		to prepare	use reaction
u	12	ammonia	$CO(NH_2)_2 + H_2O \rightarrow 2\ NH_3 + CO_2$
u	13	ammonium chloride	$NH_4OH + HCl \rightarrow NH_4Cl + H_2O$
u	14	ammonium hydroxide	$NH_3 + H_2O \rightarrow NH_4OH$
u	15	cadmium sulfide	$CdSO_4 + H_2S \rightarrow CdS + H_2SO_4$
u	16	carbon dioxide	$CaCO_3 + 2\ HCl \rightarrow CO_2 + CaCl_2 + H_2O$
u	17	chlorine	$CaOCl_2 + 2\ HCl \rightarrow Cl_2 + CaCl_2 + H_2O$
u	18	hydrogen	$H_2SO_4 + Zn \rightarrow H_2 + ZnSO_4$
u	19	hydrogen sulfide	$FeS + 2\ HCl \rightarrow H_2S + FeCl_2$
u	20	lead sulfide	$Pb(NO_3)_2 + H_2S \rightarrow PbS + 2\ HNO_3$
u	21	oxygen	$2\ KClO_3 \rightarrow 3\ O_2 + 2\ KCl$
u	22	sodium hydroxide	$Na_2O + H_2O \rightarrow 2\ NaOH$
u	23	zinc sulfide	$ZnSO_4 + H_2S \rightarrow ZnS + H_2SO_4$

Freezing mixtures

		Drop in temperature		Mixture (The figures stand for proportions by mass)	
		from °C	to °C		
u	24	+ 10	− 12	4 H_2O + 1 KCl	
u	25	+ 10	− 15	1 H_2O + 1 NH_4NO_3	
u	26	+ 8	− 24	1 H_2O + 1 $NaNO_3$	+ 1 NH_4Cl
u	27	0	− 21	3·0 ice (crushed)	+ 1 NaCl
u	28	0	− 39	1·2 ice (crushed)	+ 2 $CaCl_2 \cdot 6\ H_2O$
u	29	0	− 55	1·4 ice (crushed)	+ 2 $CaCl_2 \cdot 6\ H_2O$
u	30	+ 15	− 78	1 methyl alcohol	+ 1 CO_2 solid

Atmospheric relative humidity in closed containers

Relative humidity above the solution (%) 20°C = 65°F	Supersaturated aqueous solution		
92	Na_2CO_3	$\cdot$ 10 H_2O	u 31
86	KCl		u 32
80	$(NH_4)_2SO_4$		u 33
76	NaCl		u 34
63	NH_4NO_3		u 35
55	$Ca(NO_3)_2$	$\cdot$ 4 H_2O	u 36
45	K_2CO_3	$\cdot$ 2 H_2O	u 37
35	$CaCl_2$	$\cdot$ 6 H_2O	u 38

Drying agents (desiccants) for desiccators

Water remaining after drying at 25°C (77°F), g/m³ air	desiccant name	formula	
1·4	copper sulfate, dehydrated	$CuSO_4$	u 39
0·8	zinc chloride	$ZnCl_2$	u 40
0·14 … 0·25	calcium chloride	$CaCl_2$	u 41
0·16	sodium hydroxide	NaOH	u 42
0·008	magnesium oxide	MgO	u 43
0·005	calcium sulfate, dehydrated	$CaSO_4$	u 44
0·003	hydrated aluminum	Al_2O_3	u 45
0·002	potassium hydroxide	KOH	u 46
0·001	silica gel	$(SiO_2)_x$	u 47
0·000025	phosphorus pentoxide	P_2O_5	u 48

Hardness of a water

$$1° \text{ German hardness} \triangleq 1°d \triangleq \frac{10 \text{ mg CaO}}{1 \text{ l water}} \triangleq \frac{7·19 \text{ mg MgO}}{1 \text{ l water}} \qquad \text{u 49}$$

$$1°d = 1·25° \text{ English hardness} = 1·78° \text{ French hardness} \qquad \text{u 50}$$
$$= 17·8° \text{ American hardness (1·00 ppm } CaCO_3) \qquad \text{u 51}$$

Classification of hardness

0 … 4°d	very soft	12 … 18°d	rather hard	u 52
4 … 8°d	soft	18 … 30°d	hard	u 53
8 … 12°d	slightly hard	above 30°d	very hard	u 54

Mixture rule for fluids (mixture cross)

a	capa-	starting			a		x = |b − c|	u 55
c	city	mixed	fluid	in weight-%		c		
b	cf the	admixture			b		y = |c − a|	u 56

for water is b = 0.

Example: a = 54%; b = 92%; c shall become 62%.
One should mix thus 30 weight-sharings of a with 8 of b.

TABLES

Properties of solids

Reference conditions

Density ϱ at $t = 20°C$

Boiling point t: The values in brackets refer to sublimation, i.e. direct transition from the solid to the gaseous state.

Thermal conductivity λ at $t = 20°C$

Specific heat c for the temperature range $0 < t < 100°C$

Substance	density ϱ	melting point t	boiling point t	thermal conductivity λ	specific heat c
	kg/dm³	°C	°C	W/(m k)[1]	kJ/(kg K)[2]
agate	2·6	1600	2600	10·89	0·80
aluminum bronze	7·7	1040	2300	127·9	0·436
aluminum cast	2·6	658	2200	209·4	0·904
aluminum, rolled	2·7	658	2200	209·4	0·904
amber	1·0	300	.		
antimony	6·67	630	1440	22·53	0·209
arsenic	5·72	815	.	.	0·348
artificial wool	1·5	.	.		1·357
asbestos	2·5	1300	.	0·17	0·816
barium	3·59	704	1700	.	0·29
barytes	4·5	1580	.	.	0·46
beryllium	1·85	1280	2970	165	1·02
bismuth	9·8	271	1560	8·1	0·13
boiler scale	2·5	1200	2800	1·2...3·5	0·80
borax	1·72	740	.		0·996
brass, cast	8·4	900	1100	113	0·385
brass, rolled	8·5	900	1100	113	0·385
brick	1·8	.	.	1·0	0·92
bromine	3·14	−7·3	63	.	.
bronce (Cu Sn 6)	8·83	910	2300	64	0·37
brown iron ore	5·1	1570	.	0·58	0·67
cadmium	8·64	321	765	92·1	0·234
calcium	1·55	850	1439	.	0·63
carbon	3·51	3600	.	8·9	0·854
cast iron	7·25	1200	2500	58	0·532
cerium	6·77	630	.	.	.
chalk	1·8	.	.	0·92	0·84

[1] 1 W/(m K) = 0·8589 kcal/(h m K)   [2] 1 kJ/(kg K) = 0·2388 kcal/(kg K)

Z 2

TABLES
Properties of solids

Substance	density ϱ	melting point t	boiling point t	thermal conductivity λ	specific heat c
	kg/dm³	° C	° C	W/(m K)[1]	kJ/(kg K)[2]
charcoal	0·4	·	·	0·084	0·84
chromium	7·1	1800	2700	69	0·452
clay	1·8...2·1	1600	2980	1	0·88
cobalt	8·8	1490	3100	69·4	0·435
coke	1·4	·	·	0·184	0·84
concrete reinforce	2·4	·	·	0·8...1·7	0·88
constantan	8·89	1600	2400	23·3	0·41
copper, cast	8·8	1083	2500	384	0·394
copper, rolled	8·9	1083	2500	384	0·394
cork	0·2...0·3	·	·	0·05	2·0
diamond	3·5	·	[3540]	·	0·52
dripping, beef	0·9...1·0	40...50	350	·	0·88
duralium	2·8	650	2000	129·1	0·92
ebonite	1·2...1·8	·	·	0·17	·
electron	1·8	650	1500	162·8	1·00
emery	4·0	2200	3000	11·6	0·96
fire brick	1·8...2·2	2000	2900	0·47	0·88
glass, window	2·5	700	·	0·81	0·84
glass-wool	0·15	·	·	0·04	0·84
gold	19·29	1063	2700	310	0·130
graphite	2·24	3800	4200	168	0·71
ice	0·92	0	100	2·3	2·09
ingot iron	7·9	1460	2500	47...58	0·49
iodine	4·95	113·5	184	0·44	0·218
iridium	22·5	2450	4800	59·3	0·134
iron, cast	7·25	1200	2500	58	0·532
iron, forged	7·8	1200	·	46...58	0·461
iron-oxide	5·1	1570	·	0·58	0·67
lead	11·3	327·4	1740	34·7	0·130
leather	0·9...1·0	·	·	0·15	1·5
limestone	2·6	·	·	2·2	0·909
lithium	0·53	179	1372	301·2	0·36
magnesia	3·2...3·6	·	·	·	·
magnesium	1·74	657	1110	157	1·05
magnesium, alloy	1·8	650	1500	70...145	1·01

[1] 1 W/(m K) = 0·8598 kcal/(h m K)
[2] 1 kJ/(kg K) = 0·2388 kcal/(kg K)

TABLES
Properties of solids

Z3

Substance	density ϱ	melting point t	boiling point t	thermal conductivity λ [1]	specific heat c [2]
	kg/dm³	°C	°C	W/(m K)	kJ/(kg K)
manganese	7·43	1221	2150	·	0·46
marble	2·0…2·8	·	·	2·8	0·84
mica	2·8			0·35	0·87
molybdenum	10·2	2600	5500	145	0·272
nickel	8·9	452	2730	59	0·461
osmium	22·48	2500	5300	·	0·130
oxide of chrom	5·21	2300	·	0·42	0·75
palladium	12·0	1552	2930	70·9	0·24
paper	0·7…1·1	·	·	0·14	1·336
paraffin	0·9	52	300	0·26	3·26
peat	0·2	·	·	0·08	1·9
phosphorbronce	8·8	900	·	110	0·36
phosphorus	1·82	44	280	·	0·80
pig iron, white	7·0…7·8	1560	2500	52·3	0·54
pinchbeck	8·65	1000	1300	159	0·38
pitch	1·25	·	·	0·13	·
pit coal	1·35	·	·	0·24	1·02
platinum	21·5	1770	4400	70	0·13
porcelain	2·2…2·5	1650	·	0·8…1·0	0·92
potassium	0·86	63	762·2	1	1
quartz	2·5	1470	2230	9·9	0·80
radium	5	960	1140	·	·
red lead	8·6…9·1	·	·	0·7	0·092
red metal	8·8	950	2300	127·9	0·381
rhenium	21·4	3175	5500	71	0·14
rhodium	12·3	1960	2500	88	0·24
rosin	1·07	100…300	·	0·32	1·30
rubber, raw	0·95	125	·	0·2..0·35	·
rubidium	1·52	39	700	58	0·33
sand, dry	1·4…1·6	1550	2230	0·58	0·80
sandstone	2·1…2·5	1500	·	2·3	0·71
selenium	4·4	220	688	0·20	0·33
silicon	2·33	1420	2600	83	0·75
silicon, carbide	3·12	·	·	15·2	0·67
silver	10·5	960	2170	407	0·234

[1] 1 W/(m K) = 0·8598 kcal/(h m K)
[2] 1 kJ/(kg K) = 0·2388 kcal/(kg K)

TABLES
Properties of solids

Substance	density ϱ	melting point t	boiling point t	thermal conductivity λ	specific heat c
	kg/dm³	°C	°C	W/(m K)[1]	kJ/(kg K)[2]
slate	2·6...2·7	2000	·	0·5	0·76
snow	0·1	0	100	·	4·187
sodium	0·98	97·5	880	126	1·26
soot	1·6...1·7	·	·	0·07	0·84
steatite	2·6...2·7	1600	·	2	0·83
steel	7·85	1460	2500	47...58	0·49
sulfur, cryst.	2·0	115	445	0·20	0·70
tantalum	16·6	2990	4100	54	0·138
tar	1·2	− 15	300	0·19	· ·
tellurium	6·25	455	1300	4·9	0·201
thorium	11·7	1800	4000	38	0·14
timber, alder	0·55	·	·	0·17	1·4
" , ash	0·75	·	·	0·16	1·6
" , birch	0·65	·	·	0·14	1·9
" , larch	0·75	·	·	0·12	1·4
" , maple	0·75	·	·	0·16	1·6
" , oak	0·85	·	·	0·17	2·4
" , pitchpine	0·75	·	·	0·14	1·3
" , pockwood	1·28	·	·	0·19	2·5
" , red beech	0·8	·	·	0·14	1·3
" , red pine	0·65	·	·	0·15	1·5
" , white pine	0·75	·	·	0·15	1·5
" , walnut	0·65	·	·	0·15	1·4
tin, cast	7·2	232	2500	64	0·24
tin, rolled	7·28	232	2500	64	0·24
titanium	4·5	1670	3200	15·5	0·47
tungsten	19·2	3410	5900	130	0·13
uranium	19·1	1133	3800	28	0·117
vanadium	6·1	1890	3300	31·4	0·50
wax	0·96	60	·	0·084	3·43
welding iron	7·8	1600	2500	54·7	0·515
white metal	7·5...10	300...400	2100	35...70	0·147
zinc, cast	6·86	419	906	110	0·38
zinc, die-cast	6·8	393	1000	140	0·38
zinc, rolled	7·15	419	906	110	0·38

[1] 1 W/(m K) = 0·8598 kcal/(h m K)
[2] 1 kJ/(kg K) = 0·2388 kcal/(kg K)

TABLES

Properties of liquids

Z 5

Reference conditions

Density ϱ at $t = 20°C$ and $p = 1·0132$ bar.

Melting point and boiling point t at $p = 1·0132$ bar.

Thermal conductivity λ at $t = 20°C$. For other temperatures see Z 15.

Specific heat c for the temperature range $0 < t < 100°C$.

Substance	density ϱ	melting point t	boiling point t	thermal conductivity λ	specific heat c
	kg/dm³	°C	°C	W/(m K)[3]	kJ/(kg K)[2]
acetic acid	1·08	16·8	118	·	·
acetone	0·79	−95	56·1	·	·
alcohol	0·79	−130	78·4	0·17...0·2	2·43
benzene	0·89	5·4	80	0·137	1·80
benzine	0·7	−150	50...200	0·16	2·1
chloroform	1·53	−70	61	·	·
diesel oil	0·88	−5	175	0·13	·
ether	0·73	117	35	0·14	2·26
gas oil	0·86	−30	200...300	0·15	·
glycerine	1·27[3]	−20	290	0·29	2·43
heating oil	0·92	−5	175...350	0·12	·
hydrochlor acid {10%	1·05	−14	102	0·50	3·14
hydrochlor acid {40%	1·20	·	·	·	·
hydrofluoric acid	0·99	−92·5	19·5	2·33	2·09
linseed oil	0·96	−20	316	0·15	·
machine oil	0·91	−5	380...400	0·126	1·68
mercury	13·6	−38·9	357	8·4	0·138
methyl alcohol	0·8	−98	66	·	2·51
nitric acid	1·56[3]	−41	86	0·26	1·72
oil of resin	0·94	−20	150...300	0·15	·
oil of turpentine	0·87	−10	160	0·10	1·80
perchlor ethylene	1·62	−20	119	·	0·905
petroleum	0·80	−70	150...300	0·159	2·09
petroleum ether	0·67	−160	40...70	0·14	1·76
sulfuric acid conc.	1·84	−10	338	0·5	1·38
sulfuric acid 50%	1·40	·	·	·	·
sulfurous acid	1·49[4]	−73	−10	·	1·34
toluene	0·88	−94·5	110	0·14	1·59
trichlor ethylene	1·47	−86	87	0·16	1·30
water	1 at 4°	0	100	0·58	4·183

[1] 1 W/(m K) = 0·8593 kcal/(h m K)
[2] 1 kJ/(kg K) = 0·2388 kcal/(kg K)
[3] at $t = 0°C$
[4] at $t = -20°C$

TABLES
Properties of gases

Reference conditions

Density ϱ at $t = 0°C$ and $p = 1.0132$ bar. For perfect gases ϱ can be calculated for other pressures and/or temperatures from: $\varrho = p/(R \times T)$.

Melting point and boiling point t at $p = 1.0132$ bar.

Thermal conductivity λ at $t = 0°C$ and $p = 1.0132$ bar.
For other temperatures see Z 15.

Specific heat c_p and c_v at $t = 0°C$ and $p = 1.0132$ bar.
c_p at other temperatures see Z 13.

Substances	density ϱ	melting point t	boiling point t	thermal conductivity λ	specific heat c_p	c_v
	kg/m³	°C	°C	W/(m K)[1]	kJ/(kg K)[2]	
acetylene	1·17	− 83	− 81	0·018	1·616	1·300
air, atmosphere	1·293	− 213	− 192·3	0·02454	1·005	0·718
ammonia	0·77	− 77·9	− 33·4	0·022	2·056	1·568
argon	1·78	− 189·3	− 185·9	0·016	0·52	0·312
blast furnace gas	1·28	− 210	− 170	0·02	1·05	0·75
butane, iso-	2·67	− 145	− 10	·	·	·
butane, n-	2·70	− 135	1	·	·	·
carbon di-oxide	1·97	− 78·2	− 56·6	0·015	0·816	0·627
carbon disulfide	3·40	− 111·5	46·3	0·0069	0·582	0·473
carbon monoxide	1·25	− 205·0	− 191·6	0·023	1·038	0·741
chlorine	3·17	− 100·5	− 34·0	0·0081	0·473	0·36
coal gas	0·58	− 230	− 210	·	2·14	1·59
ethylene	1·26	− 169·3	− 103·7	0·017	1·47	1·173
helium	0·18	− 270·7	− 268·9	0·143	5·20	3·121
hydrochlor acid	1·63	− 111·2	− 84·8	0·013	0·795	0·567
hydrogen	0·09	− 259·2	− 252·8	0·171	14·05	9·934
hydrogen sulfide	1·54	− 85·6	− 60·4	0·013	0·992	0·748
krypton	3·74	− 157·2	− 153·2	0·0088	0·25	0·151
methane	0·72	− 182·5	− 161·5	0·030	2·19	1·672
neon	0·90	− 248·6	− 246·1	0·046	1·03	0·618
nitrogen	1·25	− 210·5	− 195·7	0·024	1·038	0·741
oxigen	1·43	− 218·8	− 182·9	0·024	0·909	0·649
ozone	2·14	− 251	− 112	·	·	·
propane	2·01	− 187·7	− 42·1	0·015	1·549	1·360
sulfur dioxide	2·92	− 75·5	− 10·0	0·0086	0·586	0·456
water vapor[3]	0·77	0·00	100·00	0·016	1·842	1·381
xenon	5·86	− 111·9	− 108·0	0·0051	0·16	0·097

[1] 1 W/(m K) = 0·8598 kcal/(h m K)
[2] 1 kJ/(kg K) = 0·2388 kcal/(kg K)
[3] at $t = 100°C$

TABLES
Friction numbers

$$Z\,7$$

Coefficients of sliding and static friction

material	on material	sliding friction μ			static friction μ_0		
		dry	on water	with lubrication	dry	on water	with lubrication
bronze	bronze	0·20	0·10	0·06			
	cast iron	0·18		0·08			0·11
	steel	0·18		0·07	0·19		0·10
oak	oak ‖	0·20...0·40	0·10	0·05...0·15	0·40...0·60		0·18
	oak ⊥	0·15...0·35	0·08	0·04...0·12	0·50		
cast iron	cast iron		0·31	0·10			0·16
	steel	0·17...0·24		0·02...0·05	0·18...0·24		0·10
rubber	asphalt	0·50	0·30	0·20			
	concrete	0·60	0·50	0·30			
hemp rope	timber				0·50		
leather belt	oak	0·40			0·50		
	cast iron		0·40	0·2...0·7	0·40	0·50	0·12
steel	wood	0·20...0·50	0·26	0·02...0·10	0·50...0·60		0·11
	ice	0·014			0·027		
	steel	0·10...0·30		0·02...0·08	0·15...0·30		0·10
	PE−W 1)	0·40...0·50					
	PTFE 2)	0·02...0·05					
	PA 66 3)	0·30...0·50		0·10			
	POM 4)	0·35...0·45					
PE−W 1)	PE−W 1)	0·50...0·70					
PTFE 2)	PTFE 2)	0·035...0·055					
POM 4)	POM 4)	0·40...0·50					

Rolling friction
(for section K 12 and L 9)

material on material	lever arm f of frictional force in mm
rubber on asphalt	0·10
rubber on concrete	0·15
lignum vitae on lignum vitae	0·50
steel on steel (hard: ball bearing)	0·005...0·01
steel on steel (soft)	0·05
elm on lignum vitae	0·8

‖ : movement with grain of both materials
⊥ : movement perpendicular to grain of sliding body

1) polyethylene with plasticizer   (e. g. Lupolen from BASF)
2) polytetrafluorethylene   (e. g. Teflon C 126 from Dupont)
3) polyamide   (e. g. Ultramit CA from BASF)
4) polyoxymethylene   (e. g. Hostaflon C 2520 from Hoechst)

Note: For non-circular pipes k/d is to be replaced by k/d_h.

Galvanized Steel Tubes, suitable

for Screwing to B.S. 21 Pipe Threads

(Approximate values for Medium pipes,
colour code – blue, to B.S. 1389)

Nominal bore (inches)	$\frac{1}{8}$	$\frac{1}{4}$	$\frac{3}{8}$	$\frac{1}{2}$	$\frac{3}{4}$	1	$1\frac{1}{4}$	$1\frac{1}{2}$	2
Threads per inch	28	19	19	14	14	11	11	11	11
Outside diam. of pipe (mm)	10·2	13·5	17·2	21·3	26·9	33·7	42·4	48·3	60·3
Inside diam. of pipe (mm)	6·2	8·8	12·3	16	21·6	27·2	35·9	41·8	53
Flow area (mm²)	30	61	119	201	366	581	1012	1371	2206
Ration of flow area (mm²) to nominal bore (inches)	242	243	317	402	438	581	810	914	1103

Roughness k

(according to Richter, Hydraulics of Pipes)

Material and kind of pipe	Condition of pipe	k in mm
new seamless rolled or drawn (commercial) steel pipes	typical rolled finish	0·02...0·06
	pickled	0·03...0·04
	cleanly galvanized (dipping process)	0·07...0·10
	commercial galvanized	0·10...0·16
used steel pipes	uniform corrosion pits	about 0·15
	medium corrosion, light incrustation	0·15...0·4
	medium incrustation	about 1·5
	heavy incrustation	2...4
	cleaned after long use	0·15...0·20
cast iron pipes	new, typical cast finish	0·2 ...0·6
	new, bituminized	0·1 ...0·13
	used, corroded	1 ...1·5
	incrusted	1·5 ...4
	cleaned after several years of use	0·3 ...1·5
	mean value in urban sewerage installations	1·2
	heavily corroded	4·5
pipes folded and riveted of sheet steel	new, folded	about 0·15
	new depending on kind and quality of riveting	
	light riveting	about 1
	heavy riveting	to 9
	25 years old, heavily incrusted, riveted pipe	12·5

TABLES
Heat values

Latent heat of fusion per unit mass l_f

material	$\frac{kJ}{kg}$	material	$\frac{kJ}{kg}$	material	$\frac{kJ}{kg}$
aluminum	377	glycerine	176	paraffin	147
antimony	164	gold	67	phenol	109
brass	168	ice	335	platinum	113
cadmium	46	iron	205	potassium	59
cast iron	126	lead	23	silver	109
chromium	134	manganese	155	sulfur	38
cobalt	243	mercury	11·7	tin	59
copper	172	naphthaline	151	Wood's alloy	33·5
ethyl ether	113	nickel	234	zinc	117

Latent heat of evaporation per unit mass l_d
at 101·32 kN/m² (= 760 torr)

material	$\frac{kJ}{kg}$	material	$\frac{kJ}{kg}$	material	$\frac{kJ}{kg}$
alcohol	880	hydrogen	503	oxygen	214
ammonia	1410	mercury	281	sulfur dioxide	402
carbon dioxide	595	methyl chloride	406	toluene	365
chlorine	293	nitrogen	201	water	2250

Drawing colors of steel and associated temperatures

coloring	$\frac{t}{°C}$	coloring	$\frac{t}{°C}$
pale yellow	200	corn-flower blue	300
straw- yellow	220	light-blue	320
brown	240	bluish gray	350
purple	260	gray	400
violet	280		

Colors of glowing steel and associated temperatures

coloring	$\frac{t}{°C}$	coloring	$\frac{t}{°C}$
dark-red	680	yellowish red	950
dark cherry-red	740	yellow	1000
cherry-red	770	light-yellow	1100
light cherry-red	800	yellowish white	1200
light-red	850	white	1300
light light-red	900		and above

Linear coefficient of expansion α in 1/K
at $t = 0 \dots 100°C$

material	$\alpha/10^{-6}$	material	$\alpha/10^{-6}$	material	$\alpha/10^{-6}$
aluminum	23·8	German silver	18·0	porcelain	4·0
bismuth	13·5	gold	14·2	quartz glass	0·5
brass	18·5	lead	29·0	silver	19·7
bronze	17·5	molybdenum	5·2	steatite	8·5
cadmium	30·0	nickel	13·0	steel, mild	12·0
cast iron	10·5	nickel steel	23·0	tin	
constantan	15·2	= Invar 36% Ni	1·5	tungsten	4·5
copper	16·5	platinum	9·0	zinc	30·0

Cubic coefficient of expansion β in 1/K
at $t = 15°C$

material	$\beta/10^{-3}$	material	$\beta/10^{-3}$	material	$\beta/10^{-3}$
alcohol	1·1	glycerine	0·5	petroleum	1·0
benzene	1·0	mercury	0·18	toluene	1·08
ether	1·6	oil of turpentine	1·0	water	0·18

Coefficient of heat transfer k in W/(m²K)
(Approx. values, natural convection on both sides)

material	thickness of insulating layer in mm								
	3	10	20	50	100	120	250	380	510
reinforced concrete				4·3	3·7	3·5	2·4		
insulat. cement blocks (e. g. thermalite)									
$\sigma_c = 2·45$ N/mm²						1·2	0·7	0·5	
$\sigma_c = 4·90$ N/mm²						1·6	0·9	0·7	
$\sigma_c = 7·35$ N/mm²						1·7	1·0	0·7	
glass	5·8	5·3							
glass-, mineral-wool, hard foam	4·1	2·4	1·5	0·7	0·4				
timber wall			3·8	2·4	1·8	1·7			
chalky sandstone						3·1	2·2	1·7	1·4
gravel concrete				4·1	3·6	3·4	2·3		
slag concrete						2·7	1·7	1·4	1·0
brick						2·9	2·0	1·5	1·3

double or treble glazing	2·6 or 1·9
single window, puttied	5·8
double window, 20 mm spacing, puttied [*]	2·9
double window, 120 mm spacing, puttied [*]	2·3
tiled roof without/with joint packing	11·6/5·8

[*] also for windows with sealed air gaps

Gas constant R and molecular mass M

material	R $\dfrac{J}{kg\,K}$	M $\dfrac{kg}{kmol}$	material	R $\dfrac{J}{kg\,K}$	M $\dfrac{kg}{kmol}$
acetylene	319	26	hydrogen	4124	2
air	287	29	nitrogen	297	28
ammonia	488	17	oxygen	260	32
carbonic acid	189	44	sulfuric acid	130	64
carbon monoxide	297	28	water vapor	462	18

Radiation constant C at $20°$C

material	C $W/(m^2K^4)$	material	C $W/(m^2K^4)$
silver, polished	$0{\cdot}17 \times 10^{-8}$	copper, oxidated	$3{\cdot}60 \times 10^{-8}$
aluminum, polished	$0{\cdot}23 \times 10^{-8}$	water	$3{\cdot}70 \times 10^{-8}$
copper, polished	$0{\cdot}28 \times 10^{-8}$	timber, planed	$4{\cdot}40 \times 10^{-8}$
brass, polished	$0{\cdot}28 \times 10^{-8}$	porcelain, glaz	$5{\cdot}22 \times 10^{-8}$
zinc, polished	$0{\cdot}28 \times 10^{-8}$	glass	$5{\cdot}30 \times 10^{-8}$
iron, polished	$0{\cdot}34 \times 10^{-8}$	brickwork	$5{\cdot}30 \times 10^{-8}$
tin, polished	$0{\cdot}34 \times 10^{-8}$	soot, smooth	$5{\cdot}30 \times 10^{-8}$
aluminum, unpolished	$0{\cdot}40 \times 10^{-8}$	zinc, unpolished	$5{\cdot}30 \times 10^{-8}$
nickel, polished	$0{\cdot}40 \times 10^{-8}$	iron, unpolished	$5{\cdot}40 \times 10^{-8}$
brass, unpolished	$1{\cdot}25 \times 10^{-8}$	absolutely	
ice	$3{\cdot}60 \times 10^{-8}$	black surface	$5{\cdot}67 \times 10^{-8}$

Specific heat c for liquids in kJ/(kg K)

t at $°$C	-25	0	20	50	100	200
ammonia		4·64	4·77			
benzene			1·74			
carbon dioxide			3·64			
machine oil			1·85	1·97	2·18	
mercury			0·139			
sulfur dioxide	1·25	1·355	1·389			
transformer oil			1·89	2·04	2·29	
water		4·216	4·179	4·181	4·212	4·497

Mean specific heat $c_{pm}\big|_0^t$ of various gases
in kJ/(kg K) as a function of temperature

$\frac{t}{°C}$	CO	CO_2	H_2	H_2C[1]	N_2 pure	N_2[2]	O_2	SO_2	air
0	1·039	0·8205	14·38	1·858	1·039	1·026	0·9084	0·607	1·004
100	1·041	0·8689	14·40	1·874	1·041	1·031	0·9218	0·637	1·031
200	1·046	0·9122	14·42	1·894	1·044	1·035	0·9355	0·663	1·013
300	1·054	0·9510	14·45	1·918	1·049	1·041	0·9500	0·687	1·020
400	1·064	0·9852	14·48	1·946	1·057	1·048	0·9646	0·707	1·029
500	1·075	1·016	14·51	1·976	1·066	1·057	0·9791	0·721	1·039
600	1·087	1·043	14·55	2·008	1·076	1·067	0·9926	0·740	1·050
700	1·099	1·067	14·59	2·041	1·087	1·078	1·005	0·754	1·061
800	1·110	1·089	14·64	2·074	1·098	1·088	1·016	0·765	1·072
900	1·121	1·109	14·71	2·108	1·108	1·099	1·026	0·776	1·082
1000	1·131	1·126	14·78	2·142	1·118	1·108	1·035	0·784	1·092
1100	1·141	1·143	14·85	2·175	1·128	1·117	1·043	0·791	1·100
1200	1·150	1·157	14·94	2·208	1·137	1·126	1·051	0·798	1·109
1300	1·158	1·170	15·03	2·240	1·145	1·134	1·058	0·804	1·117
1400	1·166	1·183	15·12	2·271	1·153	1·142	1·065	0·810	1·124
1500	1·173	1·195	15·21	2·302	1·160	1·150	1·071	0·815	1·132
1600	1·180	1·206	15·30	2·331	1·168	1·157	1·077	0·820	1·138
1700	1·186	1·216	15·39	2·359	1·174	1·163	1·083	0·824	1·145
1800	1·193	1·225	15·48	2·386	1·181	1·169	1·089	0·829	1·151
1900	1·198	1·233	15·53	2·412	1·186	1·175	1·094	0·834	1·156
2000	1·204	1·241	15·65	2·437	1·192	1·180	1·099	0·837	1·162
2100	1·209	1·249	15·74	2·461	1·197	1·186	1·104		1·167
2200	1·214	1·256	15·82	2·485	1·202	1·191	1·109		1·172
2300	1·218	1·263	15·91	2·508	1·207	1·195	1·114		1·176
2400	1·222	1·269	15·99	2·530	1·211	1·200	1·118		1,181
2500	1·226	1·275	16·07	2·552	1·215	1·204	1·123		1·185
2600	1·230	1·281	16·14	2·573	1·219	1·207	1·127		1·189
2700	1·234	1·286	16·22	2·594	1·223	1·211	1·131		1·193
2800	1·237	1·292	16·28	2·614	1·227	1·215	1·135		1·196
2900	1·240	1·296	16·35	2·633	1·230	1·218	1·139		1·200
3000	1·243	1·301	16·42	2·653	1·233	1·221	1·143		1·203

[1] at low pressures   [2] derived from air

Calculated from figures given in E. Schmidt:
Einführung in die Technische Thermodynamik, 11. Auflage, Berlin/
Göttingen/Heidelberg: Springer 1975.

Dynamic viscosity η of liquids in N s/m² $\times$ 10⁻⁵ *)

t in °C	−25	0	20	50	100	200
acetic acid			121·0	79·2	45·8	
ammonia	21·5	16·9	13·8	10·3		
benzene			64·9	43·6	26·1	11·3
carbon dioxide	13·0	10·1	7·0			
chloroform		70·6	56·3	42·4		
diethylene ether	38·7	29·6	24·3	18·3	11·8	
glycerine		12×10⁶	15×10⁴			
hydrochloric acid	17·0	11·0	8·6	5·4		
hydrofluoric acid	37	25·6				
hydrogen sulfide		15·2	12·6	9·4		
propane	15·8	12·7	10·2	7·1		
sulfur dioxide	47·5	36·8	30·4	23·4		
toluene		77·3	58·6	41·9	26·9	13·3
trichlorethylene		71·0	60·0	44·7		
water		175·7	100·2	54·3	27·8	13·3

Dynamic viscosity η of motor oils in N s/m² *)

SAE		0	20	50	100	
	10		0·31	0·079	0·020	0·005
	20		0·72	0·170	0·033	0·007
	30		1·53	0·310	0·061	0·010
	40		2·61	0·430	0·072	0·012
	50		3·82	0·630	0·097	0·015

Dynamic viscosity η of gases in N s/m² $\times$ 10⁻⁵ *)

t in °C	−25	0	20	100	200	400
air	1·50	1·72	1·82	2·18	2·58	3·28
ammonia	0·85	0·930	1·00	1·28	1·65	2·34
argon	1·19	2·10	2·35	2·68	3·21	4·10
carbon dioxide		1·37	1·46	1·82	2·22	2·93
chlorine		1·25	1·32	1·68	2·10	2·86
helium	1·75	1·89	1·93	2·28	2·67	3·41
hydrogene chloride		1·31	1·43	1·83	2·30	
hydrogene sulfide		1·17	1·15	1·59	1·99	
krypton		2·33	2·48	3·06	3·74	4·91
neon		2·99	3·10	3·65	4·26	5·32
oxygen	1·75	1·92	2·00	2·43	2·88	3·67
sulfur dioxide	1·06	1·17	1·16	1·63	2·07	2·80
nitrogen	1·50	1·66	1·75	2·09	2·47	3·14
water vapor		0·90	0·97	1·25	1·61	2·33
xenon		2·11	2·35	2·83	3·50	4·73

*) 1 N s/m² = 1 kg/(m s) = 1 Pa s = 1000 cP

Thermal conductivity λ of liquids in W/(m K)

t in °C	−25	0	20	50	100	200
ammonia		0·540	0·494			
benzene			0·153			
carbon dioxide			0·087			
mercury			0·304			
spindle oil			0·144	0·143	0·140	
sulfur dioxide	0·228	0 212	0·199			
transformer oil			0·124	0·122	0·119	
water		C·554	0·598	0·640	0·681	0·665

Thermal conductivity λ of vapors and gases in W/(m K)

t in °C	−25	0	20	100	200	400
air		0·022	0·023	0·029	0·035	0·047
ammonia		0·020	0·024	0 027		
carbon dioxide	0·011	0·013	0·014	0·019	0·026	
hydrogen		0·160	0·150	C·209	0·252	
sulfur oxide		0·008				
water vapor				0·022	0·030	0·050

Prandtl number Pr for liquids

t in °C	−25	0	20	50	100	200
ammonia		2·07	2·12			
benzene			7·33			
carbon dioxide			2·00			
mercury			0·023			
spindle oil			168	71	31	
sulfur dioxide	2·80	2·36	2·14			
transformer oil			481	165	60	
water		13·6	7·03	3·90	1·75	0·94

Prandtl number Pr for vapors and gases

t in °C	−25	0	20	100	200	400
air		0·715	0·713	0·707	0·685	0·685
ammonia		0·92	0·93	0·97		
carbon dioxide		0·80	0·80	0·80	0·81	
hydrogen	0·67	0·67	0·67	0·67	0·67	0·67
sulfur oxide		0·86				
water vapor				1·12	0·97	0·88

TABLES
Strength values in N/mm² [*)]

Modulus of elasticity (Young's modulus) of steel
$$E = 210000 \text{ N/mm}^2$$

BS-Standard specifications from	BS Material	USA-Standard specifications from	USA Material	Tensile strength R_m	Yield point 0.2 proof stress R_e; $R_{p0.2}$	Fatigue strength — torsion compression A p_{tA}	U p_{tU}	bending A p_{btA}	U p_{btU}	torsion A p_{qA}	U p_{qU}	Notes / sizes in mm
BS 970	050 A 20	ASTM	A 283 Grade C	340	225	153	225	170	283	99	131	$16 < d \leq 40$
	060 A 22		A 284 Grade D	410	265	185	265	205	342	119	154	
	080 M 30		A 572 Grade 55	470	285	212	285	235	392	136	165	
	080 M 40		A 572 Grade 65	570	325	257	325	285	455	165	189	
	080 M 50	SAE	1044	670	355	302	355	335	497	194	206	
	080 A 47	SAE	1045	697	481	314	481	349	582	202	279	$d \leq 16$
				657	412	296	412	329	548	191	239	$16 < d \leq 40$
				618	373	278	373	309	515	179	216	$40 < d \leq 100$
	708 A 42	SAE	4140	1079	883	486	810	540	900	313	512	$d \leq 16$
				981	765	441	735	491	818	285	444	$16 < d \leq 40$
				883	638	397	638	442	737	256	370	$40 < d \leq 100$
BS 970/2-70	823 M 30	UNS	K 31820	1226	1030	552	920	613	1022	356	593	$16 < d \leq 40$
BS 2789	– 420/12	ASTM	60-40-18	420	250	180	250	200	333	116	145	
	600/3 SGC	A 536	80-55-06	600	350	245	350	270	450	155	200	
	700/2		100-70-03	700	400	280	400	315	525	180	230	

see P 2 (for BS 2789 materials)

[*)] Allow a safety factor for the permissible stresses (see P 2 and P 18)

A: Alternating U: Undulating } see P 2

Note: The strength depends on the diameter, especially with heat-treated steel

Allowable bending and torsional stresses; E and G moduli for elastic materials in N/mm²

Material	Modulus of elasticity E	Type of loading[1]	p_{bt} A	B	C	Modulus of rigidity G	p_{qt}
Spring Steel SAE1078; hard. + temp.	210000	I II III	1000 750 500	500 350 250	150 120 80	80000	650 500 350
Yellow Brass ASTM-B134(274) HV150	110000	I II III	200 150 100	100 70 50	40 30 20	42000	120 100 80
Nickel Silver 65-18 HV160 ASTM-B122(752)	142000	I II III	300 250 200	150 120 100	50 40 30	55000	200 180 150
Tin Bronze CDA-419 HV190	110000	I II III	200 150 100	100 80 50	40 30 20	42000	120 100 80
Phosphor Bronze CDA-529 HV190	117000	I II III	300 220 150	150 110 80	50 40 30	45000	200 180 150

A: for simple springs (safety factor $\cong 1 \cdot 5$)
B: for bent and shaped springs (" " $\cong 3$)
C: for springs with no hysteresis effect (" " $\cong 10$)

[1] For explanation refer to P 1.
[2] For cylindrical helical springs use diagram on page Q 9.

Characteristic quantities for machining
(for turning outside longitudinally)

Material	Strength in N/mm² or hardness	z	$1-z$	$k_{S1.1}$ N/mm²
ASTM – A572 Grade	520	0·26	0·74	1990
UNS – K04600	720	0·30	0·70	2260
SAE – 1045	670	0·14	0·86	2220
SAE – 1060	770	0·18	0·82	2130
SAE – 5120	770	0·26	0·74	2100
SAE – 3140	630	0·30	0·70	2260
SAE – 4135	600	0·21	0·79	2240
SAE – 4140	730	0·26	0·74	2500
SAE – 6150	600	0·26	0·74	2220
SAE – L6 annealed	940	0·24	0·76	1740
SAE – L6 tempered	ASTME18-74-HRD54	0·24	0·76	1920
Mehanite A	360	0·26	0·74	1270
Chilled cast iron	ASTME18-74-HRD60	0·19	0·81	2060
ASTM – A48-40B	ASTME18-74-HRD33	0·26	0·74	1160

Specified values apply directly for turning with carbide tip
Cutting speed $v = 90 \ldots 125$ m/min
Chip thickness $h = 0.05$ mm $\le h \le 2.5$ mm | Ratio of slenderness $\varepsilon_s = 4$
Normal side-rake angle $\gamma = 6°$ for steel, $2°$ for cast iron

Permissible contact pressure p_b in N/mm²

Bearing pressure of joint bolts (Building construction DIN 1050)

Load characteristic	material	p_b	material	p_b
main load	ASTM–	206	ASTM–	304
main and additional load	A 283 Grade C	235	A 440	343

Journals and bearings, bearing plates (see q 13)

Hydrodynamic lubrication see q 47.

Mixed lubrication, shaft hardened and ground:[1], [2]

	$\frac{v}{m/s}$	p_b	Material	$\frac{v}{m/s}$	p_b
gray cast iron		5	Cast Tin Bronze CDA 902		
(836) Leaded Red Brass	1	8...12	grease lubrication	<0·03	4...12
		20[3]	quality bearings	<1	60
(938) Leaded Tin Bronze	0·3 ...1	15[3]	PA 66 (polyamide)	→0	15
			dry [5]	1	0·09
sintered iron	<1	6	grease lubrication[5]	1	0·35
	3	1	HDPE	→0	2...4
sintered iron with copper	<1	8	(high-density	1	0·02
	3	3	polyethylene)		
sintered bronze	<1	12	PTFE (polytetra-	→0	30
	3	6	fluorethylene	1	0·06
	5	4	enclosed)		
tin-bronze graphite (DEVA metal)	<1	20 ⋮ 90[4]	PTFE + lead + bronze (GLACIER-DU)	<0·005 0·5...5	80... 140[4] 1

(left column group labeled: ASTM-B 30 Cast-)

General, non-sliding surfaces: Max. values are possible up to the compressive yield point at the material ($\sigma_{dF} \approx R_e$). But normal values for good p_b are lower.

Material	Normal values of p_b under		
	dead load	undulating load	shock load
bronze	30 ... 40	20 ... 30	10 ... 15
cast iron	70 ... 80	45 ... 55	20 ... 30
gunmetal	25 ... 35	15 ... 25	8 ... 12
malleable iron	50 ... 80	30 ... 55	20 ... 30
steel	80 ... 150	60 ... 100	30 ... 50

[1] $(p \times v)_{perm}$ are closely related to heat dissipation, load, bearing pressure, type of lubrication.

[2] Sometimes a much higher load capacity with hydrodynamic lubrication is possible.

[3] Limited life (wearing parts).

[4] Specially developed metals   [5] For shell thickness 1 mm

Properties of friction materials
(C 15 ... Q 17)

Material pairing	Sliding friction coefficient μ_{slide} [4]	Max. temperature continuous °C	Max. temperature transient °C	Contact pressure p_b N/mm²	Thermal capacity per unit area q_b kW/m²
dry — organic friction lining/steel or cast iron					
general[5]	0.2 ... 0.65	150 ... 300 K H	300 ... 600 K H	0.1 ... 10	2.2 ... 23
single plate friction clutch	0.35 ... 0.4	150 ... 300	400	1	12 ... 23
automobile drum brake	0.2 ... 0.3	250 ... 300	350 ... 450	0.5 ... 1.5 2.0	
automobile disc brake	0.3 ... 0.4	400	600	10 (emergency braking)	
cast iron/steel	0.15 ... 0.2	300	600	0.8 ... 1.4	
sintered bronze/steel	0.05 ... 0.3	400 ... 450	500 ... 600	1	5.5
wet[6] — sintered bronze/steel	0.05 ... 0.1[1]	180	500 ... 600	3	12 ... 23
steel/steel	0.06 ... 0.1[2]	200 ... 250		1	3.5 ... 5.5[3]

1) $\mu_{static} = (1.3 ... 1.5)\,\mu_{slide}$
2) $\mu_{static} = (1.8 ... 2.0)\,\mu_{slide}$
3) splash lubrication lower, internal lubrication higher
4) often: $\mu_{static} \approx 1.25\,\mu_{slide}$
5) K = rubber bond; H = synthetic resin bond
6) running in oil

Z 20

TABLES
Work w and yield strength k_f

φ : logarithmic deformation ratio

w : strain energy per unit volume

For other materials see VDI 3200

k_f : yield strength

Reprinted by permission of VDI-Verlag-GmbH, Düsseldorf – VDI-Richtlinie 3200

Electrical specific resistance ϱ
and specific conductance γ of conductors at $t = 20°C$

material	ϱ $\dfrac{\Omega\ mm^2}{m}$	γ $\dfrac{m}{\Omega\ mm^2}$	material	ϱ $\dfrac{\Omega\ mm^2}{m}$	γ $\dfrac{m}{\Omega\ mm^2}$
aluminum	0·0278	36	iron (pure)	0·10	10
antimony	0·417	2·4	lead	0·208	4·8
brass – 58% Cu	0·059	17	magnesium	0·0435	23
brass – 63% Cu	0·071	14	manganese	0·423	2·37
cadmium	0·076	13·1	mercury	0·941	1·063
carbon	40	0·025	mild steel	0·13	7·7
cast iron	1	1	nickel	0·087	11·5
chromium-Ni-Fe	0·10	10	nickeline	0·5	2·0
constantan	0·48	2·08	platinum	0·111	9
copper	0·0172	58	silver	0·016	62·5
German silver	0·369	2·7	tin	0·12	8·3
gold	0·0222	45	tungsten	0·059	17
graphite	8·00	0·125	zinc	0·061	16·5

Electrical resistance ϱ of insulators

material	ϱ $\Omega\ cm$	material	ϱ $\Omega\ cm$
bakelite	10^{-4}	plexiglass	10^{15}
glass	10^{-5}	polystyrene	10^{18}
marble	10^{10}	porcelain	10^{14}
mica	10^{17}	pressed amber	10^{18}
paraffin oil	10^{18}	vulcanite	10^{16}
paraffin wax (pure)	10^{18}	water, distilled	10^{7}

Electric temperature coefficient α_{20} at $t = 20°C$

material	α_{20} 1/K or 1.°C	material	α_{20} 1/K or 1/°C
aluminum	$+0·00390$	mercury	$+0·00090$
brass	$+0·00150$	mild steel	$+0·00660$
carbon	$-0·00030$	nickel	$+0·00400$
constantan	$-0·00003$	nickeline	$+0·00023$
copper	$+0·00330$	platinum	$+0·00390$
German silver	$+0·00070$	silver	$+0·00377$
graphite	$-0·00020$	tin	$+0·00420$
manganese	$\pm0·00001$	zinc	$+0·00370$

TABLES
Electrical properties

Dielectric constant ε_r

insulant	ε_r	insulant	ε_r
araldite	3·6	paraffin oil	2·2
atmosphere	1	paraffin wax	2·2
bakelite	3·6	petroleum	2·2
casting compound	2·5	phenolic resin	8
caster oil	4·7	plexiglass	3·2
ebonite	2·5	polystyrene	3
glass	5	porcelain	4·4
guttapercha	4	pressed board	4
hard paper (laminated)	4·5	quartz	4·5
insulation of high		shellac	3·5
voltage cables	4·2	slate	4
insulation of telephone		soft rubber	2·5
cables	1·5	steatite	6
marble	8	sulfur	3·5
mica	6	teflon	2
micanite	5	transformer oil mineral	2·2
nylon	5	transformer oil vegetable	2·5
oil paper	4	turpentine	2·2
olive oil	3	vulcanised fibres	2·5
paper	2·3	vulcanite	4
paper, impregnated	5	water	80

Electro-motive series
(potential difference with respect to hydrogen electrode)

material	$\dfrac{U}{\text{volt}}$	material	$\dfrac{U}{\text{volt}}$
potassium	− 2·93	cadmium	− 0·40
calcium	− 2·87	cobalt	− 0·28
sodium	− 2·71	nickel	− 0·23
magnesium	− 2·37	tin	− 0·14
beryllium	− 1·85	lead	− 0·13
aluminum	− 1·66	hydrogen	0·00
manganese	− 1·19	copper	+ 0·34
zinc	− 0·76	silver	+ 0·80
chromium	− 0·74	mercury	+ 0·85
tungsten	− 0·58	platinum	+ 1·20
iron	− 0·41	gold	+ 1·50

Magnetic field strength H and relative permeability μ_r as a function of induction B

induction B		cast iron		steel casting and dynamo sheet steel $p_{Fe10} = 3 \cdot 6 \frac{W}{kg}$		alloyed dynamo sheet steel $p_{Fe10} = 1 \cdot 3 \frac{W}{kg}$	
		H	μ_r	H	μ_r	H	μ_r
$T = \dfrac{V\,s}{m^2}$ tesla	$\left[\; G \;\right]$ gauss	A/m	—	A/m	—	A/m	—
0·1	1000	440	181	30	2650	8,5	9390
0·2	2000	740	215	60	2650	25	6350
0·3	3000	980	243	80	2980	40	5970
0·4	4000	1250	254	100	4180	65	4900
0·5	5000	1650	241	120	3310	90	4420
0·6	6000	2100	227	140	3410	125	3810
0·7	7000	3600	154	170	3280	170	3280
0·8	8000	5300	120	190	3350	220	2900
0·9	9000	7400	97	230	3110	280	2550
1·0	10000	10300	77	295	2690	355	2240
1·3	11000	14000	63	370	2360	460	1900
1·2	12000	19500	49	520	1830	660	1445
1·3	13000	29000	36	750	1380	820	1260
1·4	14000	42000	29	1250	890	2250	495
1·5	15000	65000	18	2000	600	4500	265
1·6	16000			3500	363	8500	150
1·7	17000			7900	171	13100	103
1·8	18000			12000	119	21500	67
1·9	19000			19100	79	39000	39
2·0	20000			30500	52	115000	14
2·1	21000			50700	33		
2·2	22000			130000	13		
2·3	23000			218000	4		

━━━ practical limit

Note: p_{Fe10} see Z 24

Dynamo sheet properties

type		mild sheet steel	allow sheet steel			
			low	medium	high	
class of sheet		I 3·6	II 3·0	III 2·3	IV 1·5	IV 1·3
panel size mm × mm		1000 × 2000				750 ×1500
thickness mm		0·5				0·35
density kg/dm^3		7·8	7·75	7·65	7·6	
core losses per unit mass at f = 50 Hz W/kg (max.)	p_{Fe10}	3·6	3·0	2·3	1·5	1·3
	p_{Fe15}	8·6	7·2	5·6	3·7	3·3
induction (min.)	B_{25} V s/m^2 [gauss]	1·53 [15300]	1·50 [15000]	1·47 [14700]	1·43 [14300]	
	B_{50} V s/m^2 [gauss]	1·63 [16300]	1·60 [16000]	1·57 [15700]	1·55 [15500]	
	B_{100} V s/m^2 [gauss]	1·73 [17300]	1·71 [17100]	1·69 [16900]	1·65 [16500]	
	B_{300} V s/m^2 [gauss]	1·98 [19800]	1·95 [19500]	1·93 [19300]	1·85 [18500]	

Explanations

B_{25} = 1·53 V s/m^2 indicates that a minimum induction of 1·53 V s/m^2 [or 15300 gauss] is reached with a field strength of 25 A/cm. Thus a flux length of e.g. 5 cm requires a circulation of 5 × 25 A = 125 A.

p_{Fe10}	describes the core losses per unit mass at f = 50 Hz and an induction of	1·0 V s/m^2 = [10000 G]
p_{Fe15}		1·5 V s/m^2 = [15000 G]

Guide values for illumination E_V in lx = lm/m²

Type of establishment or location		General lighting only	General and spec. lighting	
			bench	general
workshops according to work done	rough	100	50	200
	medium	200	100	500
	precise	300	200	1000
	very precise	500	300	1500
offices	normal	500		
	open	750		
living rooms, lighting	medium	200		
	bright	500		
streets and squares with traffic	light	20		
	medium	50		
	heavy	100		
factory yards with traffic	light	20		
	heavy	50		

Luminous efficacy η

Type of lighting	Colour of illuminated surface		
	light	medium	dark
direct	0·60	0·45	0·30
indirect	0·35	0·25	0·15
street and square lighting	deep bowl reflector		widespread
	0·45		0·40

Luminous flux Φ_v of lamps

Standard lamps with single coiled filament (at operating voltage)		P_{el}	W	15	25	40	60	75	100
		Φ_v	klm	0·12	0·23	0·43	0·73	0·96	1·39
		P_{el}	W	150	200	300	500	1000	2000
		Φ_v	klm	2·22	3·15	5·0	8·4	18·8	40·0
Fluorescent lamps values for 'Warmwhite' 'Daylight'	Tubular diameter								
	26 mm	P_{el}	W		18	36	58		
		Φ_v	klm		1·45	3·47	5·4		
	38 mm	P_{el}	W	15	20	40	65		
		Φ_v	klm	0·59	1·20	3·1	5·0		
High-pressure lamps filled with mercury vapour		P_{el}	W	125	250	400	700	1000	2000
		Φ_v	klm	6·5	14	24	42	60	125

$$\varphi(x) = \frac{1}{\sqrt{2\pi}} e^{-\frac{x^2}{2}} \; ; \quad \Phi_0(x) = \frac{2}{\sqrt{2\pi}} \int_0^x e^{-\frac{t^2}{2}} \, dt \; ; \quad erf(x) = \frac{2}{\sqrt{\pi}} \int_0^x e^{-t^2} \, dt$$

x	$\varphi(x)$	$\Phi_0(x)$	$erf(x)$	x	$\varphi(x)$	$\Phi_0(x)$	$erf(x)$
0·00	0·398 942	0·000 000	0·000 000	0·50	0·352 065	0·382 925	0·520 500
0·01	0·398 922	0·007 979	0·011 283	0·51	0·350 292	0·389 949	0·529 244
0·02	0·398 862	0·015 957	0·022 565	0·52	0·348 493	0·396 936	0·537 899
0·03	0·398 763	0·023 933	0·033 841	0·53	0·346 668	0·403 888	0·546 464
0·04	0·398 623	0·031 907	0·045 111	0·54	0·344 818	0·410 803	0·554 939
0·05	0·398 444	0·039 878	0·056 372	0·55	0·342 944	0·417 681	0·563 323
0·06	0·398 225	0·047 845	0·067 622	0·56	0·341 046	0·424 521	0·571 616
0·07	0·397 966	0·055 806	0·078 858	0·57	0·339 124	0·431 322	0·579 816
0·08	0·397 668	0·063 763	0·090 078	0·58	0·337 180	0·438 085	0·587 923
0·09	0·397 330	0·071 713	0·101 281	0·59	0·335 213	0·444 809	0·595 937
0·10	0·396 953	0·079 656	0·112 463	0·60	0·333 225	0·451 494	0·603 856
0·11	0·396 536	0·087 591	0·123 623	0·61	0·331 215	0·458 138	0·611 681
0·12	0·396 080	0·095 517	0·134 758	0·62	0·329 184	0·464 742	0·619 412
0·13	0·395 585	0·103 434	0·145 867	0·63	0·327 133	0·471 306	0·627 047
0·14	0·395 052	0·111 340	0·156 947	0·64	0·325 062	0·477 828	0·634 586
0·15	0·394 479	0·119 235	0·167 996	0·65	0·322 972	0·484 308	0·642 029
0·16	0·393 868	0·127 119	0·179 012	0·66	0·320 864	0·490 746	0·649 377
0·17	0·393 219	0·134 990	0·189 992	0·67	0·318 737	0·497 142	0·656 628
0·18	0·392 531	0·142 847	0·200 936	0·68	0·316 593	0·503 496	0·663 782
0·19	0·391 806	0·150 691	0·211 840	0·69	0·314 432	0·509 806	0·670 840
0·20	0·391 043	0·158 519	0·222 702	0·70	0·312 254	0·516 073	0·677 801
0·21	0·390 242	0·166 332	0·233 522	0·71	0·310 060	0·522 296	0·684 666
0·22	0·389 404	0·174 129	0·244 296	0·72	0·307 851	0·528 475	0·691 433
0·23	0·388 529	0·181 908	0·255 022	0·73	0·305 627	0·534 610	0·698 104
0·24	0·387 617	0·189 670	0·265 700	0·74	0·303 389	0·540 700	0·704 678
0·25	0·386 668	0·197 413	0·276 326	0·75	0·301 137	0·546 745	0·711 156
0·26	0·385 683	0·205 136	0·286 900	0·76	0·298 872	0·552 746	0·717 537
0·27	0·384 663	0·212 840	0·297 418	0·77	0·296 595	0·558 700	0·723 822
0·28	0·383 606	0·220 522	0·307 880	0·78	0·294 305	0·564 609	0·730 010
0·29	0·382 515	0·228 184	0·318 283	0·79	0·292 004	0·570 472	0·736 103
0·30	0·381 388	0·235 823	0·328 627	0·80	0·289 692	0·576 289	0·742 101
0·31	0·380 226	0·243 439	0·338 908	0·81	0·287 369	0·582 060	0·748 003
0·32	0·379 031	0·251 032	0·349 126	0·82	0·285 036	0·587 784	0·753 811
0·33	0·377 801	0·258 600	0·359 279	0·83	0·282 694	0·593 461	0·759 524
0·34	0·376 537	0·266 143	0·369 365	0·84	0·280 344	0·599 092	0·765 143
0·35	0·375 240	0·273 661	0·379 382	0·85	0·277 985	0·604 675	0·770 668
0·36	0·373 911	0·281 153	0·389 330	0·86	0·275 618	0·610 211	0·776 100
0·37	0·372 548	0·288 617	0·399 206	0·87	0·273 244	0·615 700	0·781 440
0 38	0·371 154	0·296 054	0·409 009	0·88	0·270 864	0·621 141	0·786 687
0 39	0·369 728	0·303 463	0·418 739	0·89	0·268 477	0·626 534	0·791 843
0·40	0·368 270	0·310 843	0·428 392	0·90	0·266 085	0·631 880	0·796 908
0·41	0·366 782	0·318 194	0·437 969	0·91	0·263 688	0·637 178	0·801 883
0·42	0·365 263	0·325 514	0·447 468	0·92	0·261 286	0·642 427	0·806 768
0·43	0·363 714	0·332 804	0·456 887	0·93	0·258 881	0·647 629	0·811 563
0·44	0·362 135	0·340 063	0·466 225	0·94	0·256 471	0·652 782	0·816 271
0·45	0·360 527	0·347 290	0·475 482	0·95	0·254 059	0·657 888	0·820 891
0·46	0·358 890	0·354 484	0·484 656	0·96	0·251 644	0·662 945	0·825 424
0·47	0·357 225	0·361 645	0·493 745	0·97	0·249 228	0·667 954	0·829 870
0·48	0·355 533	0·368 773	0·502 750	0·98	0·246 809	0·672 914	0·834 231
0·49	0·353 812	0·375 866	0·511 668	0·99	0·244 390	0·677 826	0·838 508

$$\varphi(x) = \frac{1}{\sqrt{2\pi}}\, e^{-\frac{x^2}{2}}\,; \quad \varPhi_0(x) = \frac{2}{\sqrt{2\pi}}\int_0^x e^{-\frac{t^2}{2}}\,dt\,; \quad \mathrm{erf}(x) = \frac{2}{\sqrt{\pi}}\int_0^x e^{-t^2}\,dt$$

x	$\varphi(x)$	$\varPhi_0(x)$	erf (x)	x	$\varphi(x)$	$\varPhi_0(x)$	erf (x)
1·00	0·241 971	0·682 689	0·842 701	1·50	0·129 518	0·866 336	0·966 105
1·01	0·239 551	0·687 505	0·846 310	1·51	0·127 583	0·868 957	0·967 277
1·02	0·237 132	0·692 272	0·850 338	1·52	0·125 665	0·871 489	0·968 414
1·03	0·234 714	0·696 990	0·854 284	1·53	0·123 763	0·873 983	0·969 516
1·04	0·232 297	0·701 660	0·858 350	1·54	0·121 878	0·876 440	0·970 586
1·05	0·229 882	0·706 282	0·862 436	1·55	0·120 009	0·878 858	0·971 623
1·06	0·227 470	0·710 855	0·866 144	1·56	0·118 157	0·881 240	0·972 628
1·07	0·225 060	0·715 381	0·869 773	1·57	0·116 323	0·883 585	0·973 603
1·08	0·222 653	0·719 858	0·873 326	1·58	0·114 505	0·885 893	0·974 547
1·09	0·220 251	0·724 287	0·876 803	1·59	0·112 704	0·888 165	0·975 462
1·10	0·217 852	0·728 668	0·880 205	1·60	0·110 921	0·890 401	0·976 348
1·11	0·215 458	0·733 001	0·883 533	1·61	0·109 155	0·892 602	0·977 207
1·12	0·213 069	0·737 286	0·886 788	1·62	0·107 406	0·894 768	0·978 038
1·13	0·210 686	0·741 524	0·889 971	1·63	0·105 675	0·896 899	0·978 843
1·14	0·208 308	0·745 714	0·893 082	1·64	0·103 961	0·898 995	0·979 622
1·15	0·205 936	0·749 856	0·896 124	1·65	0·102 265	0·901 057	0·980 376
1·16	0·203 571	0·753 951	0·899 096	1·66	0·100 586	0·903 086	0·981 105
1·17	0·201 214	0·757 999	0·902 000	1·67	0·098 925	0·905 081	0·981 810
1·18	0·198 863	0·762 000	0·904 837	1·68	0·097 282	0·907 043	0·982 493
1·19	0·196 520	0·765 953	0·907 608	1·69	0·095 657	0·908 972	0·983 153
1·20	0·194 186	0·769 861	0·910 314	1·70	0·094 049	0·910 869	0·983 790
1·21	0·191 860	0·773 721	0·912 956	1·71	0·092 459	0·912 734	0·984 407
1·22	0·189 543	0·777 535	0·915 534	1·72	0·090 887	0·914 568	0·985 003
1·23	0·187 235	0·781 303	0·918 050	1·73	0·089 333	0·916 370	0·985 578
1·24	0·184 937	0·785 024	0·920 505	1·74	0·087 796	0·918 141	0·986 135
1·25	0·182 649	0·788 700	0·922 900	1·75	0·086 277	0·919 882	0·986 672
1·26	0·180 371	0·792 331	0·925 236	1·76	0·084 776	0·921 592	0·987 190
1·27	0·178 104	0·795 915	0·927 514	1·77	0·083 293	0·923 273	0·987 691
1·28	0·175 847	0·799 455	0·929 734	1·78	0·081 823	0·924 924	0·988 174
1·29	0·173 602	0·802 949	0·931 899	1·79	0·080 380	0·926 546	0·988 641
1·30	0·171 369	0·806 399	0·934 008	1·80	0·078 950	0·928 139	0·989 090
1·31	0·169 147	0·809 804	0·936 063	1·81	0·077 538	0·929 704	0·989 524
1·32	0·166 937	0·813 165	0·938 065	1·82	0·076 143	0·931 241	0·989 943
1·33	0·164 740	0·816 482	0·940 015	1·83	0·074 766	0·932 750	0·990 347
1·34	0·162 555	0·819 755	0·941 914	1·84	0·073 407	0·934 232	0·990 736
1·35	0·160 383	0·822 984	0·943 762	1·85	0·072 065	0·935 687	0·991 111
1·36	0·158 225	0·826 170	0·945 562	1·86	0·070 740	0·937 115	0·991 472
1·37	0·156 080	0·829 313	0·947 313	1·87	0·069 433	0·938 516	0·991 821
1·38	0·153 948	0·832 413	0·949 016	1·88	0·068 144	0·939 892	0·992 156
1·39	0·151 831	0·835 471	0·950 673	1·89	0·066 871	0·941 242	0·992 479
1·40	0·149 727	0·838 487	0·952 285	1·90	0·065 616	0·942 567	0·992 790
1·41	0·147 639	0·841 460	0·953 853	1·91	0·064 378	0·943 867	0·993 090
1·42	0·145 564	0·844 392	0·955 376	1·92	0·063 157	0·945 142	0·993 378
1·43	0·143 505	0·847 283	0·956 857	1·93	0·061 952	0·946 393	0·993 656
1·44	0·141 460	0·850 133	0·958 297	1·94	0·060 765	0·947 620	0·993 922
1·45	0·139 431	0·852 941	0·959 695	1·95	0·059 595	0·948 824	0·994 179
1·46	0·137 417	0·855 710	0·961 054	1·96	0·058 441	0·950 004	0·994 426
1·47	0·135 418	0·858 438	0·962 373	1·97	0·057 304	0·951 162	0·994 664
1·48	0·133 435	0·861 127	0·963 654	1·98	0·056 183	0·952 297	0·994 892
1·49	0·131 468	0·863 776	0·964 898	1·99	0·055 079	0·953 409	0·995 111

INDEX